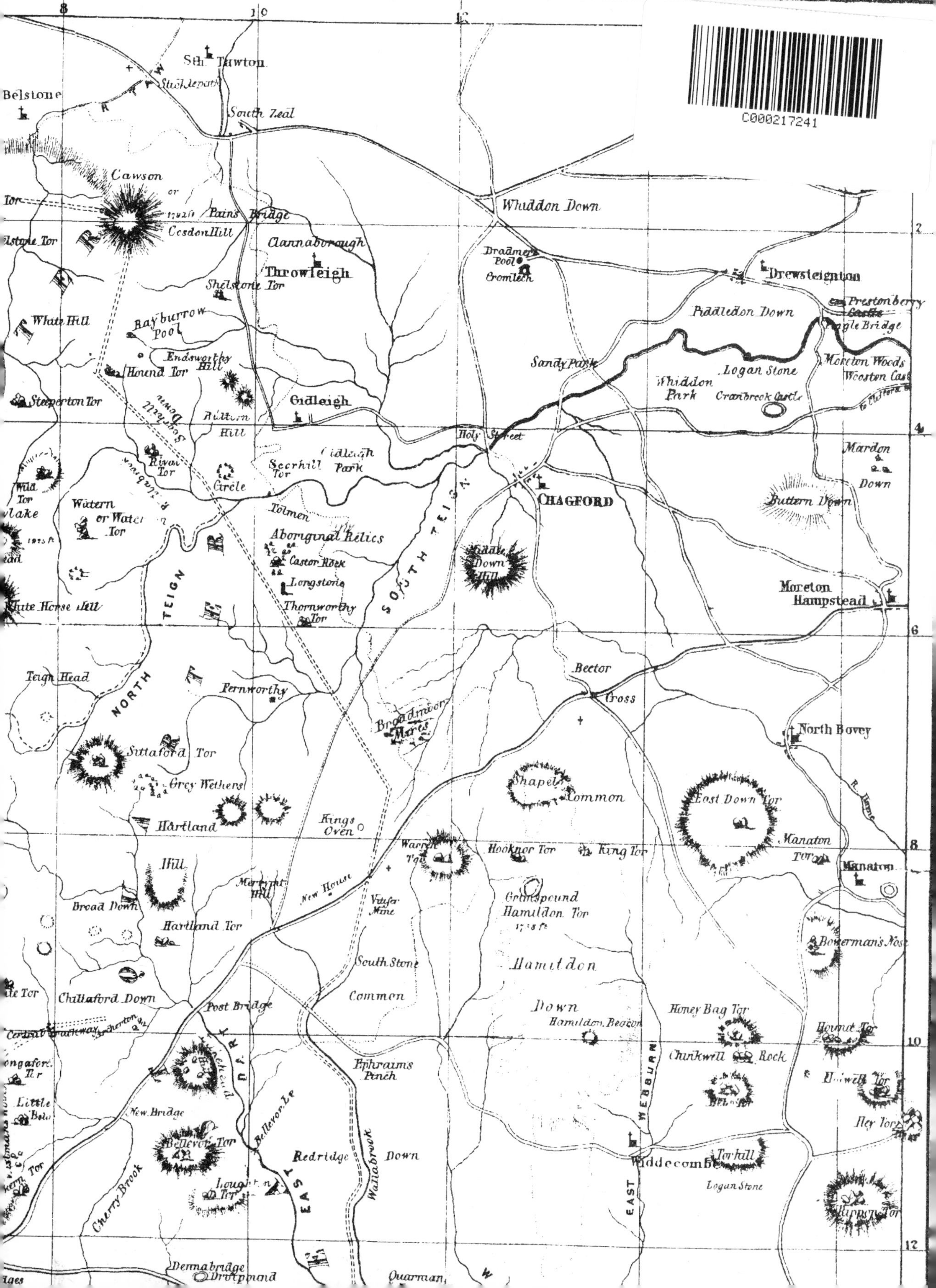

Sth. Tawton
Belstone
South Zeal
Cawson
or
Cosdon Hill
Pains Bridge
Whiddon Down
Clannaborough
Throwleigh
Shelstone Tor
Bradmere Pool
Cromlech
Drewsteignton
Preston berry Castle
Piddledon Down
Fingle Bridge
White Hill
Rayburrow Pool
Hound Tor
Endsworthy Hill
Sandy Park
Logan Stone
Moreton Woods
Wooston Cas
Whiddon Park
Cranbrook Castle
Steeperton Tor
Gidleigh
Buttern Hill
Holy Street
Mardon Down
Gidleigh Park
Seerhill Tor
Rival Tor
Circle
CHAGFORD
Buttern Down
Watern or Watern Tor
Tolmen
Aboriginal Relics
Castor Rock
Longstone
Thornworthy Tor
Middle Down Hill
SOUTH TEIGN
NORTH TEIGN
Moreton Hampstead
White Horse Hill
Teign Head
Fernworthy
Beetor Cross
Broadmoor Mires
North Bovey
Sittaford Tor
Grey Wethers
Shapel Common
East Down Tor
Hartland
Kings Oven
Warren Tor
Hookner Tor
King Tor
Manaton Tor
Manaton
Hill
Broad Down
Merripit Hill
New House
Vitifer Mine
Grimspound
Hamildon Tor
Hartland Tor
Bowerman's Nose
South Stone
Hamildon
Chittaford Down
Common
Post Bridge
Down
Hamildon Beacon
Honey Bag Tor
Hound Tor
Ephraims Pinch
Chinkwell Rock
New Bridge
Bellever Tor
Bellever Le
Redridge
Down
Widdecombe
Torhill
Logan Stone
Hey Tor
Cherry Brook
Walla brook
EAST DART
EAST WEBBURN
Dennabridge
Quarman

THE HOUND
of the
BASKERVILLES

HUNTING THE DARTMOOR LEGEND

Arthur Conan Doyle and Sherlock Holmes
Arthur Conan Doyle watching his creation leaving the old Duchy Hotel [15] for the Moor.
The mannequin and the portrait were created by The Franco-Midland Hardware Company
(The International Sherlock Holmes Study Group) in co-operation with the Dartmoor National
Park Authority in what is now The High Moorland Visitor Centre in Princetown.

THE HOUND
of the
BASKERVILLES
HUNTING THE DARTMOOR LEGEND

Being the original text of the classic story by
ARTHUR CONAN DOYLE

with a Commentary, Notes and Annotations by
PHILIP WELLER

with a Foreword by
EDWARD HARDWICKE

contemporary colour photographs by Bryan Harper

DEVON BOOKS

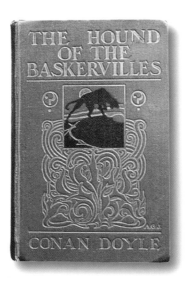

Above: Arthur Conan Doyle's original masterpiece, *The Hound of The Baskervilles.*
Below: *The Strand Magazine* in which episodes of *The Hound of The Baskervilles* appeared.

Foreword

Apart from being a thrilling story, and probably being the most celebrated of all the Sherlock Holmes cases, *The Hound of the Baskervilles* is the perfect example of Conan Doyle's understanding of his times. The late Victorians and Edwardians were, perhaps, unique in the way in which they combined their fascination with the Gothick and the Supernatural with a burgeoning interest in all aspects of scientific knowledge. Conan Doyle's creation is a man who looks at the former and logically explains it with the latter. What could be more intriguing?

The Basil Rathbone–Nigel Bruce film of *The Hound of the Baskervilles* ignited my interest in Sherlock Holmes, and that interest is something which has never left me. During the Granada Television Sherlock Holmes series, it was the story which Jeremy Brett and I most looked forward to filming. For myself, playing the part of Watson, it was a real treat, for *The Hound of the Baskervilles* is the case in which Watson's star really does shine.

A book with all the information which you have here is a must for all of us who love this adventure.

Edward Hardwicke

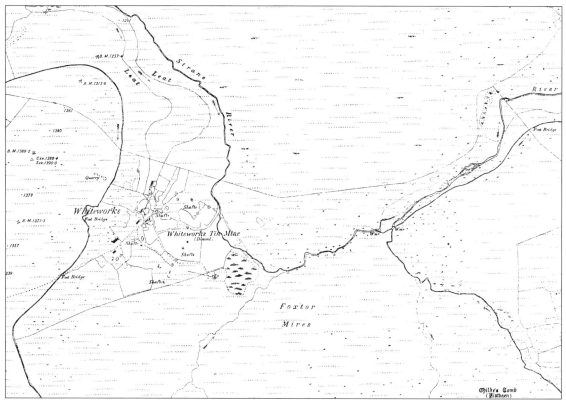

Ordnance Survey map of 1888 (based on the survey of 1885), in a scale of six inches to the mile, but reduced here, of the Fox Tor Mires (*'Grimpen Mire'*) area, with the Whiteworks tin mine prominent. The legendary Childe's Tomb Cross, which ACD will almost certainly have visited, is at the bottom-right of the map, with the remains of Fox Tor Farm just above and to the right of it. The track to Hexworthy (*'Grimpen'*) follows the course of the River Swincombe out of the top-right of the map, and Nun's Cross Farm (*'Merripit House'*) is off the map to the bottom left. The track leaving the map at bottom left leads towards Nun's Cross Farm, then curves Northwards to Peat Cot, Tor Royal and Princetown.

Endpaper Map The map used for the endpapers of this book is an earlier Victorian pictorial map. The illustrations which appear on the endpapers are typically romanticised Victorian drawings of Dartmoor archaeological sites.

Preface

Arthur Conan Doyle's book, *The Hound of the Baskervilles*, is, without question, the most influential work of fiction ever to have been written about Dartmoor, and one of the most popular detective fiction stories ever published. It has been translated into every major language in the world, and into many of the minor ones, including, for example, Swahili and Icelandic. It is a multi-million seller which has remained in print throughout the whole of its one hundred years' publishing history, and it has appeared in hundreds of different editions. It has been presented on the stage in hundreds of adaptations, and at least nineteen different film and television versions have been produced in Danish, English, German, Italian, Japanese and Russian.

There are millions of people around the world who have never visited Dartmoor, but who have a good impression of how the Moor looks and feels from reading this wonderfully atmospheric book. The many hundreds of Sherlock Holmes enthusiasts who make a pilgrimage to Dartmoor each year have not been disappointed by what they have read and then seen, with the book's references to the Moor and its many mysteries and legends, the prison, tors, stone hut circles and monuments, fog, ponies, rivers and mires. Fortunately, these pilgrims have rarely encountered escaped prisoners, but there are those who have felt that they may have experienced the presence of a gigantic hound, such is the richness of the imagery in the book.

The year 2001, which celebrates the centenary of the appearance of the first episodes of *The Hound of the Baskervilles* in *The Strand Magazine*, provides an appropriate opportunity for publishing a new edition of the book which will take advantage for the first time of some of the rare photographic archive material which exists on the nature of the Moor at the time described in the book. The opportunity is also taken to present much of the new research which has gone into the investigation of the background and production of the story. This account includes coverage of incidents which have created their own mysteries, and there is much which will be of interest to all those who love Dartmoor, as well as to literary scholars. The extensive Investigation, and the Annotations which accompany the main text, include details of many of the real places, people and history of the Moor which may have influenced Arthur Conan Doyle in the writing of his book, as well as similar details from other locations and information on some of the problems which can be encountered with the book and its history. It is hoped that these details will prove to be not only entertaining but also educational, and that they will help to increase the very real pleasure which exists in reading the main text. Such details may also encourage those who have never read the book from this sort of viewpoint to want to take part in the continuing adventure which is made possible, either on Dartmoor or in the comfort of the home, through *The Hound of the Baskervilles*.

We have been very privileged in this book not only to include many new photo-graphs, taken specifically for the book by that well-known Dartmoor photographer, Bryan Harper, but also to use photographs from the archives of that wonderful Victorian Dartmoor photographer, Robert Burnard. He was the son of the Mayor of Plymouth who was originally mentioned in the manuscript of *The Hound of the Baskervilles*, as well as a close friend of that other great Dartmoor writer, Sabine Baring-Gould, and Robert took many of his photographs at the time when the Baskerville adventure takes place, in 1889, which makes these photographs particu-larly pertinent. It is appropriate that it is the character in the story who knows Dartmoor best who says:

> *It is a wonderful place, the moor… You never tire of the moor. You cannot think the wonderful secrets which it contains. It is so vast, so barren, and so mysterious.*

This is obviously true of the Moor, with the exception of the use of the words 'so bar-ren', but it might, with the removal of those two words, equally well be a tribute to the greatest book ever to have been written about Dartmoor: *The Hound of the Baskervilles.*

Philip Weller
Chairman of The Baskerville Hounds
The Dartmoor Sherlock Holmes Study Group

Contents

THE MEN ON THE TOR
Philip Weller

❧◉☙

THE HOUND OF THE BASKERVILLES

Arthur Conan Doyle

❧◉☙

The Hound of the Baskervilles
By Sidney Paget

THE MEN ON THE TOR

A CENTENNIAL INVESTIGATION OF
The Hound of the Baskervilles

Philip Weller

The Original Men on the Tor
Arthur Conan Doyle (centre rear) and Bertram Fletcher Robinson (centre) on the *SS Briton* in July 1900, returning to England from South Africa.

General Introduction

Note. It is most strongly recommended that those who have not already read the main text of The Hound of the Baskervilles *should do so before reading 'The Men on the Tor'*

The title of this Investigation is a variation on the title of one of the chapters in *The Hound of the Baskervilles*, "The Man on the Tor". The latter title refers to the mysterious man who is seen by Dr Watson to be standing in the distance across the Moor, deep in thought, outlined against the moon, and watching the activities which are taking place on the Moor. This man becomes a brooding presence on the Moor even when he is not seen, almost as if he were an emanation of the Moor. His presence on the Moor could not have been so effectively described had not two other men ventured forth upon the Moor. These two men were Dr Arthur Conan Doyle, who wrote *The Hound of the Baskervilles*, and his friend and guide, Bertram Fletcher Robinson, who provided the initial inspiration for the creation of the book and helped with the collection of local colour for the book. The story of the production of the book is a complex one, and one which involves a certain amount of controversy. This Investigation will attempt to describe the process whereby the book was created, and attempt to resolve the controversy to some extent, but as there are so many different topics which will need to be touched upon, the key points will initially be given in outline to provide an overall view, with subsequent discussions providing more detailed information for further consideration. There will also be discussions of other topics associated with *The Hound of the Baskervilles*, including: an examination of various literary and legendary sources which may have influenced the writing of the story; some considerations of the plot of the story and of problems which exist in the text; an examination of the real-life sites, mainly on Dartmoor, which may have helped with the depiction of the locations mentioned in the story; a perusal of some of the many film versions of the story; and an assessment of what might be termed 'The Hound Phenomena', with the literary societies, memorabilia and specialist tourism which are linked to the story. This Investigation is not only the result of many years of intense archaeological, historical, biographical, literary, geographical and Holmesian study by its author in connection with the background to the writing of *The Hound of the Baskervilles*, but of an even-longer love of Dartmoor, developed over a period of four decades of teaching survival and navigational techniques on the Moor, as a former Royal Air Force Mountain Rescue Team Leader, during which a total of more than 40,000 miles of walking on the Moor have been logged, not counting the occasional casual strolls! The account is not complete, for there is, for example, much archive material associated with Conan Doyle which is not accessible for legal reasons, and it is probable that the account will never be completed fully, for there is much which has now been lost or destroyed and new investigators will almost inevitably find new questions to ask. With all explorations of Dartmoor there is never an end to what can be learned. As Holmes himself might well have said, where both *The Hound of the Baskervilles* and Dartmoor are concerned:

The Game Is Still Afoot!

That is Baskerville Hall in the middle
Holmes with his 'very large scale' map of Dartmoor.

Elliott Terrace on Plymouth Hoe, where Arthur Conan Doyle resided for a short period in 1882 [9].

A commemorative plaque on the steps of a house in Durnford Street in Plymouth, near the site of the surgery where ACD worked in 1882 [9]. It is generally accepted that ACD wrote 60 Sherlock Holmes stories, although he did also write some parodies and plays involving Holmes.

A plaque in Durnford Street in Plymouth, quoting the most famous line from *The Hound* [9].

The misleading plaque on the site of the surgery in Durnford Street in Plymouth. ACD worked here for only six weeks in 1882, and this period had almost no influence on the writing of *The Hound* [9].

The grave of Bertram Fletcher Robinson, in Ipplepen churchyard [14].

Park Hill House (right) at Ipplepen, the home of Joseph Fletcher Robinson in 1901 when ACD visited it with Bertram Fletcher Robinson [15], with the carriage house (left), where Harry Baskerville once worked [15], and from which he drove ACD onto the Moor. The lintel of the carriage house doors can still be seen above the two newer windows.

The grave of Henry (Harry) Baskerville, once Joseph Fletcher Robinson's carriage driver, in the churchyard of St Andrew's in Ashburton [86].

Very close to Harry Baskerville's grave is that of James Mortimer, the late-Victorian headmaster of Ashburton Grammar School, with the same name being used for the Grimpen doctor in *The Hound* [86].

The sepulchre containing the grave of Richard Cabell III [49], in the churchyard at Buckfastleigh which became a focal point for black magic, with the church being gutted by fire in 1992.

There is a local legend that if one circles the sepulchre backwards a set number of times and then pokes one's fingers through the grille, the Devil will bite them off.

The tomb of members of the Cabell family, capped by a heavy stone slab which has been much damaged by vandals, with the name Ricus (Richard) still being visible.

AN OVERALL VIEW

General Aims. This section of the Investigation will provide a base from which *The Hound of the Baskervilles* can be considered as a whole. Some topics will be covered in depth, where this might be necessary for those who may be new to such discussions, but others will be covered only briefly here and then expanded in the subsequent, specialist sections of this Investigation.

Quotational and Locational Conventions. In order to indicate clearly whether the locations and buildings which are being mentioned in this Investigation are taken from the text of *The Hound of the Baskervilles* or not, and whether they are real or invented, those which are mentioned in the story will be given in italics, and those which have been invented by ACD will additionally be within single quotation marks. All general quotations taken from the text will be in italics and included within double quotation marks. Quotations taken from other sources will merely be included within double quotation marks without italics. The names of three men will recur frequently throughout the Investigation, and in order to save space their initials will be used, other than in headings: Arthur Conan Doyle (ACD), Bertram Fletcher Robinson (BFR), and Sabine Baring-Gould (SBG). As the title of *The Hound of the Baskervilles* will also appear very frequently, it will henceforth be shortened within this Investigation to *The Hound*. This should not be confused with references to the phantom hound from *The Hound* which also appear within this Investigation, which is referred to as The Hound to distinguish it from any everyday hounds. One geographical convention which will be used throughout this Investigation is that it will be accepted that whenever ACD refers to *"...the moor..."*, he is referring to the high and wild moor which exists primarily on the Western side of the administrative area of the Dartmoor National Park, in what was once known as the Ancient Forest of Dartmoor. This area will be referred to as 'the Moor' in this Investigation, to distinguish it from the lower and softer areas which exist in the Eastern part of the Park, with the larger area being referred to as 'Dartmoor'. An explanation of the reason for this will be given in the first section devoted to the locations of *The Hound*.

THE HOLMES SAGA

The Early Adventures of Holmes. The first Sherlock Holmes story, a novella entitled *A Study in Scarlet*, was published in November 1887 in *Beeton's Christmas Annual*. This paper-covered magazine costing one shilling was clearly seen as being a throw-away item by most of its purchasers, in that copies are now extremely difficult to find, with recent copies having been sold at auction for over £25,000. The author, ACD, then a relatively impoverished doctor, who was to become one of the highest paid writers in the world, and to become Sir Arthur Conan Doyle in 1902, was paid the grand sum of £25 for the full rights to the story, and he later complained in his autobiography that he never earned another penny from it. Although it was well-reviewed it was not a great seller, even after it was issued as a book in its own right, and its successor, another novella, entitled *The Sign of Four*, met a similar fate, with it first being published in magazine form in *Lippincott's Magazine* in the USA in 1890. In July 1891, however, *The Strand Magazine* published the first of six short stories about Sherlock Holmes, and these were an immediate and enormous success. These short stories perfectly fitted the requirements of this new magazine, which catered especially for those, like the rapidly increasing number of railway commuters in London, who wanted something which they could read in under an hour and without the problems of serial publication, whilst maintaining the continuity of the same major characters. Their attractiveness was increased by the way in which this magazine aimed to publish at least one picture on each two-page spread. With the Holmes stories the choice of illustrator was inspired, even though it was actually a mistake. A commission for drawings for the Holmes stories was sent to the artist, Walter Paget, but it was mistakenly taken up by his artist brother, Sidney Paget. Walter became famous in connection with the Holmes stories, however, in that he was the model used by Sidney in portraying Holmes, and reality then copied art, in that Sidney's depiction quickly influenced ACD's subsequent textual descriptions of Holmes.

The Further Adventures and 'Death' of Holmes. ACD was swiftly asked to produce six more Sherlock Holmes stories for *The Strand Magazine*, but as he was completing these he informed his mother that he intended killing off Holmes, as he thought that such lightweight stories distracted him from his more-serious writings, which were mainly historical adventures. His mother persuaded him to continue with the Holmes short stories, and he accordingly produced a total of 24 of these short Holmes adventures. In the last of these, however, entitled 'The Final Problem', which was published in December 1893, he carried out his threat and 'killed' Holmes in an encounter with Professor Moriarty at the Reichenbach Falls in Switzerland, an event which was dated as taking place in May 1891. There was general dismay around the world when the news of the 'death' of Holmes arrived. In London, sober business gentlemen wore black armbands, and ACD received a letter from one lady calling him a beast! He seemed determined not to relent, and Holmes stayed 'dead' for ten years. It is not true, however, as some have claimed, that ACD rejected the possibility of writing more Holmes stories, for in the *Tit Bits* magazine of 15 December 1900, he stated

> ... I have never for an instant regretted the course I took in killing Sherlock. That does not say, however, that because he is dead I should not write about him again if I wanted to, for there is no limit to the number of papers he left behind ...

In March or April 1901 ACD was to begin writing a short novel which did not involve Sherlock Holmes, to which he gave the name of *"The Hound of the Baskervilles"*, and he soon found that he needed a strong central character for the story. Rather than invent a new one, he decided to use an existing creation - Sherlock Holmes. He did not, though, 'resurrect' Holmes at that stage, in that the story was dated as taking place at a time prior to Holmes's 1891 'death', in the October of 1889, and *The Hound* might thus have been seen as one of those limitless 'papers' which Holmes had left behind.

The Resurrected Holmes. In 1903, ACD was persuaded, primarily by a financial offer which he could not refuse, to resurrect Holmes fully, and a new series of short Holmes stories started to appear, initially in the American *Colliers' Weekly Magazine*, in September 1903, with the English edition appearing in *The Strand Magazine* the following month. A further 32 Holmes short stories and one additional novella, *The Valley of Fear*, were to appear, with the final story, 'The Adventure of Shoscombe Old Place', being published in April 1927, and with ACD dying on 7 July 1930. There was thus eventually a total of 56 Holmes short stories and four novellas, but the greatest of all of these was *The Hound*. It was a Cornish fisherman who was to suggest to ACD that Sherlock Holmes was never as good after he 'returned from the dead', and although ACD did write some extremely good Holmes stories after *The Hound*, this has a great deal of truth in it. Reference to the 'life' of Holmes may seem rather strange, but it is something which is very real to many people, as will now be discussed in order to provide the setting within which part of the continuing fascination of *The Hound* exists.

THE GREAT HOLMESIAN GAME

Holmesians and Sherlockians. One should begin any discussion of The Game by explaining to the uninitiated that 'Holmesian' is the name accepted by those, mostly in Britain, who have a particular interest in Sherlock Holmes. This term reflects the way in which Holmes is always referred to as such by his colleague and closest friend, Doctor John H Watson, which in turn reflects the correct Victorian form of address amongst men, using only surnames outside the circle of family members or family servants. In the 60 Sherlock Holmes stories Watson never once calls Holmes by his first name, and Holmes also maintains the tradition. Sherlock Holmes's brother, Mycroft Holmes, is the only person ever to call him Sherlock, although there is one rather impudent tradesman who presumed to call Holmes *"Mr Sherlock"*. It is traditional, however, for American enthusiasts to call themselves 'Sherlockians', reflecting the more informal interpersonal relationships which existed in the USA even in the Nineteenth Century. The difference has been nicely summarised as follows: "British Sherlockians prefer to call themselves Holmesians, whereas American Holmesians prefer to call themselves Sherlockians." In this Investigation we will confine ourselves primarily to using the British term, other than when referring specifically to Americans.

The Premises of The Game. Holmesians, when playing The Great Holmesian Game, accept the admittedly rather foolish premises that Sherlock Holmes and Doctor Watson were real people, that Doctor Watson wrote most of the stories of the adventures of Sherlock Holmes, and that ACD acted merely as Doctor Watson's literary agent. Many Holmesian societies, and there are well over 500 of them around the world, refuse to give any consideration to the life of ACD, and there are some where even mentioning the name of ACD, rather than referring to him as 'The Literary Agent', results in the miscreant having to buy a round of drinks for all present! Once these premises are accepted, The Game then involves the players in attempting to fit everything which happens in the 60 Sherlock Holmes recorded cases into real history and real geography. This can fairly readily be done with most of the events and locations in the stories because of the way in which ACD wrote, in that he tended to incorporate most of the things which he saw or experienced into his writing, and he had a near-photographic memory for such details. There was, of course, a certain amount of literary license involved at times, and the occasional error of time or place, but part of the fun of The Game lies in attempting to explain

away these 'errors'. It is interesting that *The Hound* became the subject of what is considered to be the earliest example of playing The Game, when Professor Frank Sidgwick, who later became the Vice Chancellor of Cambridge University, wrote an 'Open Letter to Dr Watson', which was published in *The Cambridge Review* on 23 January 1902, some three months before the story was completed. He highlighted a dozen seeming inconsistencies in Dr Watson's account, many of them being essentially chronological in nature.

Holmesian and Other Expertise. One of the great pleasures of playing The Game is that ACD included references to topics from so many different areas of interest that whatever specialist interest any particular player may have outside of the Holmesian world can be brought to the study of the contents of the Holmesian Canon, which is the name given to the collection of all 56 of the short Sherlock Holmes stories and the four Sherlock Holmes novellas. The word 'Canon' was introduced to such studies at a very early stage, in the 1920s, in deliberate imitation of the way in which some theological studies had been extended to ridiculous levels, over such arcane questions as that which asked how many angels could sit on the head of a pin. Similar levels of scholarship are often applied to Holmesian Studies, as when, for example, experiments were carried out by Holmesians in response to Holmes's casual suggestion that he had once solved a case by determining how far parsley had sunk into some butter. The experiments not only attempted to determine rates of sink at different temperatures, but also involved the use of meteorological records to determine the date when the original case took place, almost one hundred years earlier! Other investigations are far less specialised, with a favourite exercise being that of attempting to discover exactly where events took place, and Dartmoor provides a prime arena for such pursuits. Within studies of *The Hound* the knowledge of scholars from many different fields of study are called upon. We have, for example: railway historians discussing the routes used to reach Dartmoor and the timetables involved; botanists determining what sort of orchid might be growing on Dartmoor in early-October; lepidopterists discussing what sort of moth on the Moor might be the reality behind Doctor Watson's mis-recalled 'Cyclopides'; ornithologists examining the records of bitterns being seen on the Moor in 1889 and comparing recordings of bitterns 'booming' with those of hounds howling; industrial archaeologists researching disused tin mines located in the hearts of mires; newspaper historians enquiring into copies of *The Western Morning News*; cartographers comparing late-Victorian and modern place names on the Moor; with all of these topics, and many more besides, being mentioned in *The Hound*. Such studies can contribute enormously to the local history of an area like Dartmoor, and their pursuit can also, most importantly, prove to be great fun. It should not be considered that such studies are parochially tied to Dartmoor, however, in that the reference to *The Western Morning News* is contrasted in the story, for example, with *The Leeds Mercury*. Researches suggest that this Northern newspaper may have been introduced specifically to contrast with a newspaper which ACD would have known when he lived in Plymouth because the *Mercury* had attacked him recently in his political campaigning over ways of raising taxes to pay for the continuing war against the Boers.

The Limits and Limitlessness of The Game. In playing The Game one does have to attempt to overcome Doctor Watson's practice of sometimes disguising the names of locations, which he usually did in order to protect the innocent, and his frequent use of literary license, and this means that The Game is rarely completed, even within one specialist area within one particular case. The Game might easily get out of hand, and it frequently does amongst those who prefer to have no rules by which to play their version. The superior form of The Game, however, is that which was best described by Dorothy L Sayers, herself a serious player of The Game, when she wrote:

The rule of the game is that it must be played as solemnly as a county cricket match at Lord's: the slightest touch of

extravagance or burlesque ruins the atmosphere. The exercise has become a recreation; but those who like their recreation to exert a moral influence may take note of how easy it is for an unscrupulous pseudo-scholarship to extract fantastic and misleading conclusions from a literary text by a series of omissions, emendations and distortions of context.

An element of pseudo-scholarship is admitted in this, but that does not mean that poor standards of scholarship are accepted by the better Holmesian study groups, and much of what is carried on within The Game involves discussions which are far more relevant to literary scholarship than some of those which are claimed to be academically respectable by formal educational institutions. It is hoped that this Investigation and the Annotations which follow the main text of *The Hound* in this volume will encourage some of those who have never played The Game to do so, if only within their own specialist fields of interest, and that it will also encourage those who already play The Game to extend their interests. It is not suggested that the results of the studies carried out within The Game in this Investigation are definitive, for there is always more to learn and more to be incorporated, and debate is an essential part of The Game. The world's leading experts in playing The Game in connection with *The Hound*, The Baskerville Hounds, the Dartmoor Sherlock Holmes study group, will always welcome contributions from those who have a specialist interest in any aspect of Dartmoor which may be relevant to studies of *The Hound* [see the Conclusion section for contact details].

OTHER ASPECTS OF *THE HOUND*

Doylean Studies. Studies of *The Hound* are not confined to playing The Game. One can, for example, become involved in studying aspects of the real life of ACD in connection with Dartmoor through *The Hound*, and through the other books which he produced which are linked to Dartmoor in some way. He did, in fact, write a short Sherlock Holmes story about

'Dartmoor', entitled 'Silver Blaze', which was published in *The Strand Magazine* in December 1892, and set prior to the supposed death of Holmes. The quotation marks around the word 'Dartmoor' in the last sentence are meant to indicate that the Dartmoor described by ACD in that story bears little resemblance to the real Dartmoor which he later described in *The Hound*. The earlier story is based very much on the limited knowledge of Dartmoor which he gained when he lived in Plymouth for some six weeks in the late-Spring of 1882, shortly after he graduated from Edinburgh University as a physician. He lived, during that period, in the splendidly-located rented home, overlooking The Hoe, of a doctor he had met at university, George Turnavine Budd, who was something of a charlatan. ACD walked from Plymouth to Tavistock on a photographic excursion in 1882, and recorded his journey in an essay, 'Dry Plates on a Wet Moor', which was published in *The British Journal of Photography*, in November 1882. It is possible that he may have made one of his first encounters on that journey with a name which was to become important to him later, for if he had wanted to get clear of the urban clutter of Plymouth as quickly as possible, he might well have caught the Plymouth to Roborough horse bus to the outskirts of Plymouth, and that service was operated by the Baskerville family. As will be seen later, another Baskerville driver of horse-drawn vehicles was to become involved with the creation of *The Hound*. ACD also used the information which he gained from this walk in a short story, entitled 'The Winning Shot', about a shooting competition held in the Roborough Down area, which was first published in the *Bow Bells* magazine on 11 July 1883. He seems to have gained the impression that in walking from Roborough to Tavistock, where the road does have moorland on both of its sides, that he was walking across Dartmoor, in that in 'Silver Blaze' he describes Tavistock as being located at the centre of Dartmoor. Tavistock is not, in fact, on the Moor at all, let alone at its heart. The surgery where ACD practised medicine at that time was in the Stonehouse district of Plymouth, next to the old Royal Marine barracks, and Plymouth Council later mounted a plaque on the building to commemorate ACD's association with Plymouth. When the former surgery was demolished, the plaque lay for many years amongst some rubble at the rear of the site, until it was unearthed by The Baskerville Hounds, and it was subsequently re-erected on the car salesroom which was built on the site, with 'Sherlock Holmes' unveiling the plaque. Unfortunately, the beautifully cast plaque gives incorrect information, in stating that:

Sir Arthur Conan Doyle

1859 - 1930

On this site formerly stood
No, 1, Durnford Street where
between 1882 and 1884 Conan Doyle
practised medicine. His time
in Devon undoubtedly inspired
his later literary work
"The Hound of the
Baskervilles".

Kerbstones in the pavements of the Stonehouse area have been inscribed with details from some of the Sherlock Holmes stories in recent years. ACD also wrote two short stories about one of the other, great, fictional heroes he created, with the outrageous Brigadier Gerard, a French Hussar during the Napoleonic Wars, being held prisoner in Princetown Prison, or Dartmoor Depôt as it was more-correctly called at that time. Gerard did something which many inexperienced walkers on Dartmoor have done since, when he escaped at night, walked on the Moor through wind and rain, and ended up in the morning back at the point where he started, through having kept the wind bearing on one cheek all night as he walked. The wind had, of course, changed its direction gradually as he walked. The accuracy of ACD's description of the Moor improves dramatically between the Gerard story about Dartmoor which he wrote before his 1901 visit to gather local colour for *The Hound*, and the Gerard story about Dartmoor which he wrote after that visit.

Baskerville Horse Omnibus. The photograph from the Taylor Collection is of the omnibus owned by the Baskerville family which ran between Plymouth and Roborough at the time of ACD's short residence in Plymouth, and it is thus possible that ACD might have used this transport to get out of Plymouth for his rural walk to Tavistock. There were many Baskervilles living on and around Dartmoor at the end of the 19th Century, especially in the South-West area of the Moor. It may be noted that the advertisements for a very popular brand of soap on either side of the driver, which also appeared on horse omnibuses in London, recalls the name of Sherlock Holmes's landlady at 221B Baker Street. [9]

Dartmoor Historical and Literary Studies. ACD always attempted to learn as much as possible about the background to be used for any of his novels, and this includes *The Hound*. Although we do not have a reading list of the books which he may have consulted in writing his great Dartmoor epic, there are indications of some of the sources which he may have used, with these including articles and stories from magazines, non-fiction books, accounts of legends, and novels. One can even identify phrases which he may have 'borrowed' from other works. There are authors who will be well-known to all lovers of the litera-

ture of Dartmoor, such as SBG, R D Blackmore and Eden Phillpotts, but there are many others who are far less well-known. An extensive study of possible sources for parts of *The Hound* is included in this Investigation, but there are many more literary and historical influences which might be discovered by those who are specialists in Dartmoor geography, folklore, literature and history.

The Authorship Controversy. Shortly after the first episodes of *The Hound* had been published in *The Strand Magazine*, the suggestion was raised by an American critic that most, if not all, of the story had been written by ACD's friend, BFR, and not by ACD. In spite of ACD stating categorically that he could vouch for the book being all his own work, the accusation that ACD had put his name to work which he did not write was to be resurrected at regular intervals, mostly in the USA, and latterly with the support of Harry Baskerville, the Fletcher Robinson family's carriage driver who drove ACD and BFR around Dartmoor. Little consideration, if any, has been given to the writing skills of BFR in suggesting that he wrote most, if not all of *The Hound*, and arguments in favour of his authorship have frequently omitted evidence for ACD having been the sole, or the primary, author. The opportunity is taken in this Investigation to discuss this controversy more-fully than it has been elsewhere, and although it is accepted that the full story can probably never be uncovered now, it will be seen that the balance of the evidence currently available suggests that ACD's integrity remains unimpaired.

Films of *The Hound*. There can be few stories which have attracted the cinema and TV camera so frequently, with at least 19 film and TV versions of the story having been produced between 1909 and 2000. The universality of the attractions of the story is also revealed by the fact that it has been filmed using six different languages. There is much still to be discovered about the Dartmoor locational filming involved in those films which were actually made on the Moor, and there may well be film specialists or Dartmoor enthusiasts who can help with research into those films. One does need to be wary here, however, for this particular commentator still recalls the excitement of being put into contact with an elderly lady who had been reported as having been involved with one of the films which had been made on Dartmoor, with that excitement being instantly deflated when the lady concerned began talking about Basil Rathbone filming on the Moor, when his version of the story was made entirely in a Hollywood studio!

The *Hound* Phenomenon. There are many other associations with *The Hound* which will interest different sorts of enthusiasts, with some of these catering for the Dartmoor tourist, others for the Dartmoor historian and most for the Holmesian. With the last of these there are numerous Holmesian and Sherlockian societies around the world which have been named after some specific element of *The Hound*. The leading group here is, of course, Dartmoor's own specialist study group, The Baskerville Hounds, which, when the society was formed during the centenary year of the events of the story, 1989, initially encountered some problems with animal rights groups who thought that they might be a hunting organisation! This group, in addition to its studies of *The Hound*, also carries out research into the other Dartmoor books of ACD, mentioned above, and interacts with local Dartmoor societies, giving talks at village society meetings, or with more-widely-based groups which have some Houndianly-relevant association with Dartmoor.

The Continuing Game. It will quickly be seen that there are some widely differing opinions on some of the topics which are mentioned in this Investigation, and those who have never been involved in the Great Holmesian Game should appreciate that debate is an essential element of playing that game. It has rightly been said that if ten Holmesian authorities were asked to form a consensus opinion on any of the major topics of Holmesian discussion, then the result would be eleven opinions, with the consensus opinion and ten individual opinions which all differ from the consensus in their own way. No apologies are offered for the occasions when the recorded opinions of others are criticised in this Investigation, since that process is all part of the fun of the thing, and no apology is offered for the passion which might be detected in the explications given here! Holmesian studies inevitably involve strong reactions if they are worthwhile, in that everyone who enjoys the works of ACD to the full tends to feel strongly about those works to begin with. The reader is, however, reminded that the opinions which are expressed in this Investigation by this present commentator should not be accepted passively as definitive or conclusive, since in reacting to those opinions the reader will be playing the game which those opinions are meant to encourage.

ORIGINS AND DEVELOPMENTS

Scattered Locations and Changing Nature. The creation of *The Hound* began in Norfolk and was concluded in Surrey, having passed through several other counties and through at least one truly major change in its nature.

THE NORFOLK DAYS

South Africa and Cromer. ACD served as a doctor in a civilian field ambulance unit in what he later called The Great Boer War in the Spring and early Summer of 1900. During his voyage home on the *SS Briton* he developed a friendship with BFR, who had been serving as the special war correspondent of *The Daily Express* in South Africa, although there are some indications that the two men had met earlier. BFR was known to his very close friends as 'Bobbles', but ACD normally referred to him in the formal Victorian manner as 'Robinson', or as 'Fletcher Robinson'. A French army officer travelling on the boat, Major Roger Raoud Duval, repeated a common accusation from the war, by stating, in ACD's presence, that British troops had used dum-dum bullets in South Africa. ACD, being a fierce patriot and having written most of what was to be his history of the war whilst in South Africa, called Duval a liar. BFR intervened, and Duval eventually retracted his statement and apologised handsomely in writing to ACD, although the latter refused to mention Duval's name when recording the incident in his own autobiography almost a quarter of a century later. Whilst in South Africa ACD had contracted enteric fever, a disease which was to kill more British soldiers than were killed in action during that war, and early in 1901 ACD suffered from a recurrence of the disease. To recuperate he spent some time in March or April in the then newly popular Norfolk seaside resort of Cromer, staying at the Royal Links Hotel in the company of his friend, BFR, with ACD having stayed at that hotel as early as September 1897. The two men played golf, but on a cold and windy Sunday afternoon when play was impossible the two friends stayed in the hotel and ended up discussing one of the many hound legends of Dartmoor, and they may well have discussed other hound legends, as will be seen. They obviously agreed to collaborate in the writing of a book, for ACD wrote to his mother, from the Cromer Hotel:

> Fletcher Robinson came here with me and we are going to do a small book together *The Hound of the Baskervilles* - a real creeper.
>
> Cromer, Norfolk
>
> Your own, A.

Some time thereafter, ACD also wrote to the editor of *The Strand Magazine*, Herbert Greenhough Smith, about this proposed story:

> I have the idea for a real creeper for "The Strand". It is full of surprises, breaking naturally into good lengths for serial purposes. There is one stipulation. I must do it with my friend Fletcher Robinson, and his name must appear with mine. I can answer for the yarn being all my own in my own style without dilution, since your readers like that. But he gave me the central idea and the local colour, and so I feel his name must appear. I shall want my usual £50 per thousand words for all rights if you do business.

It will be seen in this second letter that ACD has already announced that he will be writing the story, although he wants to recognise BFR's contribution. What must be noted, however, is that the story at that time entitled *The Hound of the Baskervilles* was not the story which we now recognise under that title, for it did not include

The Royal Links Hotel. The hotel in Cromer where Arthur Conan Doyle was staying in 1901 when he was inspired to write *The Hound of the Baskervilles.* [12]

Sherlock Holmes. We know this because ACD subsequently wrote to Greenhough Smith and asked for a higher fee for the story because it by then included Holmes. One year after the Cromer meeting, in April 1902, the month when the final episode of *The Hound* appeared in *The Strand Magazine*, an account of the birth of the Holmes version of the story was published in an English literary magazine entitled *The Bookman* by J E Hodder Williams:

With his friend Mr. Fletcher Robinson he found himself at Cromer, where a long Sunday was spent together in friendly chat. Robinson is a Devonshire man, and he mentioned in conversation some old county legend which set Doyle's imagination on fire. The two men began building up a chain of events, and in a very few hours the plot of a sensational story was conceived, and it was agreed that Doyle should write it. When he came to working out the details, he found, however, that some masterful central figure was needed, some strong man who would influence the whole course of events, and his natural reflection was: "Why should I invent such a character when I have him already in the form of Holmes?"

Thus, clearly, it was agreed that ACD would write the non-Holmes version of *The Hound of the Baskervilles*, which, to avoid confusion, will be referred to hereafter in this Investigation as the "Proto-Hound", and this agreement was later confirmed by BFR, as will be seen. It will be appreciated that once Holmes was included in the subsequent version of this story, the contribution of ACD was even greater and there was less reason for mentioning BFR's contribution, although ACD did acknowledge BFR in all the editions which were published. We shall return to these statements later, as they are crucial to other matters, and we will also see that there is a possibility that BFR had a hound story of his own in mind when he went to Cromer, which may have formed a major part of the initial basis of the "Proto-Hound", if not of the final version of *The Hound*.

Bertram Fletcher Robinson. As is shown by the quotation from Hodder Williams used immediately above, BFR is frequently described as having been a Devonshire man, and he has almost equally as often been described in discussions of the origins of *The Hound* as having been born in Ipplepen in Devonshire. BFR was, to some extent responsible for this, in that he exaggerated his connection with Dartmoor, in claiming in 1905, for example, that his home was on the borders of Dartmoor when he had only inherited that house two years previously. He was, in fact, born near Liverpool, and spent more time in that city and in the city of London than he did in Devonshire. He moved to Devonshire in 1882, at the age of 11, when his father, Joseph Fletcher Robinson, bought Park Hill House on the Totnes to Newton Abbot road, in the village of Ipplepen, which lies some seven miles, as the bittern flies, from the high moorland of the South-Eastern edge of the Moor. BFR attended Newton Abbot College whilst living in Ipplepen, but in 1890 he entered Jesus College, Cambridge, where he studied law and where he earned a blue for rugby and rowed for his college. In 1894 he graduated and moved to London, but he never practised law, as he became employed as a journalist, following in the footsteps of his uncle, Sir John Robinson, who was the editor of *The Daily News* in London. BFR wrote occasional articles for various newspapers and magazines, and he eventually became an assistant editor of *The Daily Express*, and an editor of *Vanity Fair* and of *World*. He was, like ACD, an all-round sportsman, and he provided technical information for several books on a variety of sports. In 1904 he collaborated with J Malcolm Fraser in writing an adventure novel involving a lengthy chase across Europe, entitled *The Trail of the Dead*. He also wrote a series of short detective stories, published originally in the *Lady's Home Magazine* in 1904, which were collected in 1905 as *The Chronicles of Addington Peace*, wherein the eponymous hero

and his 'Boswell' are poor imitations of Holmes and Watson. There are differing accounts of BFR's death, at the age of 35, in 1907, including some hype by his fellow journalists about the suddenness of his demise under the supposed evil influence of an Egyptian mummy-case, newly arrived at the British Museum, about which he had been writing an article. He actually died far more-mundanely from peritonitis, following the perforation of his intestine after he had been ill with enteric fever for three weeks.

Differing Hound Legends. There are those who have suggested that it was one specific hound legend or another from Dartmoor which BFR told ACD in Cromer, but no direct evidence as to which particular legend was told has ever been produced, and it has to be admitted that the hound legend which is included in *The Hound* is very different from any of those which have been recorded about Dartmoor hounds. The legend which BFR told ACD may, therefore have been one which he had adapted or embroidered or misremembered, or ACD may have changed it drastically himself in recording it. There is no question about the fact that BFR did tell ACD some sort of Dartmoor hound legend, however, for ACD clearly registered this fact, as will be seen later. What is of interest is to consider what may have encouraged BFR to tell ACD a hound legend in Cromer, and the answer may well be the legends of another phantom hound, called 'Black Shuck', 'The Dog Shuck', 'Shuck', or, using the Scandinavian name which is still sometimes used in Norfolk, 'Scucca'. There are several legends about this giant black hound, which supposedly still haunts the coasts of Norfolk, and especially the Cromer area, which bear a very close resemblance to the legend contained in *The Hound*, but there are also suggestions that the legend which inspired ACD came from the Welsh borderlands, where the main branch of the ancient Baskerville family lived, as will be discussed later in the Investigation.

BFR's Initial Involvement. ACD was clearly excited by the legend, or legends, which he was told, and he directly attributed the inspiration for

The Hound to BFR when the first episode of the story was published in *The Strand Magazine*, in August 1901, and, in slightly varying ways, in the first editions of the story when it appeared in book form. Before the full Sherlock Holmes story could develop, however, ACD and BFR would explore Dartmoor and gather the sort of atmospheric detail which still brings the book to life a century after it was created.

THE DEVONSHIRE DAYS

Henry 'Harry' Matthews Baskerville. After the short holiday in Cromer, ACD visited London to clear up some urgent matters, and he then travelled down to Devonshire to stay, some have claimed, with BFR at the home of BFR's father, at Park Hill House in Ipplepen. Joseph Fletcher Robinson's carriage-driver, Henry Baskerville (usually known as Harry), bore the name used for one of the leading characters in the story, Sir Henry Baskerville, and Harry later claimed on many occasions that BFR, and even ACD, had asked for his permission to use the name. This is at least partial nonsense, in that it has been seen here that ACD and BFR had decided upon the Baskerville part of the name of the book whilst they were still in Cromer. Perhaps the forename 'Henry' was decided upon after the two writers met up again in Devonshire, or BFR may have mentioned his father's carriage driver to ACD in Cromer, but Harry Baskerville seems to have been a sharp operator in terms of subsequently capitalising upon his connection with the book, with his name later appearing in the local and even national newspapers. He certainly exaggerated both his connection with the book and the contribution of BFR to it whilst being interviewed by clever journalists, who saw the advantages of potential scandal, or by gullible Sherlock Holmes enthusiasts who thought that they had uncovered a new insight on the book. Suffice it to say for now that Harry Baskerville, and others, were erroneously to claim that BFR wrote much, if not all, of the book.

Princetown and Holmes. By the time that ACD reached Dartmoor, or soon thereafter, he had decided to include Holmes in the story, and this must have completely changed the nature of the book. Harry Baskerville later described ACD and BFR working on the book together until late in the night at Park Hill House, and he also described the way in which he drove them over the Moor in the Fletcher Robinson family carriage to visit places which were to be mentioned in the book. What Harry Baskerville never seems to mention in any of his many interviews is the fact that ACD and BFR actually stayed at what was then Rowe's Duchy Hotel in Princetown, a building which has since become the High Moorland Visitor Centre operated by the National Park Authority, whilst they were gathering the local colour for the book. In this building there is now a permanent Sherlock Holmes exhibition, including a life-size mannequin of Holmes and a full-size portrait of ACD watching his famous creation going out onto the Moor, as well as other exhibits. From the hotel, ACD wrote to his mother, saying:

Dearest of Mams,

Here I am in the highest town in England. Robinson and I are exploring the moor over our Sherlock Holmes book. I think it will work out splendidly - indeed I have already done nearly half of it. Holmes is at his very best, and it is a very dramatic idea - which I owe to Robinson.

We did 14 miles over the moor today and we are now pleasantly weary. It is a great place very sad & wild, dotted with the dwellings of prehistoric man, strange monoliths and huts and graves.

Previous discussions of this topic have included only the above two paragraphs from this letter, with the well-known authority on ACD, Richard Lancelyn Green, referencing the collection at the Château de Lucens as the source. Professor Christopher Frayling, in his excellent Introduction to the Penguin Classics edition of *The Hound*, continued the letter as follows:

Bertram Fletcher Robinson and Harry Baskerville. Bertram (third from left in rear row) and Harry (second from right in front row) in the Ipplepen Cricket Team. [15]

In those old days there was evidently a population of very many thousands here, and now you may walk all day and never see one human being. Everywhere there are gutted tin mines.

Tomorrow we drive 6 miles to Ipplepen where R's parents live. Then on Monday Sherborne for cricket, 2 days at Bath, 2 days at Cheltenham. Home on Monday the 10th. That is my programme.

All of the biographers who mention this letter claim that it was written on 2 April 1901, but this letter may actually have been written on 2nd May or, more probably, on 2nd June 1901. The writer chosen by the family to write the 'official' biography of ACD, John Dickson Carr, remarked that after his four-day stay with BFR in Cromer in 'March' 1901, ACD had to give a dinner at the Athenæum Club before he could travel down to Devonshire, and Carr mentions the names of five of the guests at that dinner, including James Barrie and Winston Churchill. The Athenæum has kept all of the records for dinner parties having more than three persons present up until 1910, and there is only one such party listed for ACD in 1901, where he had 11 guests to dinner on 30 April. ACD seems to have been celebrating his very recent election to membership of the Athenæum, where he was, unusually, selected by Committee choice rather than by election by the members, since in addition to a choice of four other wines he pushed the boat out with eight bottles of the 1884 Moet et Chandon Champagne at 8 shillings a bottle! According to Dickson Carr's statement, however, ACD cannot have reached Devonshire before May 1901. Richard Lancelyn Green, has indicated that one of ACD's account books shows a payment made to the Royal Links Hotel in Cromer on 30 April 1901, and he suggests that there is other evidence that ACD stayed at the hotel on 27-28 April in that year, which would fit nicely with the journey back to London for a party on 30 April. In another account, updating the Gibson and Green bibliography of ACD's works, there is a small note stating that ACD did not visit Dartmoor until late May. This suggests that 2nd June might be the correct dating of ACD's letter from the Duchy Hotel to his mother, and it may be noted that the only month when the 10th fell on a Monday in 1901, as mentioned in the letter's programme, was June. Professor Frayling has stated that there is evidence for ACD playing cricket at Sherborne on 3-4 June, at Bath on 5-6 June, and at Cheltenham on 7-8 June, which very strongly supports the June dating.

THE PUBLICATION OF THE STORY

The Completion of the Story. ACD returned to his recently-completed home, "Undershaw", in Hindhead, on the Surrey-Hampshire border, where he lived with his wife, Louise, and his two children, Mary, aged 12, and Kingsley, aged 9. It was in this naturally-dark house, being built on a platform cut into the side of a hill and being over-shadowed by a clump or 'shaw' of trees, that ACD had installed his own electricity generating plant, rather in the way that Sir Henry Baskerville announced that he would install an electric light system at 'Baskerville Hall' to relieve its naturally-dark appearance. In a service buildings block at the rear of the house, ACD kept his own carriage and horses, tended by his carriage driver, rather in the way that Sir Henry Baskerville had his own carriage and driver, with the latter being named Perkins. It was at "Undershaw" that *The Hound* was completed, but only after ACD had renegotiated the fee with the editor of *The Strand Magazine* to the higher rate of £100 per thousand words over the inclusion of Sherlock Holmes. Given that *The Hound* contains almost exactly 60,000 words, the fee paid for the initial magazine serialisation of the story, at some £6,000, was a very large sum indeed for those

days, considering that the large house which had been built to ACD's design, and the extensive grounds which surrounded it in what was then known as the 'Little Switzerland' of Surrey, had cost about the same amount. There was, of course, more to come, with the book rights, and with the overseas publication rights. Not that the financial advantages were all one-way, in that the inclusion of *The Hound* in *The Strand Magazine* almost doubled the sales in the UK, to 300,000.

Serial and Book Publication. The story appeared initially in nine parts in consecutive monthly issues of *The Strand Magazine*, between August 1901 and April 1902. Each of the nine episodes of the serialisation appeared in the American edition of *The Strand Magazine* one month after the English episodes. Very shrewdly, financially, the first book edition of the story, published by George Newnes Ltd who also published *The Strand Magazine*, appeared on 25 March 1902, prior to the publication of the final episode of the story in *The Strand Magazine*, with 25,000 copies being produced in the first English printing, at a cost of 6 shillings each. A copy of this edition of the book, complete with its dustjacket, was sold at auction in 1999 for £80,700, which indicates the value of the dust-jacket when it is appreciated that good copies of the same edition, but without the jacket, could be obtained for £2,000 in the same year. This also explains why there had earlier been an attempt at selling a forged copy of the dustwrapper! A similar, pre-serial-conclusion marketing process was used in the USA, with the first American book edition, published initially by McClure, Phillips & Company at a price of $1.25, appearing on 15 April 1902, and with the final episode of the story in the American edition of *The Strand Magazine* not appearing until the following month. This clever ploy obviously encouraged the sale of the book to those who could not wait a further month to discover the full solution of the story, and there were clearly many of these, with discussions having taken place in national newspapers over the solution. As a result, 50,000 copies of the book were sold during the first ten days of publication in the USA. There were eventually to be many hundreds of different editions of the story, from many different publishers, even within one country, and with numerous translations.

TEXTUAL AND PLOT CONSIDERATIONS

The Text. Non-Holmesians might be surprised to find that, in spite of *The Hound* being a classic, there are several different versions of the text in print in English, quite apart from the numerous foreign language editions. The differences between these texts are mostly minor, but there is one fairly major variation which was introduced by the author. Some of the minor differences are also the result of changes made by the author, which are entirely justified, but others have been made by publishers, both intentionally and unintentionally, and yet others have been made at the suggestion of Holmesian scholars, and not all of these are justified. The only important versions of the text are: that of the holograph manuscript, that which appeared in serial form in *The Strand Magazine* between August 1901 and April 1902, and that of the first book edition, from Newnes, of March 1902. The whereabouts of most of the manuscript is not known, and it is thought that much of it may no longer exist, because of the deterioration of the high acid content paper upon which it was written. In addition, individual pages from the manuscript were sent out to booksellers throughout the USA to be put on display as part of a publicity campaign, as if the publication of such an important book needed publicity! The whole of Chapter XI of the manuscript does exist, in the Berg Collection of the New York Public Library, and this does reveal, in spite of the general claim which is made for ACD making very few changes within his manuscripts, that numerous alterations were made within the manuscript of this book. Some 15 single pages of manuscript are also known to exist. The version of the text used in this centenary edition of *The Hound* is that which appeared in *The Strand Magazine*, warts and all, because it was the version through which the story was introduced to the world a century ago. Most of the errors

which existed in that version are truly minor, especially in connection with ACD's sometimes excessive use of commas (a habit shared to a lesser extent by the author of this Investigation!), and with a certain amount of inconsistency in the use of capitalisation. Others are, however, very significant, and some of these will be discussed elsewhere in this Investigation, where there will also be an examination of some of the 'improvements' which have been made in other important editions of the story. Some of the minor variations will be mentioned in the Annotations which accompany the main text. The changes which were made when the story first appeared in book form will also be included in the Annotations. One might add that in 1980 an American Sherlockian, Bliss Austin, made a claim that ACD had produced a play version of *The Hound*, but the evidence for this is far from conclusive. There have certainly been far too many dubious play adaptations by others!

Scholarship Editions of the Text. Because of the variation which exists between different editions of the Sherlock Holmes stories, a 'standard', single-volume edition of the complete stories is used by most Holmesians, as published by Doubleday in 1929, entitled *The Complete Sherlock Holmes*, which has subsequently been re-issued by several other publishers, with the most significant re-issue being that from Penguin Books. Although that edition is primarily based on the texts issued by *The Strand Magazine* (the first two Sherlock Holmes novellas never appeared in that magazine), it does introduce many new errors, including the Americanisation of some of the text. The other significant edition of the Sherlock Holmes stories, in nine volumes, is that published by Oxford University Press in 1993. This series attempted to produce a 'definitive' edition of the stories, and it was far more successful in doing this than any previous attempt, but the volume containing the text of *The Hound* was probably the least successful in the series, in that the editor of that volume, unlike the editors of the other volumes, was not a Doylean specialist, let alone a specialist on *The Hound*. The introduction and annotations of

Rowe's Duchy Hotel. This is the building as it was in 1889, but it was altered slightly by the time that ACD stayed there in 1901. The building now houses The High Moorland Visitor Centre, and upon entering one finds a life-size mannequin of Sherlock Holmes descending the hotel's main staircase under the watchful eye of a life-sized image of ACD. The building beyond the cart on the left is The Plume of Feathers. The road leading to the horizon heads for Yelverton and Plymouth, whilst the road to the right passes the main entrance to Dartmoor Prison to join the main road across the Moor, from Moretonhampstead to Tavistock. [15]

that volume contain numerous errors of fact and interpretation, and the text is certainly not accepted as being definitive by all students of *The Hound*.

The Plot. There is a major flaw in the three other Holmes novellas which is not present in *The Hound*, in that they each contain a central 'flash-back' section which tends to hold up the action in an unacceptable way. These flashbacks also involve another flaw which presents itself too-frequently in ACD's novels, in that they all contain, in varying degrees, too much petty and slightly irrelevant detail, which ACD seems subconsciously to have insisted upon including to indicate the amount of research he had carried out during the writing of the book. ACD was a superb teller of short stories, and each of the other three Holmes novellas seems to be an excellent short story, marred by the extraneous centre sections. In 1987, in celebration of the centenary of the publication of the first of the Holmes novellas, *A Study in Scarlet*, an adaptation of the story was presented in the Kings Theatre in the city where the story was written, Portsmouth, wherein the central third of the original story was

replaced by some ten lines of narrative, and the result was vastly superior to the original. In *The Hound*, there is no such irrelevant digression from the development of the main plot, but we do have the strange situation whereby the hero of the story, Sherlock Holmes, disappears for around one third of the book. The centre stage is held during that period, and well-held, by Dr Watson, and the information which he gives us is all entirely relevant to the main theme of the story. This is certainly Watson's case *par excellence*, and it is therefore a great shame that his star performance has been ruined in many of the film adaptations by having him played as a bumbling idiot. In spite of Holmes's absence, we do still feel that he is present, in that Watson's various narratives, letters, reports and diary entries from '*Baskerville Hall*' are written as if they were half of a conversation with Holmes at '*221B Baker Street*'. The first third of the story is more-classically like the Holmes short stories, with Holmes, for example, carrying out a model example of his deductions, inductions and abductions over Mortimer's walking stick. There is plenty of action on the Moor in the final third of the story, with only the final chapter, 'A

Retrospection', being disappointing, in that it involves far too many loose ends having to be tidied up, and in that some of the explanations given are rather dubiously based.

The Atmosphere. There is, in fact, given its relative length, very little detection in the story, and it might just as easily be described as being a Gothick Novel, instead of being described as a Detective Novel, in that it evokes some dark fear from within ourselves. This can be seen on even a very mechanical level, in the way in which the word 'dark' appears 36 times and the word 'black' appears 39 times in the story, with much of the action, indoors and out on Dartmoor, taking place at night. The word 'fear' arises on 23 occasions. ACD is often accused, wrongly, of having characters who are one-dimensional, but there is a large degree of depth in the portrayal of some of the minor characters in *The Hound*, as well as with the major characters. ACD has also, equally wrongly, been accused of lacking a sense of humour in all but the crudest of his comedies. There is a good deal of subtle humour in *The Hound* to relieve the darker moments, ranging from Frankland threatening to take an archaeologist to court for removing the human remains from a prehistoric grave without the permission of the relatives, to Sir Henry saying, in connection with the legend of The Hound that: *"...it's the pet story of the family..."*! It is with the re-creation of the atmosphere of the Moor itself, however, that the book really excels, and there is nothing to match it for this. This is, perhaps, best revealed by the way in which one can find so many suitable candidates for most of the invented Dartmoor locations from the book on the real Moor.

Holding it only an inch or two from his eyes
Holmes, discovering what turns out to be a vital clue,
although he does not pass it on to Watson.

HISTORICAL SOURCES

INTRODUCTION

General Points. In his *A Book of Dartmoor* (published by Methuen in 1900), SBG wrote, primarily in condemnation of those who had developed Druidical explanations for many of the antiquities on Dartmoor:

> The old school of antiquaries started with a theory, and then sought for illustrations to fit into their theories, and took facts and distorted them to serve their purpose, or saw proofs where no proofs existed. The new school accumulates statistics and piles up facts, and then only endeavours to work out a plausible theory to account for the facts laboriously collected and registered.

This might almost be taken to be a re-working of the statement made by Sherlock Holmes in the first of the short Sherlock Holmes stories, 'A Scandal in Bohemia' published in *The Strand Magazine* in July 1891:

> It is a capital mistake to theorize before one has data. Insensibly one begins to twist facts to suit theories, instead of theories to suit facts.

ACD certainly had plenty of historical and prehistorical data about Dartmoor available to him when he began writing *The Hound*, in many of the works of The Big Four of Nineteenth Century Dartmoor historical writing: Samuel Rowe, SBG, Richard Hansford Worth and William Crossing. One should, perhaps, note that much of the content of ACD's earliest sources might more-appropriately be called antiquarian, or even anecdotal, rather than historical, but standards of scholarship were improving enormously in connection with the Moor at the end of the century. Amongst the earlier writings on Moor matters, one of the most notable was

Samuel Rowe's compendious *A Perambulation of Dartmoor* from 1848 (the field work involved was carried out in 1827-28), but there was a vast increase in available material after the foundation of the Devonshire Association in 1862, with its annual *Transactions* providing a treasure trove of local research which continues today. At the time that ACD visited the Moor, Rowe's *Perambulation* had been updated and expanded by his grand-nephew, J Brooking Rowe, in 1896, but much of its by-then discredited Druidical explanation for antiquities on the Moor was left untouched. William Crossing had already published several of his books on the Moor, and much of the material of his *Hundred Years on Dartmoor*, which was not published in book form until August 1901, had been released in article format in *The Western Morning News* (a newspaper mentioned specifically in *The Hound*) in 1900. SBG had not only produced his general account of Devon, *A Book of the West: Volume 1 - Devon* (1899), but his more-specialised account of Dartmoor, *A Book of Dartmoor* (1900), in addition to scores of items on Dartmoor in journals, magazines and newspapers.

PREHISTORY

The Broader Victorian View. Many of the early excavations on Dartmoor were carried out by treasure seekers, who destroyed vital evidence and left no details of the sites prior to their activities. This might rightly be condemned, but, given the length of the periods with which they deal, too many modern archaeologists condemn the activities of their more-serious, late-Victorian predecessors, without appreciating that their own activities might equally well be condemned, or their theories looked upon as ridiculous, by future archaeologists. Although we might wish that the late-Victorians had carried out their excavations in the modern way, we should accept that without the advances made by the Victorians we would not now be in a position to make our own contributions. Non-specialists might also welcome something like the bold way in which the Victorians were not afraid to produce large-scale views of prehistory from their work, in comparison with the way in which many modern specialists within archaeology tend to spend forever polishing their spectacles without ever looking through them! The late-Victorians should be better appreciated as the giants upon whose shoulders the modern archaeologists stand.

The Dartmoor Exploration Committee. The 1890s saw a giant leap forward in the study of the archaeology of Dartmoor, especially under the influence of the Devonshire Association, which set up a Committee on Dartmoor in 1877 to record antiquities on the Moor in the face of their increasingly rapid disappearance. In 1879 they set up a Devonshire Barrow Committee, and although this initially excluded Dartmoor,

that area was added in 1882, and Richard Nicholls Worth prepared the findings of the group within the *Report and Transactions of the Devonshire Association* (usually just referred to as the *Transactions*) until 1896. His son, Richard Hansford Worth, then took over until 1950, and established far higher standards of accuracy in the surveying of sites and the recording of details, although only rarely carrying out excavations himself. In 1894 a six-man Dartmoor Exploration Committee was formed within the Devonshire Association, which overlapped to some extent with the personnel and activities of the Devonshire Barrow Committee. The Secretary was SBG, but his work could never be claimed to be a model of care and accuracy, in contrast to that of his friend and fellow Dartmoor Exploration Committee member, Robert Burnard, who created a wonderful collection of photographs of the Moor, its antiquities, buildings and people, and some of his

Grimspound – Hut No 7. Robert Burnard's own handwritten caption for this photograph, taken on 28 April 1894, refers to the 'hearth' and to the 'flatstone' in the bottom of this stone hut circle. It will be recalled that Watson mentions the *"...flat stone..."* in the middle of the stone hut in which Holmes stayed on the Moor, and the *"...stone slab..."* upon which Neolithic (sic) man had once slumbered in that hut, as well as the way that *"...ashes of a fire were heaped in a rude grate."* [22]

extremely interesting photographs have been included in the present study. Burnard was the son of a Mayor of Plymouth, and it will be recalled that ACD had originally mentioned the Mayor of Plymouth in the manuscript of *The Hound*. A third founding member was Dr Arthur Prowse, who had been, like Watson, an Army surgeon, although the former had been far more successful than the latter, in reaching the rank of Lieutenant Colonel. Two other members were father and son Worth team, R N and R H. The final member was the Reverend W A Gordon Gray. In Dr Mortimer we appear to have an amalgamation of several of these figures, with him being a professional man who seems to have devoted more interest to his hobby than to his profession, but the primary influence is certainly SBG, who summarised the work of the others until 1905 in the 'Reports' published in the *Transactions*. Interestingly, ACD's companion on the Moor, BFR, included a reference in his 1904 short Dartmoor story, 'The Tragedy of Thomas Hearne', to the narrator acquiring a knowledge of Dartmoor archaeology from "...the reports of that worthy society the Devonshire Association." The direct influence upon ACD might have come from BFR's father, Joseph, who was a member of that august society, and who received its *Transactions* until 1903, whilst BFR had moved his primary and professional interests to London. In 1894 the Committee carried out the first, and still-largest in scale, excavation at Grimspound, the hut circle enclosure which seems to have played an important rôle in the creation of the name of the *'great Grimpen Mire'*, and which is reflected in the number of references to groups of stone hut circles, with ACD and BFR having visited Grimspound in 1901. The speed with which the group worked does, of course, justify some of the modern criticisms, in that 15 of the 24 huts at Grimspound were excavated within 17 Days! The group did, however, carry out some of the earliest experimental archaeology, by eating their lunches within some of the hut circles and then throwing the chicken bones outside in order to examine further the area within bone-throwing distance.

SABINE BARING-GOULD

Themes Ancient and Modern. The paragraph title used here might be excused, and explained for those not in the know, by reference to the title of the hymnal, *Hymns Ancient and Modern*, in that SBG was the writer of 'Onward Christian Soldiers' and other popular hymns. Archaeologically, he contributed annual reports, on behalf of the Dartmoor Exploration Committee, to the journal of the Devonshire Association, including one devoted to Grimspound in 1894. He also published more-popular accounts of Grimspound in *The Western Morning News* in the Summer of that year. These would all have been readily available to ACD when he stayed at the home of Joseph Fletcher Robinson in 1901, as the latter was a keen member of the Devonshire Association, having become a member in 1884, and he was accorded an obituary in the *Transactions* in 1904. Joseph would also almost certainly have had copies of SBG's previously-mentioned books on Dartmoor, with *A Book of Dartmoor* containing an extended account of Grimspound. It would thus probably have been from SBG that ACD suggested, through the pen of Dr Watson and the mouth of Stapleton, that the hut circles on Dartmoor were Neolithic, when they are now accepted as being Bronze Age. The details of Holmes's stone hut on the Moor are very much in accordance with SBG's descriptions of the hut circles at Grimspound. There are, however, a few Neolithic remains on the Moor, including the remnants of some long barrows. It will be recalled that Mortimer was excavating a barrow on Long Down when he found *"...a prehistoric skull..."* There is no Long Down on Dartmoor, so perhaps this may have been a private name allocated by Mortimer to a down upon which there existed a long barrow. One splendid example would be the megalithic chamber tomb near Corringdon Ball Gate, which is close to several other relevant Houndian sites. It is located on a gentle slope of Brent Fore Hill which could certainly be described as being a down, and the modern Ordnance Survey map labels this antiquity as 'Long Barrow'. There

Grimspound - Main Gateway. Robert Burnard's own handwritten caption for this photograph, taken on 4 May 1894, reads: "In this S.B.G. has entered and is admiring his handiwork in assisting to clear this pre-historic gateway. Camera pointing North - Hookney Tor in the distance." The hill on the far horizon is the Northern end of the Birch Tor ridge. This gateway is mentioned in 'A Tale of a Dartmoor Fog', with the escaped convict hiding behind the wall as the hero approaches the gate from the direction of the camera. [22]

appear to be no records as to who excavated this magnificent tomb, but it is extremely unlikely that Mortimer would have found a skull in it, or in any other site on Dartmoor, since the soil of the Moor quickly destroys bone and no prehistoric skulls have been found.

Populations Old and New. It might be thought that the influence of SBG was present in the way in which Watson, who at least had the grace to admit that *"I am no antiquarian..."*, suggests that ancient man *"...lived so thickly on what must always have been most unfruitful soil."* SBG's very young colleague in the Dartmoor Exploration Committee, Richard Hansford Worth, later severely criticised SBG's exaggeration of both the number of huts which existed on the Moor and the number of their occupants. SBG had suggested that "With regard to the numbers of people who lived on Dartmoor in prehistoric times, it is simply amazing to reflect upon. Tens of thousands of their habitations have been destroyed; their largest and most populous settlements, where are now the 'ancient tenements', have been obliterated, yet tens of thousands remain." Worth suggested that nowhere near so many habitations had been destroyed, and that about 1,500 hut circles remained, and modern assessments suggest something between 2,000 and 2,500. Watson seems to have exhibited an early, and more-extreme, version of Worth's estimation of the number of remaining hut circles, in that he says *"...many hundreds of them are scattered throughout the length and breadth of the moor..."*, and his comment about the inability of the Moor to support many people is echoed by Worth. There is another suggestion for the influence of SBG which links both the ancient and the Victorian people of the Moor. Frankland boasts that he had closed the woods where the Fernworthy folk used to picnic, and he says that: *"I have no doubt, for example, that the Fernworthy* *folk will burn me in effigy to-night."* There are no records of this sort of practice on Dartmoor in Victorian times, although it is perfectly possible with such a strongly minded group of people as the Moormen. Shortly before ACD's visit, however, the Dartmoor Exploration Committee had carried out a series of excavations at Fernworthy, and it was noted that the soil within the large stone circle there was covered with charcoal, suggesting that some form of ritualistic burning had possibly been carried on in Fernworthy in the distant past. Watson, Mortimer, Stapleton and Frankland were not the only characters in *The Hound* to comment on matters archaeological, however, in that Barrymore refers to the ancient inhabitants of the hut circles as *"...the old folk..."*, much in the way that many Moormen refer to the early tin miners as 'The Old Men', and that great Dartmoor writer, William Crossing, actually refers to them on occasion as 'the Old Folk'.

Other Writings by Sabine Baring-Gould. SBG's range of writings was truly vast, but he was very much interested in all forms of general antiquarian information. In December 1889 he published a book entitled *Old Country Life*, which included a chapter on 'Family Portraits'. This includes a real-life account of a member of a family being identified by sitting under a portrait of an ancestor, much in the way that Stapleton is recognised as being a Baskerville from his resemblance to a portrait of the wicked Hugo Baskerville, but the book also involves a lengthy discussion of atavism. It will be recalled not only that Holmes discusses Stapleton in terms of him being an atavistic throwback, but that Dr Mortimer had supposedly written an article for *The Lancet* in 1882, entitled 'Some Freaks of Atavism'. It may be noted that in 1891 SBG published a book entitled *Freaks of Fanaticism*. One historical connection with Fox Tor Mires which might have been suggested by SBG comes from his 1900 book, *A Book of Dartmoor*, where it is recorded that:

Fox Tor Mire bore a very bad name. The only convict who really got away from Princetown and was not recaptured was

last seen taking a bee-line for Fox Tor Mire. The grappling irons at the disposal of the prison authorities were insufficient for the search of the whole marshy tract.

This can, of course, be taken to mean merely that this prisoner escaped in a Southerly direction, or that he sank into the mire. ACD may also have derived some inspiration from SBG's 1900 account, in *A Book of Dartmoor*, of the Seventeenth Century inheritance problems involving the old house of North Wyke near South Tawton. There were complicated plans for cheating on the inheritance, a woman escaping from the house to seek refuge at a farm, litigation which lost a fortune, and the villain, Richard Weekes, crying: "I am come to do the devil's work and my own!"

Legal and Postal Matters. SBG frequently included purely historical elements in his novels, and a striking example occurs in his 1897 novel, *Bladys of the Stewponey*, which reveals a common interest between SBG and ACD over the condemnation of savage forms of personal treatment which were sanctioned by the law. In this book SBG comments upon the way that, exactly one hundred years before the events described in *The Hound*, a woman could, and was, tied to a post and burned to death for committing a crime against her husband. SBG further commented, in his 1896 novel, *Guavas the Tinner*, on the way in which in Elizabethan times a man could be condemned by the Dartmoor Tinners' Parliament to be tied to a post and semi-crucified. In *The Hound* ACD can be seen to be condemning the way in which a husband could, at the time depicted in the story, still legally imprison and beat his wife, by the way Beryl Stapleton is graphically described as having been whipped and tied to a post. This is, in fact, a further justification for the 1889 internal dating of the story, since the law on wife-beating was changed in 1891, although ACD continued to fight for divorce law reform, in favour of women, into the next century, and he eventually became the Chairman of the Divorce Law Reform League, with his opinions here being reflected in his comments on the deplorable marital situation of Laura Lyons.

Judging of Distances and Naming of Parts. We may, with the help of an anecdote recorded by SBG, be able to solve a geographical problem which occurs in *The Hound*, which also names two parts of Devonshire relevant to that story. Holmes suggested to Watson that Princetown Prison was *"…fourteen miles away…"* from 'Baskerville Hall', but nowhere can be fourteen miles away from Princetown Prison and still be on the Moor. In *A Book of the West - Volume 1 - Devon*, of 1899, however, SBG noted a Dartmoor practice whereby Moormen might be thought to refer to any distance which was more than a stroll as being 'fourteen miles' in length. He recorded the following encounter:

> The other day a bicyclist was spinning down the road to Moreton Hampstead. Not knowing quite where he was, and night approaching, he drew up where he saw an old farmer leaning on a gate. 'I say, you Johnnie, where am I? I want a bed.' 'You'm fourteen miles from Wonford Asylum,' was the quiet response, 'and fourteen from Newton Work'us, and fourteen from Princetown Prison, and I reckon you could find quarters in any o' they - and suitable.'

As there is nowhere which could be fourteen miles from all three of the locations mentioned, we have the same situation here as we had later with Holmes. It may be noted that in his Duchy Hotel letter, ACD suggests that it is a 6-mile drive to Ipplepen from Princetown, when it is actually 18 miles!

THE FLETCHER ROBINSONS

Personal Historical Influences. It may have been BFR's father, Joseph Fletcher Robinson, who provided some historical basis for several of the background touches of *The Hound*. Joseph was a keen huntsman, riding with the South Devon Foxhounds and the Dart Vale Harriers, and it may be noted that there was much discussion amongst huntsmen in the Dartmoor area at the time of ACD's visit with regard to the cross-breeding of hounds to increase their size. These discussions are well illustrated in a Dartmoor book of 1916 which covers the relevant period, J H W Knight-Bruce's *Dartmoor Days with the Forest Hunt*, and there are other discussions in that book which may reflect the influence of *The Hound*. One notices, for example, the way in which one particular foxhunting horse is described: "Belliver Tor, steadiest and best of hunters, of whom Tom said that he ought to be called Fox Tor Mire, 'for there was no getting to the bottom of him'…" There are similar discussions in the wonderful series of recollections by a Victorian Moorman, Harry Terrell, recorded by William Collier in two books, *Harry Terrell: A Dartmoor Philosopher* (1896) and *Country Matters in Short* (1899). All of these recollections have recently been re-issued within a single cover by Halsgrove, under the title of *The Hound and the Horn*. Joseph Fletcher Robinson would certainly have been well aware of all such discussions, and BFR himself wrote about foxhunting, whilst ACD had recently become a member of the local hunt near his home in Hindhead. The possible canine interest at the Fletcher Robinson home may be reflected in the references to the cross-breeding of The Hound. It is to be noted that although Watson detected elements of the mastiff in The Hound, which would account for its ferocity, it is the hound element which must have predominated, as is indicated by the title of the story, although Watson specifically mentioned bloodhound rather than foxhound. Contrary to popular belief, bloodhounds have not been used regularly on Dartmoor in pursuit of escaped prisoners, as trials proved them to be of little use. On a point of literary politics, Sir Charles Baskerville is recorded in the *Devon County Chronicle* account of his death as having been *"…the probable Liberal candidate for Mid-Devon at the next election…"* Joseph Fletcher Robinson's obituary in the *Transactions* of the Devonshire Association records: "In politics he was a strong Liberal, an active member of the Ipplepen Liberal Club, a personal friend of the

Grimspound. The Bronze Age settlement to the North of Widecombe, on the saddle between Hameldown Tor, on the Southern horizon, and Hookney Tor, from which Robert Burnard took this photograph on 27 July 1889, just two months before the events depicted in *The Hound.* The original gated entrance to the settlement is at the top of the enclosure wall. The water supply stream, Grimslake, enters the enclosure at the bottom left and leaves at the bottom right. Several of the individual stone hut circles can be seen, including Hut No 3 in the centre of the enclosure, where ACD and BFR probably smoked their pipes in 1901. The enclosure is estimated to have been occupied around 1300 BCE. [22]

late Charles Seale-Hayne, M.P., also a very close friend of Garibaldi." Sir Charles Seale-Hayne had been the Liberal Member of Parliament for the Mid-Devon Division, in addition to having the same title and forename as Sir Charles Baskerville. There is also a rather exotic, Southern-hemispherical connection between Sir Charles Baskerville and Joseph Fletcher Robinson, with the former having spent his adventurous days in South Africa and the latter having spent his in South America. It will be recalled that ACD too had experienced some adventures recently in the Southern hemisphere, with the War in South Africa, and he was, in another decade, to write about a different sort of adventure in South America, with his novel, *The Lost World.*

OTHER WRITERS

Small Historical Points. Various Victorian Dartmoor historians have been proposed as having provided information which ACD seems to have used in *The Hound*, but it is difficult to identify one particular source with some of these

possible references. It has been mooted, for example, that the references to Selden being in hiding near '*Baskerville Hall*' and being provided with food and clothing by the Barrymores, and of rewards being paid for information leading to the capture of escaped prisoners is a combination of several stories which include Royalists being thus supplied during the Civil War, as well as French and American prisoners of war and escaped convicts being thus provisioned and hunted. Such stories were commonplace on the Moor in Victorian times, when it was common for those who lived near prisons to leave food, drink and clothing outside the house whenever news of an escape was announced. This practice continued until the late-20th Century amongst the members of this commentator's own family, and with others who lived near Parkhurst Prison on the Isle of Wight, and it was done partly to prevent an escaped prisoner having to break into the house to obtain such things, but also out of a sense of sympathy for the escaped prisoner. Numerous writers also mentioned the fact that a reward was available to those who reported information which led to the capture of escaped prisoners, but there was a general reluctance about claiming this, exactly as Perkins mentions: *"...the chance of five pounds is but a poor thing compared to the chance of having your throat cut..."*. It might reasonably be thought that ACD obtained oral information from the horse's mouth, in that he did meet some of the senior staff from the prison whilst he was staying at the Duchy Hotel in Princetown in 1901, but BFR seems to deny that possibility in writing:

> The morning after our arrival Doyle and I were sitting in the smoking-room, when a cherry-cheeked maid opened the door and announced 'Visitors to see yeou [sic], gentlemen.' In marched four men, who solemnly sat down and began to talk about the weather, the fishing in the moor streams and other general subjects. As they left I followed them into the hall of the inn. On the table were their cards. The governor of the prison, the deputy governor, the chaplain and the doctor had come, as a pencil note explained, 'to call on Mr. Sherlock Holmes'.

One nicely confirmatory historical, or natural historical, reference comes from Rowe's updated *Perambulations*, in that Rowe's extensive listing of birds to be seen on the Moor, which includes rare visitors as well as regular residents, contains no reference to bitterns existing on the Moor, seven years after Stapleton suggested that the last of the bitterns might have been heard. One might, incidentally, find an indication of the influence of Rowe's Druidical theories in Dr Watson's references to the *"...temples..."* of the ancient people of the Moor. There is a hint, though, of the most dramatic line in the whole of *The Hound* in the report made by William Crossing which was later included in his *One Hundred Years on Dartmoor*. One of the earliest of Dartmoor's agricultural 'improvers', Edward Bray of Tavistock, visited the famous Cranmere Pool in September 1802, and in the peaty soil he found the footprints of a fox. Foxes were then very common on the Moor, so what can have encouraged him to record this particular sign? Might this have been an unusually large fox? The foxes of the North Moor were, according to Crossing, certainly larger and greyer than their Southern counterparts at that time. Bray may, therefore, have experienced something of the shock which caused Mortimer to say: *"Mr Holmes, they were the footprints of a gigantic hound!"*

LITERARY SOURCES

The Breadth of Doylean Reading. Once again, it must be stressed that ACD read widely in researching his longer stories, and there are many elements of *The Hound* which may echo themes which ACD had read in the works of others, especially when such works involved the topics which are touched upon in his story, and particularly when they involved Dartmoor. It must also be remembered that ACD had a near-photographic memory for tiny details in literary works, and he often noted very small changes which had been made to a text years after he had first read it.

SABINE BARING-GOULD

General Considerations. ACD may well have read several of SBG's works prior to visiting the Moor, in that many of them were published in serialised form in the same magazines which published ACD's works. *Red Spider*, for example, had been published in *Temple Bar* in 1887, but that book dealt with the area around Lew House in Lewtrenchard, rather than the Moor itself. *Urith: A Tale of Dartmoor*, published in 1891, would have been more useful for local colour, but this too was based on an area to the West of the Moor, around Lydford. It was in his earlier Dartmoor novel, *John Herring* (1883), that SBG not only introduced the story with an account of the Gubbins, a group of savages who once lived in burrows just beyond the Western rim of Dartmoor, but had them bringing animals across the whole width of the Moor to avoid detection, rather in the way that Stapleton does with The Hound, and we will return to an even earlier depiction of the Gubbins later in this Section. Some of the non-fictional accounts of Dartmoor may certainly have been used by ACD, and these are discussed elsewhere, but there is, however, one novel by SBG which is very much pertinent to *The Hound*: this was *Guavas the Tinner*.

Guavas the Tinner. The book, first published in November 1896 (although the title page of the first edition bears the date 1897), with a second edition quickly being produced in 1897, is based in Elizabethan times, but it is the geographical and character elements which are of great significance. The narrative wanders across many of the areas involved in *The Hound*, from Yealm Head in the South, across the headwaters of the Erme and Avon, through Fox Tor Mires and down the Swincombe Valley. It also extends along the route which ACD and BFR possibly followed, through Bellever to a tin mine in Chaw Gully, close to Grimspound. There exists, interestingly, a photograph by Robert Burnard of SBG in Chaw Gully in the same year as that of *The Hound*, 1889, with the gully looking like an ideal representation of the '*Cleft Tor*' which is mentioned in *The Hound*. Two of the major *Guavas* characters follow a path which heads along the Southern side of Fox Tor Mires, exactly as Watson and Stapleton walked along the Southern edge of the '*Great Grimpen Mire*' on their journey to '*Merripit House*'. There is a description of a bullock floundering into Fox Tor Mires and disappearing beneath it after a desperate struggle, exactly like that of the pony which Watson and Stapleton see. There is a fog which arises over Fox Tor Mires, exactly as happens in *The Hound*, and this fog makes it impossible to see the wands (the same word is used by ACD for Stapleton's way markers in the '*Great Grimpen Mire*') which are normally used to navigate through the mire. Characters in the story are terrified by a large, savage canine, in this case a wolf, which is kept tethered by a chain, and which is also deliberately kept in a starved condition to make it attack its victims. In the mire the wolf becomes covered with a substance which is phosphorescent, and which thus makes it glow in the dark. There is difficulty in *The Hound* over explaining the nature of the "*...cunning preparation...*" of phosphorous which is used to make The Hound glow, since phosphorous would have

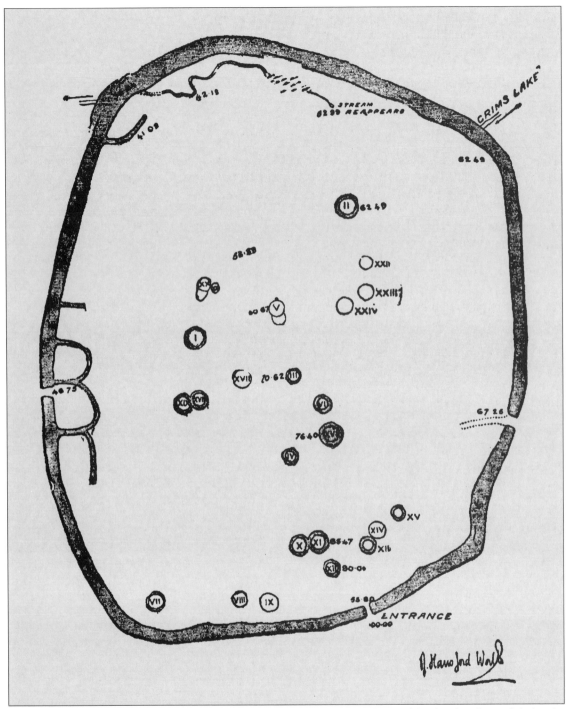

Grimspound. The plan drawn by R Hansford Worth, the colleague of Sabine Baring-Gould and Robert Burnard during the 1894-95 excavations, showing all 24 of the stone hut circles within the enclosure wall, and it would have been available to ACD in Sabine Baring-Gould's *A Book of Dartmoor* of 1900. The over-restored Hut 3 is seen in the centre of the enclosure, and Hameldown ridge leading to Widecombe is at the bottom of the drawing, with Hookney Tor at the top. A few of the huts still remain unexcavated. [22]

harmed The Hound and ruined its sense of smell. It is possible that SBG's phosphorescent substance was something like the non-injurious *Schistostega osmondacea* moss, which SBG mentions in his *A Book of Dartmoor* of 1900. It may be noted here that SBG said that this moss "...has a metallic lustre like green gold...", and that in the dark the ground where it occurs "...seems to be blazing with gold." It is also of interest that two of the places where he said that it occurred were Hound Tor and the Swincombe Valley, but it should be noted that its light was very dim and it tended to disappear when smeared onto the fingers. As with *The Hound*, a supernatural manifestation is blamed for the death of one of the Moor's inhabitants in *Guavas the Tinner*, and several of the Moor's residents claim to have seen this monster. The wolf is described as being a familiar of the Devil, but the hero of the story is convinced from the start that the creature is entirely natural, being the last of the Cornish wolves. It is the wolf, in fact, which drives one of the villains into the mire, where the man dies, and the wolf savages the throat of the other villain. When the first villain sees the wolf coming across the Moor at night he remarks: "...the sight of him makes my blood clot in my veins and my marrow freeze.", whilst Sir Henry Baskerville, upon first hearing The Hound says: "*...that sound seemed to freeze my very blood.*" Another connection between the two books occurs with the way in which both writers use the raven near places of death, with that bird being the traditional harbinger of death in European mythology. Physical cruelty is graphically described in both books, as is discussed in the Historical Sources section of this present 'Investigation', and both books are concerned with amatorial jealousy and materialistic envy, with property rights being important in both. Many of SBG's Dartmoor novels include real people, rather in the way that ACD is supposed to have included the name of a real Dartmoor prison warden, Selden, and this happens in *Guavas the Tinner*, where the heroine's mother is called Joan Ford, with this character living near the site of the real Joan Ford Intake kistvaen in the Swincombe Valley.

FREDERICK ADYE

General Considerations. It is rather sad that Frederick Adye's novel, *The Queen of the Moor* (published by J & R Maxwell in London in 1885, with a second edition being released by Macmillan in London in 1897) is now almost completely forgotten, for it is far superior in many ways to the numerous Princetown Prison escape stories (or, more-correctly, Princetown Depôt escape stories, since they are almost all concerned with escaping prisoners of war during the Napoleonic and American wars in the early Nineteenth Century, rather than with the convicts who occupied the building after it became a prison in 1850), but it is hoped that it will see a revival with a new edition being published in 2001 and with this discussion. Frederick Adye was the pen name of the Reverend William Frederick Adye, who had been the curate of the churches at Plymstock (1872-74) and at Lydford (1874-76), during which periods he gained an extensive knowledge of Dartmoor. *The Queen of the Moor* is a relatively lengthy novel, having initially been produced in a triple-decker format to meet the requirements of the then-dominating subscription libraries market, and being more than three times the length of *The Hound*. It is concerned with the escape of two French prisoners, a Captain and a Sergeant, and it is locationally centred on the Depôt and on the area around Tor Royal, including Fox Tor Mires, although it also diverts briefly to the Battle of Waterloo. The novel has the almost inevitable high degree of Victorian melodrama, but there is a directness of approach, a lightness of touch and a highly modern sense of humour which is missing in the later examples of this sub-genre. It also shows the influence of the late-Nineteenth Century 'New Woman' movement. ACD had fulfilled a death-bed promise, two years before he wrote *The Hound*, to complete the unfinished novel, *Hilda Wade*, of his friend Grant Allen, who had been a leading light in this feminist movement. ACD would have had a great interest in the Napoleonic War elements of the Adye novel, in that he was clearly fascinated by the Emperor, writing as he did three novels, two volumes of short stories and a play about the period. One major difference between *The Queen of the Moor* and *The Hound* is the way that Adye uses many more real buildings, such as Tor Royal (between Princetown and Fox Tor Mires), Oakery (or Okery) Cottage (beside Blackaton Bridge on the Princetown to Two Bridges road) and Parson's Cottage (beneath Crockern Tor) for important elements of his story, and he also bases some of his characters and incidents on real people and events, as with the real French Army Sergeant who escaped from the Depôt in the clothes of the Depôt doctor. This does sometimes create conflicts for those who know their Dartmoor history, in that we know, for instance, that Sir Thomas Tyrwhitt, and not the heroine of the novel, was living at Tor Royal at the time of the story (SBG moved Sir Thomas to Prince Hall in another of his Dartmoor novels, *Royal Georgie*, and he too had an interest in the French Emperor, in that he wrote a biography, *The Life of Napoleon Bonaparte*, in 1897).

Geographical Links. ACD would almost certainly have seen some geographical writing by Adye, albeit in an anonymous presentation, about a part of Devonshire, with numerous references to Dartmoor, including the prison. Adye's uncredited article, 'Winter on Exmoor', followed immediately after the first part of one of ACD's favourite stories of his own creation, *The White Company*, when that story began its serialisation in *The Cornhill Magazine* in January 1891. There are some wonderful descriptions of Exmoor in this article, including Adye and his pony getting stuck in a mire, and some even-better descriptions of Dartmoor in *The Queen of the Moor*, with the opening of the latter including the dreary arrival of a traveller at Tor Royal being followed by a total change of atmosphere in the morning, exactly as happens after Watson's arrival at '*Baskerville Hall*'. A lot of Adye's action takes place around Fox Tor Mires, and one of the major characters has to be rescued when his horse gets stuck in that mire. The character explains that the mire "...had appeared a capital bit of galloping ground...", which closely matches Watson saying, on seeing the great

Grimpen Mire for the first time: "*It would be a rare place for a gallop.*" Many of the locations mentioned in the Adye book are also mentioned in *The Hound*, including the prison, Bellever Tor (spelled 'Belivor' in this case), Merripit, and Lafter Hole (with that spelling being even closer to the '*Lafter Hall*' of *The Hound* than the present day Laughter Hole Farm). Indeed, the hunt in the story follows part of the route which ACD and BFR followed, down the Swincombe Valley and over Bellever Tor, past Laughter Hole Farm. Perhaps ACD chose that very route in attempting to recapture the atmosphere of the story which he had read? When Stapleton tries to explain away the sound of The Hound which he hears in the company of Dr Watson, he says that "*It's the mud settling, or the water rising, or something.*", and then goes on to suggest that "*Yes, I should not be surprised to learn that what we have heard is the cry of the last of the bitterns.*" In his book, Adye suggests that one of the few sounds which can be heard near the mire of Cranmere Pool, where the mud does settle and the waters occasionally rise, is "...the booming of the bitterns...", and yet by the time that ACD visited Dartmoor there were fears of the bitterns having become extinct. This is not the first time that ACD had referred to bitterns in this sort of way, in that he had used this phrase far more closely in the opening paragraph of his 1891 romantic adventure, *The White Company*, in describing the atmosphere of the New Forest. There he wrote, of the sound of the great bell at Beaulieu Abbey: "It was a common sound in those parts - as common as the chatter of the jays and the booming of the bittern." There may be other indications of the early influence of *The Queen of the Moor*, in other Sherlock Holmes stories, such as when Adye mentions silver cups for horse racing at Whitchurch Down, with ACD subsequently mentioning the training of racehorses on the Moor near Tavistock in 'Silver Blaze', published in *The Strand Magazine* in December 1892. Many Holmesians and Sherlockians, ignorant of the differing aspects of the Moor, have wrongly condemned ACD for suggesting that racehorses could have been trained on the rough and rocky Moor, without knowing that such training was

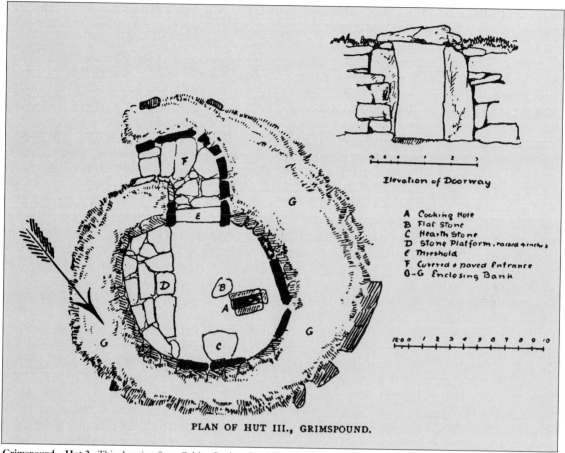

Elevation of Doorway

A Cooking Hole
B Flat Stone
C Hearth Stone
D Stone Platform, raised 4 inches
E Threshold
F Covered & paved Entrance
G-G Enclosing Bank

PLAN OF HUT III., GRIMSPOUND.

Grimspound – Hut 3. This drawing from Sabine Baring-Gould's *A Book of Dartmoor* would have been available to ACD during his 1901 visit to the Moor. It shows several of the features of the stone hut in which Sherlock Holmes spent some of his time on the Moor, including the *"…flat stone…"* and the *"…rude grate…"* with the cooking hole. It will also be seen how the wind-break curved porch would have prevented Watson from seeing directly out of the hut. [22]

carried on at Whitchurch even after the race-course closed, or that even rougher forms of horseracing took place at the annual Bellever Week gathering. Holmesians would instantly think of the *"…ancient and cobwebby bottles…"* which Dr Watson mentions in 'The Adventure of the Noble Bachelor', published in *The Strand Magazine* in April 1892, when they read Adye's reference to *"…cobwebby bottles…"* in *The Queen of the Moor*. Students of ACD's other works might well note the way in which Adye's French General confidently expects to receive his Marshal's *bâton* from Napoleon, in exactly the way that ACD's other hero, Brigadier Etienne Gerard constantly expects to receive his *bâton* from Napoleon, with the first example of his

expectation being included in 'How the Brigadier Slew the Brothers of Ajaccio', published in *The Strand Magazine* in June 1895.

Other Links. As with *The Hound*, there is a pack of hounds involved in *The Queen of the Moor*, and the name of one of Adye's hounds, 'Roysterer', recalls the three most-daring of the companions of the wicked Hugo Baskerville, who were referred to as *"…roysterers…"*. Reference is made by Adye to a post-hunt *"…carouse…"* being held regularly at Holne Chase, after there has been a reference to the hunt passing a tor with a cleft in it. Hugo's roys-terers are described as settling down to *"…a long carouse, as was their nightly custom."*, and a 'Cleft

Tor' is mentioned as being near *'Baskerville Hall'*. There is no *'Cleft Tor'* on Dartmoor, but there is a Cleft Rock at Holne Chase. There is an extremely fierce dog in Adye's story, which is, like Stapleton's hound, a cross-breed, and it is kept chained to a ring in a wall, and it goes for its victim's throat, exactly like Stapleton's hound. In Adye's hunt scene the quarry is reported as follows: "...they can see him ahead of the hounds, which are now running mute...", whilst the shepherd in the Baskerville legend reported that: "...*Hugo Baskerville passed me upon his black mare, and there ran mute behind him such a hound of hell as God forbid should ever be at my heels.*" When one of the ladies in Adye's story mentions suitable hobbies for a husband she suggests entomology, which is practised by Stapleton, and the card game of écarté, which is played by Mortimer and Sir Henry, even though that game had fallen out of fashion by the end of the Nineteenth Century. It is one of the servants of the house in Adye's story who goes to Plymouth to arrange a passage overseas for the escaped prisoner, whilst it is Barrymore who arranges a similar passage for Selden. There are scores of other small details which occur in both novels, with one leading character having just returned from Canada, and with another amusing himself by watching people in the park in London, exactly as Sir Henry and Dr Mortimer do, respectively, in both instances. There are tors on the horizon which are named, the sound of a hound seeking its quarry on the Moor, the Moor referred to unusually as a prairie, an old gentleman who sweeps the Moor with his telescope, and family portraits in the dining-hall including a reference to Reynolds.

Ill-Treating POWs. ACD collected and preserved many obsolescent words, and if he did read *The Queen of the Moor*, as seems highly likely, he may have tucked away one example for later revival, when the narrator in Adye's book, in commenting on the severity with which the authorities had dealt with a riot in the Princetown Depôt, suggested that "...in some places, especially in New York, there was considerable animadversion." That riot is based on the real riot of 6 April 1815, when seven prisoners were killed and over 60 wounded, and with most of the casualties being Americans who were angry at the delays over repatriation, with the American war having been concluded more than three months before the riot. An official enquiry decided that the Americans had been attempting to escape, and only mildly criticised the Depôt Governor for ordering his troops to open fire on them. Interestingly, one of the prisoners offering evidence was called Holmes! Between 1916 and 1919, ACD was strongly, and quite rightly from a historian's viewpoint, condemned by an anonymous reviewer in the *Times Literary Supplement* as each volume of ACD's six-volume history of the First World War, *The British Campaign in France and Flanders*, was published. When ACD eventually discovered that the unknown critic was the Royal Librarian, The Hon J W Fortescue, he complained about the way in which the latter, who was in fact an experienced military historian, had been "...picking out the pettiest details for animadversion." By that time ACD had written a propagandist booklet on the ill-treatment of prisoners of war, entitled *The Story of the British Prisoners*, in which he attacked the Germans but ignored the activities of British soldiers on Dartmoor during 1815 and in South Africa during what ACD called The Great Boer War.

ANON

General Considerations. It is even sadder when the author of a good story is not known, and when, as in this case, this is because of the poor regard which magazine publishers had for their authors, in that many of the magazines which became increasingly popular in the 1890s had a policy of not giving the names of the authors of the short stories which they published. This was the case with a short story entitled 'A Tale of a Dartmoor Fog', which appeared in *Chambers's Journal* on 22 April 1893. This story was clearly written by someone who knew the Moor very well, at least the part which he or she describes. It is also written by someone who knew their Dartmoor history very well. It seems, in fact, very probable that the anonymous author was Frederick Adye, for the style of writing is very similar in 'A Tale of a Dartmoor Fog' to that in the earlier *The Queen of the Moor*, as is the level of knowledge of Dartmoor, the types of interest revealed, and some of the phraseology. It might be noted that several of Frederick Adye's short stories and articles appeared anonymously in major magazines at the time that 'A Tale of a Dartmoor Fog' was published.

Geographical Links. 'A Tale of a Dartmoor Fog' is a story of a prisoner who has escaped from the Dartmoor Depôt, with the prisoner in this case being a British sailor who had traitorously served with the American Navy. Many of the 'American' sailors in the war of 1812-14 were, in fact, British sailors who acted for mercenary reasons, for political causes, or in rejection of the press gang enlistment used in Britain. The scene of action in this short story lies between Widecombe-in-the-Moor, along Hameldown, through Grimspound, then on to the former hamlet of Fernworthy before heading up the ridges through Hound Tor to Cawsand (Cosdon) Beacon and Belstone. The story involves the villain being driven by what appears to have been a spectral apparition into Raybarrow Pool, where he disappears. One cannot read the explanation about Squire Brewer's mare in the short story without recalling the extended version of the same explanation being given for the name of one of the leading characters in *The Queen of the Moor*. Thus we have, in 'A Tale of a Dartmoor Fog': "...he mounted his famous chestnut mare Jenifer (west-country for Guinevere)...". In *The Queen of the Moor* we have the fuller explication: "You will, probably, want to know how she got her curious name of Jenifer. It was given her by her god-parents, most likely with the idea that they were naming her after the consort of good King Arthur, who, it will be remembered, lived not far away in his castle by the Cornish sea. At least, Jenifer is a common name in Devon and North Cornwall, and probably is a corruption of Guinevere." When looking for a suitable location on the Moor to be used as an example of a place where one might die in a mire, both the short

story and the long novel choose Cranmere Pool, in spite of the fact that the pool was nothing of the sort in the 1890s, having been drained, although it may have been far more dangerous at the time in which the two stories are set, at the beginning of the Nineteenth Century.

EDEN PHILLPOTTS

General Considerations. Any examination of the possible influences of a book about Dartmoor written after 1894 would be incomplete if it did not include a consideration of the work of another of the Dartmoor literary giants, Eden Phillpotts, who remains the most prolific writer of novels about Dartmoor. His first book about Dartmoor, a triple-decker entitled *Some Everyday Folk*, was published in 1894, and he followed this with ten short tales about Dartmoor and its neighbourhood, *Down Dartmoor Way*, two years later. In 1898 he published the first of what was to be a 20-volume series of books which are known as 'The Dartmoor Cycle', with *Children of the Mist*, and this was followed by *Sons of the Morning* in 1900. The third volume, *The River*, was not published until 1902, but it was written during 1901, at almost the same time as *The Hound*. Each volume of the Dartmoor Cycle, with the exception of the two volumes of short stories, concentrates upon one particular area of the Moor, and Phillpotts stayed at each of these areas in turn in order to collect local colour, and 'colour' is a word to which we will return. The first three volumes were concerned with the Chagford, Gidleigh, and the West Dart and Two Bridges areas respectively, and they are thus not especially concerned with the areas involved in *The Hound*. It was not until 1911 that Phillpotts dealt with the Holne area, in *Demeter's Daughter*, and then it was in 1920 that he covered the Whiteworks and Fox Tor area in *Miser's Money*. The Avon Valley area was dealt with in 1923, in *Children of Men*, with that being the last novel of the Dartmoor Cycle. Although the Shaugh Prior area is not connected geographically with *The Hound*, other than through the possible association of the Devil and his black hounds at the Dewerstone, the 1909 volume, *The Three*

Grimspound – Hut No 3. The stone hut circle which was rather over-imaginativly restored by Sabine Baring-Gould and his companions in the Dartmoor Exploration Committee in 1894 (with further excavations in 1895). This photograph was taken by Robert Burnard on 28 April 1894. A railing was later erected to protect this hut, but the rails and the balanced lintel stone have since been removed. The rocky outcrop on the Northern skyline is Hookney Tor. [22]

Brothers, does concentrate on the Baskerville family, with the main Dartmoor branch of the real Baskerville family living in that area, and Eden Phillpotts cannot have been unaware of the new *frisson* associated with the word 'Baskerville' on Dartmoor. Phillpotts wrote many more books about Dartmoor, and one which rings a Houndian locational bell is *The Master of Merripit*, from 1914.

Doylean Connections. Obviously, the volumes of the Dartmoor Cycle published after 1902 cannot have influenced *The Hound*, but one should consider the possible influence of the first three volumes, for Eden Phillpotts was, when he worked as a writer in London, a personal friend and neighbour of ACD. They were both members of the group of writers who produced material for the *Idler* magazine, run by Jerome K Jerome, Robert Barr and George Brown Burgin, and they attended the frequent tea parties at the magazine's offices which often trailed on into uproarious dinner parties. The regulars included

J M Barrie, with whom ACD collaborated in the writing of a play, as well as Anthony Hope, and Israel Zangwill, with the last being a well-known writer of detective stories at that time. Phillpotts was, then, the Assistant Editor of the popular magazine, *Black and White*, and ACD provided that magazine with some short stories, including one entitled 'A Straggler of '15', which he later re-wrote as his Napoleonic play, *Waterloo*. Henry Irving bought the acting rights and had a huge success with it. Phillpotts later recalled ACD at length in his short memoir, *From the Angle of 88*, published in 1951 at the age of 88, although he was wrong in claiming that he knew ACD before the latter created Holmes, but he was correct in suggesting that ACD was "A big man in mind and body..." When ACD stayed at the Duchy Hotel in Princetown in 1901, Phillpotts was living in Torquay, but he had moved up to the Moor to research his latest book, *The River*, just as ACD was doing for *The Hound*. In fact, Phillpotts stayed at the Two Bridges Hotel, less than two miles from where ACD stayed, and although no records of a meeting have been located, one would certainly have been arranged had the two men known that they were temporary neighbours. Phillpotts was one of the few who remained appreciative of ACD after the latter became tainted by his involvement in the Cottingley Fairies affair, wherein ACD wrote extensively in support of two small girls who were only much later shown to have faked pictures of fairies which they had supposedly seen. One must also note another literary connection between ACD and Phillpotts, in that they both wrote detective stories, with some of those by Phillpotts appearing under the pen name of 'Harrington Hext'.

A Question of Style. There seem to be no specific examples of the influence of Phillpotts' Dartmoor Cycle in *The Hound*, although ACD would have gained an excellent understanding of Moor life from the volumes already published. ACD's style, however, would not have allowed him to use the sometimes excessive purple prose so frequently employed by Phillpotts although one may, in *The Hound*, see some of the affinity of the natural poet which is essential to the great story-teller. One constantly finds that Phillpotts discovers colour in the Moor, even at times when there was little natural colour available, and even though the plots of Phillpotts' novels frequently involved a Hardyesque element of disastrous relationships. As has been mentioned earlier, *The Hound* is very much lit in terms of black and white, although there is the occasional example of colour, mainly through Dr Watson's notorious predilection for the ladies, but Watson did also occasionally introduce the subtle colouring of the Moor, as with the description of the view on his arrival on the high Moor: *"Bronzing bracken and mottled bramble gleamed in the light of the setting sun."* The situation is slightly different with Phillpotts' own Dartmoor Depôt escape novel, *The American Prisoner*, which is not part of the Dartmoor Cycle, but this was not published until 1904. It, like *The Hound*, seems to reveal the influence of Adye's *The Queen of the Moor*. If it be thought that the suggestion that Phillpotts may have influenced ACD slightly is

strained, however, then it should be appreciated that Phillpotts actively attempted to influence the writing of many of his friends, and another example involves a fictional detective who is almost as well-known as Holmes, in that Phillpotts advised the young Agatha Christie when she was creating her first Hercule Poirot novel, *The Mysterious Affair at Styles*, part of which she created as she walked the hills of Dartmoor. She later wrote a murder novel about the Moor, *The Sittaford Mystery* (entitled *Murder at Hazelmoor* in the USA). The suggestion of one Sherlockian, Nancy Blue Wynn, however, that Christie 'embarrassingly' borrowed from *The Hound* in the latter book, solely on the grounds of an escaped convict hiding on the Moor and relying on the help of mysterious relatives, is a gross exaggeration.

R D BLACKMORE

General Considerations. Eden Phillpotts would certainly have recommended the Dartmoor works of Richard Doddington Blackmore to ACD, or anyone else, in that Phillpotts constantly championed the cause of Blackmore as a great writer. One might note that Phillpotts was involved in the creation of a memorial window and a marble cameo portrait of Blackmore in Exeter Cathedral. Blackmore had mentioned one element of the fringes of Dartmoor which may have influenced ACD in the same way that it did SBG, with his account of the Gubbins, a disreputable band of near-naked savages who lived in burrows just beyond the Western rim of the Moor, near Brentor, and who existed mainly by stealing sheep on the Moor. The Gubbins were recorded by Thomas Fuller as being extinct by the mid-Seventeenth Century, in his *Worthies of England* of 1882, but it will be noted that Dr Watson described Selden's first appearance as follows: *"Foul with mire, with a bristling beard, and hung with matted hair, it might well have belonged to one of those old savages who dwelt in the burrows on the hillsides."* Blackmore's short account appeared in *The Maid of Sker* (1872), where he wrote: "And truly the place was chosen well; for the hollow not far below it, might be found those savage folk.... Scarcely any of the men had more than a piece of old sack upon him; and as for the women, the less I say, the more you will believe it." Of the children of the Gubbins he wrote: "These little creatures, all stark naked, seemed to be well enough of for food, of some sort or another, but to be very badly off for want of washing and covering up. And their little legs seemed to be growing crooked; the meaning of which was beyond me then; until I was told that it took its rise from the way they were forced to crook them in, to lay hold of one another's legs, for the sake of natural warmth and comfort, as the winter-time came on when they slept in the straw all together." It has already been mentioned that SBG later used the Gubbins in 1883, in a way which is reflected in *The Hound*. The horrific ending of Blackmore's book, with the villain dying as a result of what is described as "...ignominious canine madness...", has much the same atmosphere as that involved in the death of the wicked Hugo Baskerville. Reference has been made above to the occurrence of the word 'Roysterer' in both *The Hound* and *The Queen of the Moor*, but the influence of this unusual word may have been given to both by Blackmore, for it occurs in *The Maid of Sker*, significantly in connection with a Dartmoor hunt. Blackmore provided far more information on life on the Moor with his later book, *Christowell* (1881).

L T MEADE & ROBERT EUSTACE

'Followed'. In 1996, Richard Lancelyn Green, one of the world's leading Doylean scholars, suggested that the origin of *The Hound* could be found in *The Strand Magazine*, and specifically in the December 1900 issue, where a short story by the well-known mystery-writing duo, L T Meade and Robert Eustace, appeared. The story, entitled 'Followed', involves a bride-to-be, Flower Dalrymple, meeting her eccentric mother-in-law-to-be, Lady Sarah, at 'Longmore Hall' on Salisbury Plain. Lady Sarah kept snakes, and she attempted to kill Flower by allowing her to go out onto the Plain with a substance on her brown boots which encouraged a very large, black snake to attack her. Flower ran to Stonehenge and

fainted on the Slaughter Stone as the snake approached, but she was saved by Lady Sarah, who had overcome her insane jealousy for the attentions of her son, and who shot the snake. There are several similarities between this story and *The Hound*, with Flower going out onto the plain through a wicket-gate like that at 'Baskerville Hall', and with her boots being used to attract the attacking creature. The snake chasing Flower across the Plain by moonlight is similar to The Hound chasing Sir Henry across the Moor by moonlight, although there is no fog in the former case. Perhaps the closest similarity was with one of the illustrations which accompanied the story, with the snake-shooting scene looking very much like the Hound-shooting scene in *The Hound*, but then this was because the two pictures were by the same artist, Sidney Paget, who seems almost to have re-hashed the 'Followed' picture for depicting the demise of The Hound. In both stories Paget's illustration was allowed to ruin the story, with the pictures of the deaths of the snake and The Hound being placed by the publisher at the start of the crucial part of the story. Lancelyn Green acknowledges that 'Followed' was not the only source of inspiration for *The Hound*, but it is fairly certain that ACD will have read this issue of *The Strand Magazine*, as it was a special tenth anniversary number which included an expression of thanks from the Editor, Greenhough Smith, to those who had helped make the magazine such a success, and no-one had contributed more to that success than had ACD. There is, however, little similarity in the plots or the locational details of the two stories, with ACD's masterpiece being concerned primarily with property, as were so many of his stories, whereas 'Followed' is essentially concerned with maternal jealousy, and there is no mystery about the identity of the villain in 'Followed', as it is a simple horror story. There is, however, a firm connection between one of the authors of this story and Dartmoor, in that Robert Eustace provided technical assistance when Dorothy L Sayers wrote her own novel about a murder on Dartmoor, *The Documents in the Case* (published in 1930), although that case takes place in the softer Bovey Tracey - Manaton

- Lustleigh Cleave area, away from the wild Moor.

OTHER WRITERS

Arthur Conan Doyle. One should not forget the influence of ACD's own earlier writings, with Gothick elements appearing in several of the stories which he wrote prior to the first Sherlock Holmes story being published. There is, for example, ACD's first published work, 'The Mystery of Sasassa Valley', written in 1879, which includes the legend of a frightening beast, with the glowing red eye of that beast being seen at the base of a remote crag. More importantly, there is the story of 'Uncle Jeremy's Household', published in January 1887, which contains much of the atmosphere and detail of *The Hound*, although it takes place on the Yorkshire Fells. The narrator is a medical man (his friend's hobby is chemistry, and he has acid-stained fingers, just like Holmes!) with an eye for the ladies (just like Watson), and there is one of ACD's favourite ploys for creating an air of mystery (a beautiful woman with a touch of foreign blood). There is a jealous rival for this lady's attention, and the narrator comments on the loneliness of the place for such a beautiful woman. The narrator (who lives in Baker Street), arrives at a wayside station and is driven over monotonous hills, broken by jagged peaks, to the isolated country house, were there is a dilapidated gatehouse with gateposts surmounted by stone creatures, and a long tree-lined driveway opening out in front of the house. There has been a mysterious death in the shrubbery outside the house, and there are reports of a spectral apparition at night. Food is left outside the house for a murderer, and a secret, late-night rendezvous is arranged in the grounds of the house, at which the woman does not arrive, and at which the man dies.

A Great Variety of Possible Sources. Given ACD's practice of reading widely on any subject which he pursued, one may expect that there were many other writers about Dartmoor that he might have consulted. One influence which has been suggested by a Holmesian scholar is that of the father of the detective story, Edgar Allan Poe, who wrote of a "…grey hound…" on Dartmoor. This, however, was not in one of his novels, but in a literary review of the work of Mrs Felicia Hemans, who is nowadays known, if at all, almost solely for writing the line "The boy stood on the burning deck…" She was, however, very popular in Victorian times, and she did write a prize-winning poem about Dartmoor in 1821, but Poe misquoted her, in that what she wrote of was "…a greyhound…"! Although ACD's close neighbour and friend, Grant Allen, died more than a year before ACD began writing *The Hound*, he may have discussed Dartmoor with ACD, and the latter may have seen some of Allen's factual writings about Dartmoor in two of the magazines which published work from both writers, *The Cornhill Magazine* and *The English Illustrated Magazine*, or in *Longman's Magazine*. In the first of these, in November 1882, Allen published an examination of the origins of the place names in the Southern half of Devonshire, entitled 'A Corner of Devon', and it may be noted that ACD had Holmes investigating the Phoenician language in another of his West Country adventures, 'The Devil's Foot'. In *Longman's Magazine*, in an article entitled 'An Ancient Lake Bottom' in June 1884, Allen discussed the geology of the area between Bovey Tracey and Newton Abbot. Most significantly, however, Allen examined the whole of the valley of the River Dart in 'From Moor to Sea' in *The English Illustrated Magazine* in December 1889, which is the year in which *The Hound* is temporally located, with some charming illustrations of the area being provided by W Biscombe Gardner. Grant Allen dwells upon the popularity of Holne Chase for tourists, and it will be recalled that this is the location of Cleft Rock, which is the only site on Dartmoor bearing a name resembling that of ACD's *'Cleft Tor'*. Interestingly, although there was no direct literary link, it was in 'From Moor to Sea' that Allen establishes a different sort of connection between the words 'Holmes' and 'Holne', in suggesting that the two words are locationally associated with the holly tree, and it might be recalled that ACD used a similar, archaic-linguistic, locational connection in naming the house in which he completed *The Hound*, 'Undershaw', which uses the Saxon word 'shaw' for a clump of trees. In discussing the origins of the name of the *'great Grimpen Mire'*, it should also be noted that it was Grant Allen who revived the use of that rare English verb, 'to grimp' (meaning to climb - from the French *grimper*) in 1893, in his book *Scallywag*, in writing "How the little beasts grimp...". This meaning is also involved in T S Eliot's use of

ACD's *'Grimpen'*, when Eliot wrote "On the edge of a grimpen, where is no secure foothold." in *East Coker* in 1940. We too have no secure foothold in examining possible influences on *The Hound*, but the fact that ACD was influenced in this sort of way is a well-established reality, and readers are encouraged to look into their own specialist readings on the Moor and its associated topics to attempt to identify possible sources other than those given here.

His body was discovered
Barrymore, drawn by Paget before ACD's description of Barrymore had been published.

Welcome, Sir Henry!
Barrymore, drawn by Paget to better match ACD's description of the butler.

LEGENDARY SOURCES

Originality. There are some literary critics who seem to be determined to prove that certain writers never produced anything original in their lives, and this is certainly the case where ACD and *The Hound* is concerned. It is true that ACD was at least as influenced by earlier writers as anyone, and that he always carried out an enormous amount of background research for his books, but he added much to what he read, and enriched anything which he used with his own style, so that what he produced was definitely original. With *The Hound* he produced what is not only the best Gothick detective story ever written, but also one of the most interesting books ever written about Dartmoor and its history. In doing this ACD incorporated much of what he had read about Dartmoor, revealing that he had a good knowledge of the written material about the Moor which was available at that time, including some of the misunderstandings which that involved. Those who are familiar with the literature of Dartmoor will certainly recognise stories and factual recordings which they have read before, but there is always that special element of Doylean magic involved in the presentation. Although most of the classics from the literature of the Moor have been examined for evidence of influence in *The Hound*, there may well be readers who detect other influences not mentioned here, which can only add to the pleasure of the Game. We will here, however, examine the influence which initially inspired the writing of the story, which is concerned with a West Country legend about a spectral hound. What should constantly be borne in mind, though, is that ACD merely acknowledged the inspiration provided by this legend. Far too many scholars have assumed that it provided the basis for the story of *The Hound*, or for the hound legend recorded in that story.

INDIVIDUAL LEGENDS

Single Sources. Various commentators have adopted some pet legend, to repeat the pun about dogs which ACD included in *The Hound*, in claiming that it alone was responsible for the legend which inspired the story, or for that included in the story. That such an isolationist approach is totally wrong for the second aspect of such claims is revealed by the fact that none of the legends recorded as existing prior to the writing of *The Hound* matches that which is included in the story. The legend which provided the inspiration for the story need not, however, match the story's legend, but this is a point which is not appreciated by many of those who have become involved in the discussion. It would be easy to ridicule many of these efforts, but one might more-profitably concentrate on what has undoubtedly been the most extensive contribution made so far on the topic. This is the case presented by Janice McNabb, in her generally excellent monograph entitled *The Curious Incident of the Hound of Dartmoor*, which had the sub-title of 'A Reconsideration of the Origins of *The Hound of the Baskervilles*', and which was published in Canada in 1984. However, whilst giving a wide coverage of potential sources and an excellent analysis of the problem, it omitted mentioning some important sources, and it made assumptions about the then-existing situation which were not valid. The opening paragraph reads:

> Ask any serious Sherlockian about the origins of Doyle's *The Hound of the Baskervilles*, and with very little prompting, you will hear again some variation on the familiar tradition that surrounds this singular adventure. It is universally accepted that the story is based on an old Dartmoor legend, which was told to Doyle while he holidayed on the moors with his friend, Fletcher Robinson. In

Chaw Gully. Robert Burnard's [25 May 1894] photograph shows Sabine Baring-Gould standing near the summit of the gully which he used in his Dartmoor murder story, *Guavas the Tinner.* That book, like *The Hound*, involved a ferocious canine coated with a phosphorescent substance which makes it glow in the dark on the Moor and has animals and men being swallowed in a mire. ACD may well have passed through Chaw Gully *('Cleft Tor')* on his walk from Fox Tor Mires *('Grimpen Mire')* to Grimspound. Sabine mentions a raven nesting in the gully ('chaw' is a word used on the Moor for the raven and other members of the corvine family), almost certainly for the same reason that ACD mentions the same bird in *The Hound*, which is its traditional image as a harbinger of death. [29]

gratitude and courtesy, Doyle then dedicated this story to his friend.

Even in 1984 it would have been difficult to find a serious Sherlockian or Holmesian who accepted these points. No-one could really accept that the story was *based on* an old Dartmoor legend, since it had only been suggested that the story was *inspired by* such a legend, and the legend occupies only a small part of the full story. No-one accepted that ACD was told this legend whilst holidaying on 'the moors', since they had all been led to understand at that time that ACD was told the legend in Cromer. No-one can have accepted that ACD dedicated the story to BFR, because he never dedicated it to anyone. It was therefore incorrect to suggest that the postulated response was "…universally accepted…" McNabb continues to present incorrect situations throughout the monograph, such as suggesting, whilst discussing legends of Whisht Hounds, that: "…Doyle cleverly puts the definition of their habits into the unsympathetic mouth of Stapleton…", when Stapleton actually uses the explanation that: *The peasants say it is the sound of the Hound of the Baskervilles calling for its prey.*, with *'Hound'* and *'its'* clearly indicating a singular Hound, when the Whisht Hounds are a pack. There are numerous factual errors, often relying upon the authority of others, such as when it is mentioned, without contradiction, that BFR was a Devonshire man (he was actually from Liverpool), and that there were convicts in Dartmoor Prison in 1806 (they were Prisoners of War, and there were no convicts prior to 1850). The whole discussion is diminished, in a broader sense, when it is opined that "…careful study played little part in the story which was begun in March and published in August of the same year.", since a wider reading of potential sources, rather than just hound legend sources, reveals that there are signs of in-depth study in many fields. ACD was capable of carrying out a great deal of research within a four-month period, and there is actually no indication that ACD had completed the story in August, merely that he had completed the first episode by then. Janice McNabb had, in fact already carried out an extensive and impressive investigation of BFR, which has sadly not been published, although this concentrated on his London literary associations, rather than on his contribution to *The Hound*.

BERTRAM FLETCHER ROBINSON'S LEGEND

Traditional or New? As has already been mentioned, and will be discussed at length below, there is a controversy over how much BFR contributed to the writing of *The Hound*, but what is incontrovertible is the fact that it was a West Country legend which he told to ACD which provided the inspiration for the story. ACD published four slightly different acknowledgements for the assistance provided by BFR in the creation of *The Hound*, and these will be given in full in discussing the authorship controversy, but the key point here is that in a letter to BFR about the book ACD wrote: "It was your account of a west country legend which first suggested the idea of this little tale to my mind." As will be seen, there are those who consider that this reference to a 'west country' legend indicates a legend from the West of England, near the Welsh border, rather than a legend from the South-Western peninsula of England (which is often referred to within the UK as 'The West Country'). It should be noted immediately, however, that in his final acknowledgement of BFR, in 1929, ACD wrote:

> Then came *The Hound of the Baskervilles*. It arose from a remark by that fine fellow, whose premature death was a loss to the world, Fletcher Robinson, that there was a spectral dog near his home on Dartmoor.

There are others, including this present researcher, who consider that the legend which formed the basis of the folk tale which ACD included in the story did not primarily come from either of the 'West Country' areas mentioned, but from East Anglia or possibly from the Severn Valley area, although that does not deny the claim that the initial inspiration came from

Dartmoor. BFR did claim, in 1905, that he had told some Dartmoor legends to ACD when they were on the Moor, but this was after ACD had been inspired to write *The Hound*, and the legends which BFR mentions do not involve a singular, spectral hound, but ghostly hounds in the plural, headless riders and devils, as will be discussed further in connection with the author-ship controversy. Although some commentators have suggested that BFR was an authority on folk tales, there are only a few, minor, invented, folk tale elements in his works, which were recorded after *The Hound* was published, and he produced no documentary comments on the subject. If BFR did tell ACD a Dartmoor legend about a hound when the two men met in Cromer, as seems probable, then it is possible that he gave his own interpretation of that legend, or that ACD changed the story dramatically himself. It is also possible, as will be seen, that when BFR told his legend, this encouraged the telling of another, and that it was the second legend which provided the basis for that contained in *The Hound*, with BFR's legend providing only the initial inspiration and the dramatic location for ACD's greater story.

THE CROMER LEGEND

The Cromer Tale. Unfortunately, we do not know exactly what happened on the Sunday afternoon at the Royal Links Hotel in Cromer in 1901 when ACD was inspired to write what even-tually became *The Hound*. There are some fairly well-detailed accounts, but these are recorded by those who were not there, and they clearly contain elements of surmise. BFR certainly seems to have given an account of some sort of legend about a spectral hound on Dartmoor to ACD at some time, but there is very little simi-larity between any of the Dartmoor hound legends and the one in the story, and it is possi-ble that the telling of BFR's story was encour-aged by, or encouraged, the telling of another hound legend: the local Cromer legend of Black Shuck, which bears a far closer resemblance to the legend of the story than do any of the Dartmoor legends.

The Legends of Black Shuck. Shuck was, unlike most of the Dartmoor spectral hounds, a solitary hound, and he ranged chiefly along the Northern and Eastern coastline of Norfolk, with Cromer at the centre of his wanderings. According to a local historian, J Westwood, Shuck had some regular routes, including one which ran from the beach at Cromer, up a deep-cut, sandy lane, now called Mill Road, past the Royal Links Hotel where ACD and BFR stayed. From there Shuck would run across the hill, which has *"…stunted oaks and firs which had been twisted and bent by the fury of years of storm…"* and then down to the grounds of Cromer Hall, which lie in a small *"…cup-like depression ..…surrounded by trees…"* in the valley, with that building matching the description of 'Baskerville Hall' more-closely than any building on Dartmoor. Here another remarkable coincidence occurs, in that Shuck would run along the back of the Hall where, until partially destroyed by the Great Storm of 1987, there existed a fine yew alley, and it was in a *"…yew alley…"* behind 'Baskerville Hall' that The Hound caused the death of Sir Charles Baskerville. In some versions of the Norfolk legend, Shuck is described as *"…a black, shaggy dog, the size of a small calf…"*, and it will be recalled that Sir Charles Baskerville was horrified when he saw something which Mortimer took to be *"…a large black calf passing the head of the drive."* at 'Baskerville Hall'. Shuck is also described as having *"…eyes glowing like coals in the night…"*, and it is said that anyone upon whom Shuck casts his fiery gaze will die within the year. It may be noted that The Hound seen by three of the wicked Hugo's companions had *"…blazing eyes…"* and that of these men *"One, it is said, died that very night of what he had seen, and the other twain were but broken men for the rest of their days."* Perhaps The Hound did not cast his gaze directly upon the twain! The legend of Shuck had been revived at the end of the Nineteenth Century, and a former Cromer vicar, Joseph Gurney Barclay, had attempted to lay the ghost of Shuck. The story gained popularity when some young men attempted to scare the vicar by chasing a sheep draped in a sheet down a narrow lane after him one night. It is not claimed here that ACD used any of the various legends about Shuck in *The Hound*, but the coincidences between that legend and the Dartmoor legend told by BFR, and the other connections which existed between Cromer and Dartmoor (discussed below) may well have inspired him to have created his greatest story, and may have generated the excitement which sent him hurrying off to Dartmoor.

The Contribution of Max Pemberton. BFR's friend, Max Pemberton, who, as editor of the Isthmian Library books on sports commissioned BFR to write on rowing, rugby, football and cycling, claimed, in an article in the *Evening News* of 25 May 1939 , that he had given the legend of Black Shuck to BFR, who passed it on to ACD. Pemberton wrote:

> The late Fletcher Robinson, who collaborated with Doyle in the story, was dining at my house in Hampstead one night when the talk turned upon phantom dogs. I told my friend of a certain Jimmy Farman, a Norfolk marshman, who swore that there was a phantom dog somewhere on the marshes near St. Olives and that his bitch had met the brute more than once and had been terrified by it. 'A Great black dog it were,' Jimmy said, 'and the eyes of 'un was like railway lamps. He crossed my path down there by the far dyke and the old bitch a'most went mad wi' fear…Now surely that bitch saw a' summat I didn't see…

> Fletcher Robinson assured me that dozens of people on the outskirts of Dartmoor had seen a phantom hound and that to doubt its existence would be a local heresy. In both instances, the brute was a huge retriever, coal black and with eyes which shone like fire.

> Fletcher Robinson was always a little psychic and he had a warm regard for this apparition; indeed, he expressed

some surprise that no romancer had yet written about it. Three nights afterwards, Fletcher Robinson was dining with Sir Arthur. The talk at my house was still fresh in his mind and he told Doyle what I had said, emphasising that this particular marshman was as sure of the existence of the phantom hound as he was of his own being. Finally, Fletcher Robinson said 'Let us write the story together.' And to his very great content Sir Arthur cordially assented.

BFR cannot have spoken to 'Sir Arthur' of this legend at that undetermined time, since ACD was not knighted until after *The Hound* was published, but we will excuse this slip as being a polite, if incorrect, pre-dating of the honour. It must, however, be noted that the dog involved in BFR's Dartmoor account was not a hound, but a retriever, whereas ACD referred to BFR telling him a phantom hound legend, and almost all of the legends on Dartmoor do involve hounds.

Pemberton may well have been one of those who have attempted to increase their own standings at the expense of others when the occasion was right, for he did repeat this account of his influence on *The Hound* in *The Citizen* of 28 June 1939 at a time when there was a great deal of revived interest in *The Hound*, because of the news of the making of the 20th Century Fox film version of the story in that year.

Whatever the degree of exaggeration here, BFR may have been aware of one of the Shuck legends, as well as the Dartmoor legend which ACD acknowledged, and the environment of Cromer would clearly have been one which encouraged the telling of the first of these, which seems in turn to have encouraged the telling of the second.

SOME 'WEST COUNTRY' LEGENDS

The Hound of the Vaughans. Having dealt with one non-Dartmoor legend, we now consider the suggestion that the legend used in *The Hound* comes from the West of England, even though that term is commonly used for the South-Western peninsula of England, and even though the Welsh borderlands of England are more often referred to as the West Midlands. ACD's first wife, Louise, had family and property in that area, and some of that property bordered that of the Baskerville family. The main branch of the Baskerville family lived at Eardisley Castle in Herefordshire, near Hay-on-Wye, at the end of the Nineteenth Century, with part of the family living just across the nearby Welsh border at Clyro Court, in the hamlet of Clyro, in what is now Powys and was then Radnorshire. It is claimed that one of the Baskerville homes on the English side was known as 'The Moor'. Clyro Court has some minor similarities to 'Baskerville Hall', including yew trees, but it has no hound legend. The Baskervilles were, however, inter-married with the Vaughan family who resided at the nearby Hergest Court, just outside the small town of Kington. It was the editor of *The Strand Magazine*, Herbert Greenhough Smith, who sug-gested, shortly after ACD's death, that BFR's share in the creation of *The Hound* was merely "…to draw the attention of Conan Doyle to the tradition of the fiery hound in a Welsh guide-book." It has already been seen that ACD did not agree with this, but a descendant of the main branch of the Baskerville family, Major Geoffrey Hopton, is recorded as having discussed the contact supposedly made between his grand-mother, Dorothy Nesta Baskerville, and ACD:

> Everybody knows that Conan Doyle heard the tale of the phantom hound that haunted the Vaughans of Hergest Court, 10 miles from here. He asked my grandmother if he could use the family name because Baskerville was more romantic than Vaughan. She agreed, provided he spirited the hound far away from here into the West Country, and that is that.

Many scholars have queried the reliability of this account, but it is possible that ACD was well aware of the main branch of the Baskerville family before he decided to call his story *The Hound of the Baskervilles*, in that he may have visited the Welsh borderlands with his wife in 1897 or 1898, and there are unsubstantiated accounts of him staying at Kington, and he may thus have been aware of the Vaughan family hound legend. That legend merely involved a spectral hound which appeared just before one of the Vaughans died, but it received an element of exaggeration and mild popularity in a novel by W S Symonds, entitled *Malvern Chase*, published in 1881, wherein the phantom hound frightens to death the dog of a visitor at Hergest Court.

The Baskerville Mynors Account. One of Britain's leading authorities on dog and hound legends, Theo Brown, provided, in her book *Devon Ghosts*, another tale of a Baskerville hound, from a member of the Baskerville family. She recorded an account from a Miss Cicely Botley, relaying a story told to the latter by Mrs Baskerville Mynors in 1963, when those two ladies were both living in the same hotel in Tunbridge Wells:

> Once upon a time an ancestor of the family was in his castle hall in Herefordshire (perhaps Eardisley) drink-ing. As he had been trained to do, his black hound (an Irish wolf hound) ran in baying to announce the approach of an enemy, but his master, who seemed to have reached the fuddled-irritable stage, simply lifted his spear and ran the faith-ful creature through the head (hence the crest). The deed had scarcely been done when in dashed a retainer with news of the attack.

> Henceforth the death of a head of the family was announced by the baying of a hound.

The crest which this account mentions is one of many crests held by the Baskerville family, but with this particular one having a dog's head, which looks like that of a greyhound, with a spear thrust through it. This crest appeared for many years on the old pub sign of the

Cleft Rock. Robert Burnard's handwritten caption for this photograph, taken on 14 January 1891, indicates that it is in Ausewell Wood, above Holne Bridge, and suggests that the cleft is the result of an old mining excavation. It is a rare opportunity for seeing this site, since public access is not available, not just because it is on private property, but because it is now dangerously overgrown. The name is the closest to that of the *'Cleft Tor'* which appears in *The Hound.* [29]

Baskerville Arms in Clyro, although the dog on the pub sign has since been replaced by a jocular, beagle-like hound wearing a deerstalker and smoking a calabash!

The Norville Hound. It is possible that ACD was familiar with a far more significant hound legend from the West Midlands area close to the Welsh border, with a story about Norville Hall in the village of Beauton Norton, in the Severn Valley area. A solitary shepherd is said to have seen a spectral re-enactment of a scene which bears many close resemblances to the legend from *The Hound.* It is recorded that there are documents suggesting that at the end of the Seventeenth Century, Sir Lucius Beauton Norville seized a maiden one Christmas Eve and carried her off to Norville Hall, where an orgy took place. Some sort of tragedy followed, in which Sir Lucius died, and he was buried hastily on Christmas

Day, with no religious ceremony, in the park of Norville Hall. In more-recent times, a shepherd, Tom Phillips, saw a young woman in white, running down the driveway of the by-then empty Hall, and heard the sound of hounds following her. A pack of hounds then appeared, followed by men on foot and a man on a large black horse. The men were wearing old-fashioned clothing, with breeches, lace around their wrists and wigs. The hounds caught and attacked the maiden, even though the rider dismounted and attempted to drive them off with his whip, but he was too late and the hounds tore the maiden to pieces. A new, larger, black hound, with red eyes and flames playing around its jaws, then appeared from the driveway and attacked the rider, tearing out his throat. Once again, however, this legend does not seem to have been recorded until well after *The Hound* was written, and the book may thus have influenced the recording of the legend, for this legend certainly matches that of the book far better than any other.

DARTMOOR LEGENDS

Introduction. Most of the hound legends on Dartmoor are not concerned with solitary hounds, but with packs of hounds, and this includes the main legends which are most often considered to have been the source of inspiration for *The Hound*. These hound packs are derived not only from earlier legends, such as those connected with Thor, but also from the large number of packs which were used for hunting on Dartmoor. The most infamous of these legendary packs on the Moor is that known as The Whisht Hounds, which belonged to the Devil, or Dewer as he is sometimes called on the Moor, and which is often described as being used to hunt the souls of unbaptised babies. It may be noted that the wicked Hugo Baskerville, when he discovered that his captive maiden had escaped *"...cried aloud before all the company that he would that very night render his body and soul to the Powers of Evil if he might but overtake the wench."* Dewer and his hounds usually ride at night, and it is significant that the good Hugo Baskerville concludes his account of the Baskerville legend by warning that his sons *"...should forebear from crossing the moor in those dark hours when the powers of evil are exalted."* One of the homes of the Devil on Dartmoor is the Dewerstone, and ACD included the Dewerstone, with a mysterious phantom figure first appearing there, in his story *The Winning Shot*, and he may well have visited this extremely popular beauty spot on the walk which he carried out in 1882, from Plymouth to Tavistock.

Fernworthy – The Farmhouse. The home of some of those who are referred to by Frankland as *"the Fernworthy folk"* This is almost certainly the farm mentioned in 'A Tale of a Dartmoor Fog', although it would have been much improved by the time that Chapman & Son took this photograph in the early Twentieth Century, in comparison with the Napoleonic War period of that story, although the older part of the building can clearly be seen to the right. Interestingly the Dartmoor writer Paul Rendell identifies the two workmen as being from the Mortimer family. Little is now visible of the ruins of the farm and its outbuildings. [71]

Richard Cabell. The real-life man behind the Dartmoor legends which are most frequently claimed to have been those told to ACD by BFR is Richard Cabell, he being the third of that name to live on Dartmoor. He was a local squire, living at Brook Manor, a few miles to the North of Buckfastleigh, but there is no evidence to support the knighthood sometimes attributed to him. He was extremely unpopular in the area, being known as 'Dirty Dick', and he gave himself airs as the lord of the manor which others may have resented. His unpopularity may also have been due to the fact that he controlled the local mills, and he went to court to insist that everyone living in the area had to use his mills to grind their corn. In addition, there would have been further resentment of the fact that his family had managed to avoid losing their lands when they ended up on the wrong side in the Civil War, with the account of the legend given in *The Hound* recommending the account of that conflict given by Lord Clarendon. There are also anecdotal rumours that Cabell kept mistresses at Hawson Court, close to his manor house. Cabell built a penthouse tomb, a small house-like structure containing a raised tomb with a heavy capstone, for his father and grandfather immediately outside the entrance to what was the parish church of Buckfastleigh. It is assumed that the third Richard was later buried in the same tomb, although the records for this are missing, but the single word 'Ricus' does exist on the opposite side of the slab covering the tomb to that on which the names of the first two Richards are recorded. The third Richard died in 1672, according to the leading authority on the history of this branch of the Cabell family, Susan Cabell Djabri. Some authorities claim that Richard died in 1677, but this seems to have been a case of everyone copying a poorly researched dating. The direct line of this branch of the family ended there, with his only daughter, Elizabeth, marrying Cholmeley D'Oyly, who turned out to be a bigamist, and who was very distantly descended from the same family as ACD. Interestingly, given the name of the villain behind The Hound, when D'Oyly died Elizabeth married Richard Fownes from Stapleton House, Stapleton, in Dorset.

The Cabell Legends. SBG seems to have been the first to have recorded any of the legends about Richard Cabell, but he did so in his little Methuen guide, *Devonshire*, which was not published until 1907, and it is possible that the story had by then been corrupted by the legend contained in *The Hound*. He wrote, in describing the church:

> Before the S. porch is the enclosed tomb of Richard Cabell of Brook, who died in 1677. He was the last male of his race, and died with such an evil reputation that he was placed under a heavy stone, and a sort of penthouse was built over that with iron gratings to it, to prevent his coming up and haunting the neighbourhood. When he died, the story goes that fiends and black dogs breathing fire raced over Dartmoor and surrounded Brook, howling.

It will be noted that SBG has the wrong date for the death of Richard, and his account incorrectly suggests that the penthouse tomb, or 'sepulchre' as it is known locally, was built to hold Richard. It is also pertinent that we have 'dogs' rather than hounds involved, and that they were accompanied by 'fiends'. More significantly, these dogs merely howl, rather than attacking anyone, but they do at least breathe fire. There is a less-frequently told alternative to this legend, which is closer to that of *The Hound*, and which claims that Cabell was hunted to his death across Dartmoor by black dogs. Again we have the pack, and dogs rather than hounds, but there is no record of this legend existing outside discussions of sources of *The Hound*, and it may thus be yet another case of making the evidence fit the argument. A third legend associated with Cabell is that on the anniversary of his death, on 5 July (which was Mid-Summer's Night, a night when all sorts of demons and ghosts arose, before the calendar was changed in 1752) he escapes from his tomb and rides headless down the drive to Brook Manor on a great black horse, followed by a pack of hounds. All of these legends have resulted in a local story, whereby children are dared to poke a finger through the keyhole of the door of the sepulchre, or to walk backwards around the sepulchre thirteen times and poke their fingers through the grille, with the threat being that the Devil will bite off the offending finger or fingers. More seriously, these legends and stories may well have attracted the attention of black magic worshippers to the church, with rumours of black masses being held in the church and in the churchyard. Nearby Totnes has been described as having become the black magic centre of England in recent years, and the suggestion arose that it was some sort of black magic ceremony which resulted in the fire which almost totally destroyed the church in 1992.

Some Other Cabell Accounts. There is what might be called a modern myth associated with the Cabell legends, although 'myth-take' might be a better description! This is contained in a highly imaginative re-writing of the history of Richard Cabell by Anthony Howlett, which was unfortunately presented as if based on factual accounts. It was suggested that Richard Cabell, thinking that his wife had been unfaithful, beat her with a whip, and then, when she escaped from the house, hunted her across the Moor and stabbed her to death, with her favourite dog being found fatally wounded near her body the next day. The body of Richard Cabell was also found nearby, with his knife in his hand, but with his throat torn out as though by a savage beast. This account seems to be influenced more by the Hammer Films version of *The Hound of the Baskervilles*, and by the account of a legend which Basil Rathbone had heard on the set of his film version of the story, than by fact, for Richard Cabell's wife outlived him by 14 years (or by 9 years if the 1677 date is accepted). Some further confusion has been added to the Cabell legends by the intrusion of a once-popular American writer, James Branch Cabell, who, in his 1933 collection of essays entitled *Ladies and Gentlemen*, complained about ACD's interference with the history of his ancestors, although he also claimed that there were no accounts of scandal or of Satanic connections in the family.

Other Dartmoor Hound Legends. Of the few solitary hound legends on Dartmoor, none seems to match that of the story. There is the black hound which runs ahead of the ghostly coach of Lady Howard, but this runs along the road from Tavistock to Okehampton. There is one hound legend which William Crossing recorded, although not until 1914, where the hound chased someone through areas associated with *The Hound*, including Pupers Hill, but this hound merely snapped at the heels of his quarry, and the first narrator of this legend was accused of having been involved with a different sort of spirits, of the liquid variety, before getting home late after encountering his phantom hound! Another black hound legend involves the small stream which flows beside the best locational candidate for '*Baskerville Hall*', Hayford Hall. A weaver died in the hamlet of Deancombe, near Buckfastleigh, and his ghost continued to weave until the priest threw a handful of soil from the churchyard into his face, turning him into a black hound. The hound was given the task of emptying a pool in the adjacent Dean Burn, using a nutshell with a hole in it, and the pool has since been known as Hound Pool. Clearly, these legends, and there are more like them, bear little resemblance to that told in the story.

Some Legendary Conclusions. According to the limited evidence available from BFR, the Dartmoor legends which he told ACD were not like that which appears in *The Hound*. It is also rather strange that there is no record of any of the powerful legends about Richard Cabell prior to SBG's account of 1907, for he does not appear in R Polwhele's *History of Devonshire* (3 Vols, 1797-1806), or in Daniel & Samuel Lysons' *Magna Britannia* (Vol 6 covering Devonshire, 1822), although these works do mention similar anecdotes. Certainly the best matching legend is that from the Severn Valley, closely followed by that of Black Shuck. The only accounts of Dartmoor hounds which match that of the story in any significant manner may have been influenced by the story itself, for even with SBG's reasonably early account it must be recalled that the turn of the century was a time when a great deal of interest was being developed over the recording of folk tales and legends, and it was also an important time for 'old' legends to be newly invented. BFR may well have developed his own version of one of the existing Moor legends, and ACD was perfectly capable of ignoring whatever legends he heard about Dartmoor and of inventing his own legend or of importing and modifying one which he had heard elsewhere. The most reliable accounts of the Richard Cabell connection are those provided by Mrs Susan Cabell Djabri, and the profits from her inexpensive booklet entitled *The Story of the Sepulchre* go towards the maintenance of the Cabell family tomb.

It was a stranger pursuing me
Homes meeting Stapleton on the 'Baskerville Hall' to
'Grimpen' road, with the Moor to the West.

REAL HOUNDIAN LOCATIONS

INTRODUCTION

Sources of Locations. Spirit of place is a crucial element of *The Hound*, with its highly Gothick atmosphere contributing to the air of suspense and mystery, and the enjoyment of the story is enhanced enormously for those who are familiar with the real locations which are mentioned and with the locations which may have influenced the invented sites, with many of the latter possibly being amalgamations of real places. It is possible to identify most of the locations in the story because of the way in which ACD wrote, in that he wrote so much that he continually used locations which he had visited, or combinations of elements of places which he knew, in his writings. This is not to suggest that imagination did not play a part in ACD's creations, but it does add the possibility of sharing some of his experiences, especially since so many of the places which ACD visited on Dartmoor have changed so little. Many of the places to be mentioned here are private property, and so an indication will be given when public access to a particular location is not available, although almost all of the sites referred to can be viewed from points of public access, albeit at a considerable distance in a few cases.

Real and Invented Locations. This section will deal with the real locations which are mentioned in *The Hound*, but there are some general locational points which apply to both the real and invented locations in the story. As usual with ACD, some of the places he mentions are easily located, in being still known by the name which he uses, or by a slight variation in some examples. Others are fairly easily identifiable, but yet others seem to be a combination of two or more real locations, conjoined to simplify, enhance dramatically or to disguise. Although the Dartmoor National Park is relatively small in scale, occupying some 369 square miles, there are many thousands of locations which might prove to be

relevant to this discussion within that area, but, fortunately, we do not need to consider the whole of this artificially created, roughly circular, administrative area, as much of it is lowland and softer in nature than the high and wild moorland involved in the story. When ACD, through Watson, refers to *"...the moor..."*, we can generally accept this as being the geographical area bounded by the limits of the Ancient Forest of Dartmoor, existing primarily in the Western two thirds of the Dartmoor National Park, and this area has been referred to in this Investigation as "the Moor", with the larger area of the Dartmoor National Park being referred to as "Dartmoor". It is stressed that in this context, the word 'Forest' has nothing to do with trees, in that it was a technical term for an area of land where hunting was solely the privilege of the monarch. The Ancient Forest area was bounded by certain set points, and although there is some minor disagreement over the identity of all of these points, they run in an anti-clockwise direction from the most Southerly point as follows:

> Eastern White Barrow, Huntingdon Cross, Ryder's Hill, O Brook Foot, Dartmeet, Runnage Bridge, King's Oven, North Walla Brook, Heath Stone, Long Stone, Batworthy Corner, White Moor Stone, Cosdon Beacon, Cullever Steps, Rowtor, Sandy Ford, Steng-a-Tor, Rattlebrook Head, Rattlebrook Foot, Western Redlake Foot, Limsboro' Cairn, Dead Lake Foot, Great Mis Tor, North Hessary Tor, South Hessary Tor, Nun's Cross, Eylesbarrow, Plym Steps, Erme Pits Ford, Western White Barrow.

One can further localise the majority of the candidates for worthwhile consideration to the area surrounded by this Forest boundary which lies to the South of a line drawn from a point slightly North of Dartmeet to North Hessary Tor, and when Watson talks about travelling along the edge of *"…the moor…"*, then he is almost certainly referring to the roads which run around the South-Eastern part of the Ancient Forest boundary. The crucial area as far as *The Hound* is concerned is, primarily, one which is cut off from the rest of Dartmoor by the road which runs from Ashburton or Buckfastleigh to Hexworthy, Two Bridges, Princetown and Tavistock. There are high moorlands outside of the Ancient Forest boundary area, but they tend to be intruded upon by soft lowlands. It is stressed that it is not claimed that the identifications made herein are definitive, for it will be seen that it is almost impossible to establish absolute identifications for many of the locations, and there are disagreements over candidates, but this situation is to be welcomed in that the game of attempting to identify Houndian locations can continue forever! An attempt will be made here to mention a variety of options for some of the important locational candidates where major disagreements exist. This game is, of course, best played on foot, on the Moor itself, but it can also be enjoyed to a lesser extent by those who may be less-mobile, and by those who are unable to explore the Moor itself on a regular basis. Even for those who visit the Moor to carry out such explorations, much of the pleasure is derived from the anticipation and from the preparations carried out with the book and a good map, and with other reference sources, with this element of exploration being available to all. Consideration will also be given in the Investigation to locations associated with *The Hound*, real and invented, other than those on Dartmoor. It is repeated here that to avoid confusion, the locations, including buildings, which are mentioned in the story are printed in italics in this Investigation, with the invented locations additionally being printed in single quotation marks.

Reliability Warning. There is clearly a great deal of room for debate between the merits of contending candidates for some of the invented locations, and it may sometimes only be a matter of personal choice as to which is seen as the best. Some of the proposals which have been made by those who really do not know Dartmoor are,

however, completely wrong. In his *The Annotated Sherlock Holmes*, W S Baring-Gould extracted a drawing from his grandfather's book, *A Book of Dartmoor*, which he states is of Black Tor. It is actually of Sharpitor and Leather Tor. As an extreme example, one might take a well-known American Sherlockian, David L Hammer, who has published several books about Holmesian locations, and who introduces his section on the Holmesian locations of the West Country with a suitably misty photograph of a Dartmoor hill. The caption for this reads: "The melancholy Brent Tor, topped by the church of St. Michael of the Rock, was Doctor Watson's first glimpse of Dartmoor." It would be difficult to get more wrong in one short sentence. Firstly, the photograph is of Hound Tor, and not of Brent Tor, and the 'church' is therefore merely one of the rock outcrops. Secondly, the church at Brent Tor is more-correctly dedicated to St Michael de Rupe. Thirdly, to have seen Hound Tor, Watson would already have travelled through part of Dartmoor, since it cannot be seen from outside of the Dartmoor boundaries. Fourthly, Watson would have had to have been travelling from Cornwall, not London, for Brent Tor to have been the first part of Dartmoor that he saw. It is possible that Brent Hill, near South Brent would have been the first part of Dartmoor that he would have seen when travelling from London, as it can be seen from the railway on the way from Totnes to South Brent, but there is no church on that hill. Fifthly, this would not have been Watson's first glimpse of Dartmoor, since he had visited the Western edge of Dartmoor when investigating the case of 'Silver Blaze', the year before the crucial events of *The Hound*. One would also need to be cautious in using the map which Hammer provides, for although one might accept Hammer's obvious lack of familiarity with Dartmoor for the way in which the map fails to include Ashburton, the largest town on Dartmoor, one cannot allow the map's proliferation of Tors. Close to his symbol for a Tor which he calls 'Hound Tor', which is close to the location of the real Hound Tor, between Manaton and Widecombe, he includes a symbol for a newly discovered Tor, which he calls 'Great Hound Tor'. There is a real Great

Houndtor close to the site of this new Plutonic (with apologies to Walt Disney!) eruption, but that is the name of a farm, and not of a Tor. It is also true to say that some reliable maps have shown a Great Hound Tor, but when they did this it was as an alternative name for Hound Tor, not an indication of another Tor. Hammer almost certainly copied this error, as he did so many others, from W S Baring-Gould, without carrying out any research of his own. One might also search in vain for Mr Hammer's 'Foxton Mires', or the farm which is elevated to the status of being 'Leighon Hall'. Mr Hammer is certainly not alone in making such basic errors, and one must accept that not everyone can devote the sort of time which is required to be able to understand the real nature of the Moor. The author of the Introduction and Explanatory Notes of the Oxford edition of *The Hound*, for example, clearly did not have any real knowledge of Dartmoor, and although he kindly acknowledged the assistance of the present commentator's monograph, *The Dartmoor Locations of "The Hound of the Baskervilles"*, in connection with discussing such locations, most of the locational statements which he made are, like Watson's deductions made from Mortimer's stick, erroneous. Care is needed before accepting the pronouncements of those Holmesian and Sherlockian writers whose knowledge of Dartmoor is limited to that obtained from minimal research or through the windscreen of a car during a fleeting visit. Perhaps one should create a new version of the warning of the good Hugo Baskerville:

Forebear from crossing the moor
in those dark hours
when the powers of unbridled
invention are exalted!

Safety. On a more serious point, for those who are not familiar with the Moor or with hill-trekking, some warning notes should be sounded. Many of the Houndian locations can be reached by car and on clearly-defined tracks, but when venturing forth upon the wilder parts of the Moor one should be aware that fog or rain can descend very quickly on Dartmoor, and the inexperienced can very easily become lost. All of the usual precautions for walking in wild country should be taken, including the use of appropriate hill-walking and survival kit, and the leaving of notification of intended routes and return times with some responsible person. Large parts of the Northern Moor are used by the Ministry of Defence, and there are artillery and mortar ranges in these areas where live ammunition is used, but one is allowed to venture into most of these areas on non-firing days. These military areas are clearly marked on the Ordnance Survey maps, and they are surrounded by notice boards and posts, with red flags flying on firing days. Fortunately, these areas are not involved in the main Houndian explorations, but before entering them walkers should have checked with the local Tourist Information Centres over firing times, and in such areas explorers should be careful not to touch any suspicious-looking hardware lying on the Moor.

Environmental Care. One should adhere at all times to The Country Code, and on Dartmoor special emphasis should be given to preserving what is a very fragile and very precious environment, and to not becoming a nuisance to those who have to earn a living from the Moor. Although public access to the Moor is generally very good, the land does all belong to someone. Be warned in particular that a carelessly parked car might be found, after a walk, to have been moved by a farmer with the aid of a tractor! Leave your car only in a clearly designated parking area - parking on grass verges can cause irreparable damage, as well as blocking access for wide farm vehicles, but it should also be noted that it is illegal to drive a vehicle more than 15 metres onto the Moor from a road. These warnings should not put anyone off visiting the Moor, nor should the dangers be exaggerated. One need merely follow the excellent advice given on signs beside roads at the boundaries of Dartmoor, for the benefit of the Moor, those who live on the Moor, and those who visit the Moor:

Take Moor Care

THE SOUTH-EASTERN QUADRANT OF THE MOOR

Introduction. There are some general references in the story which indicate that most of the dramatic events of the story take place in the South-Eastern quadrant of the high Moor, and primary amongst these are the descriptions of the railway approaches to the major Dartmoor locations of the story and the references to the road approaches to '*Baskerville Hall*'.

The Railway Approaches. In the year when the adventure takes place, 1889, there were two main railway approaches to Dartmoor, with each travelling around the edges of the greater Dartmoor area from Exeter to Plymouth, one travelling in an anti-clockwise direction and the other in a clockwise direction. We will deal initially with the first of these, because it is the simpler of the two in its involvement, and because it indicates that the second is the more important. Jack Stapleton is described as travelling to Dartmoor from London with his Hound as follows:

> He brought it down by the North Devon line and walked a great distance over the moor so as to get it home without exciting any remarks.

What ACD refers to as the "*…North Devon line…*" is recognised by railway historians as being part of, or a branch line extension of, the old rail route from Exeter to Barnstaple, which was completed in 1854, and although this extension was started by other companies it was quickly taken over by the great London and South Western Railway Company. This company had a strategic aim connected with the North Devon line, which was to run another line from it to travel around the Northern and Western edges of Dartmoor to reach Plymouth from Exeter via Okehampton and Tavistock, thus breaking the monopoly of the Great Western Railway which had a line travelling around the Eastern and Southern edges of Dartmoor to reach Plymouth via Newton Abbot and Totnes. This aim was achieved in 1876, albeit, at first, using the lines of other companies for part of the journey. The

normal route for reaching somewhere lying in the Eastern, South-Eastern or Southern areas of the high Moor would have been the Great Western line, and in mentioning that Stapleton used the '*North Devon line*' to reach his home, '*Merripit House*' which lay in the neighbourhood of '*Baskerville Hall*', without attracting attention, Sherlock Holmes is indicating that the '*North Devon line*' is not the normal line which would have been used to get to the '*Baskerville Hall*' area. It is stated that Stapleton walked a long way across the Moor to reach his home, and as the Ancient Forest part of the Moor is only some 17 miles long across its greatest dimension, this strongly indicates that '*Merripit House*' must have been in the Southern half of the Moor. Indeed, one of the greatest distances that one could travel in a reasonably straight line across the Moor, without passing through inhabited areas, would be from Okehampton, on an extension of the '*North Devon line*', in a South-South-Easterly direction, with major tracks assisting such a transit. The rail approach to '*Baskerville Hall*' would thus have been made through Newton Abbot, Totnes or South Brent, possibly with a change to a branch line at one of the first two of these, and with the third being unlikely, in that, being a main-line station, it was not a "*…wayside station…*".

The '*Baskerville Hall*' Road Approaches. The text of the story gives us an enormous amount of information about the relative location of '*Baskerville Hall*'. By far the most important reference here is the description of the carriage journey made to '*Baskerville Hall*' by Dr Watson, in the company of Sir Henry Baskerville and Mortimer, from the wayside station which they reach after their railway trip from London. This is supplemented by the descriptions of the route from '*Coombe Tracey*' to '*Lafter Hall*', of the route from there to '*Baskerville Hall*', and of that from there to the hamlet or village of '*Grimpen*'. Crucial within these descriptions are the facts that '*Lafter Hall*', '*Baskerville Hall*' and '*Grimpen*' all lie on the edge of the high Moor, that '*Baskerville Hall*' lies roughly to the North of '*Lafter Hall*' and that '*Grimpen*' lies roughly to the North of *'Baskerville Hall'*. When we add the final, major locational fact, that the only clear view of the high Moor from *'Baskerville Hall'* is from the Westernmost window on the first floor of the *'Hall'* to the general limitation of the required area to the Ancient Forest boundary of the Moor, we are left with the conclusion that *'Baskerville Hall'* lies on the East-South-Eastern rim of the high Moor. There is far more evidence available for this conclusion, and some of this will be presented when other locations in the area are mentioned.

SPECIFIC REAL DARTMOOR LOCATIONS

Introduction. There are some real locations on Dartmoor, both within and outside the South-Eastern quadrant, which we know that ACD visited, and there are others which he may well have visited, which may have influenced his descriptions of certain locations and events connected with Dartmoor in *The Hound*.

'Princetown Prison'. Although the name of this location title has been included in single quotation marks, which normally indicates an invented name in this Investigation, this is only because the correct name of the institution which is undoubtedly being referred to is Her Majesty's Prison Dartmoor, not *'Princetown Prison'*. It is from here that the prisoner involved in the story, Selden, escapes, but the reference to the prison does arouse a point of caution where the details of the story are concerned. It is frequently said by Holmesians that Dr Watson was terrible at calculating distances, in that he often seems to have doubled or halved the distances involved in his accounts of the adventures of Sherlock Holmes. In this particular case Dr Watson has Holmes saying, when looking at a map of Dartmoor: *"That is Baskerville Hall in the middle...Then fourteen miles away the great convict prison of Princetown."* Both *'Baskerville Hall'* and *'Princetown Prison'* are meant to be on Dartmoor but, as has already been indicated, it is not possible to find somewhere which is fourteen miles from Dartmoor Prison which is also on Dartmoor, given that the prison lies close to the

centre of the Moor and that none of the radius lines from it to the edges of Dartmoor are more than 12 miles in length. Perhaps Holmes was calculating the distance between the two locations by road, and such considerations need to be made whenever Watson mentions distances, as must the possibility that he may have been attempting to disguise actual locations, although it would be difficult to disguise Dartmoor Prison!

Belliver (Bellever) and **Vixen** Tors. A different sort of salutary lesson might be learned from the way in which one Holmesian, Anthony Howlett, criticised Dr Watson for saying that he climbed a hill and found that: *"A haze lay low upon the farthest sky-line, out of which jutted the fantastic shapes of Belliver and Vixen Tor."* Mr Howlett commented that: "Watson was mistaken in thinking he saw them both...there is no point on the Moor from which he could have seen them both." This indicates not only a lack of awareness of the geography of the Moor, but of the fact that the uninterrupted lines of sight from North Hessary Tor to Bellever Tor and Vixen Tor can easily be determined from a map. Although we do not have a record, there is a strong possibility that ACD, who was a keen hill-walker and occasional mountaineer, would not have been able to ignore the easy track which starts at the rear of the hotel where he stayed in Princetown, and which winds its way invitingly up to the summit of North Hessary Tor, less than one mile away. This provides what is one of the best viewpoints available in that part of Dartmoor, supplying views of much of the area of the Moor over which ACD was to walk with BFR whilst staying at the Duchy Hotel. On one memorable occasion, whilst commemorating the centenary of the death of The Hound on a night marathon around the Moor in October 1989, some fell-running members of The Baskerville Hounds, including the present commentator, clearly saw Vixen Tor and Bellever Tor by moonlight from the summit of North Hessary Tor and commended Watson's superiority on this point.

Black Tor. There is a problem with identifying the *'Black Tor'* which is mentioned in *The Hound*,

Dartmoor Prison. The main gateway in the outer wall of the prison, which still exists, with warders in their dress uniforms, including an officer wearing his ceremonial sword. The photograph was taken by Robert Burnard, but is undated, although the fact that there is a Queen's Crown, as opposed to a King's Crown, on the notice indicates that it was taken in Victorian times. The Latin motto, 'Parcere Subjectus' means 'Spare the Vanquished', indicating that the establishment was built to house prisoners of war, rather than convicts. It will be noted that the walls are not particularly high, but then the main deterrent to escaping was the Moor itself. [56]

and it is not just the geographical one which arises from the fact that there are at least four Black Tors on Dartmoor, if one includes one clearly identified as Blacka Tor, which is a spelling which emphasises the way in which Moormen tend to avoid any harsh syllabic breaks between two words. One might suggest that there are, in fact, as many as six Black Tors, if one allows a second, rather dubiously-identified Blacka Tor, and a Blackey Tor which reflects the previously-mentioned phonetically harmonious speech practice on Dartmoor. The two Black Tors which might be significant to the creation of *The Hound* are that overlooking the River Meavy, near Princetown, and, more-favourably, that

overlooking the River Aune, significantly close to Shipley Tor and Shipley Bridge (with the fictitious *'Shipley's Yard'* being mentioned in the book), near South Brent. The other problem associated with the *'Black Tor'* mentioned in the book is the fact that it was not always referred to in that way in the original published text, or in the manuscript. We thus have one reference to *"...the black Tor..."*, one reference to *"...the Black Tor..."*, and one reference to *"...that Black Tor..."*. There is the possibility that these variations are simple typographical errors, and that the references are merely to a Tor which has a black appearance, rather than to a specifically-named Black Tor, as the use of the prefixes 'the' and 'that' suggest, with these being absent from all the references to actual Tors in the story. Unfortunately, the surviving manuscript of Chapter XI of The Hound does not help here, even though it includes two of the three references to a black Tor, or a Black Tor, in that it has one example of *"...black Tor..."* and one example of *"...Black Tor"*.

Hound Tor. Much to the disappointment of some visitors (with others being conned without realisation), and of various commercial and tourist agencies, there is no reference to a Hound Tor anywhere in *The Hound*, in spite of the fact that there are now two tors with the name of Hound Tor, and another with the name of Little Hound Tor, on Dartmoor. One of these real Hound Tors, and the real Little Hound Tor, will be mentioned again shortly, in connection with their proximity

to a great 'mire', Raybarrow Pool. This 'mire' will be seen to be unsuitable as a candidate for the *'great Grimpen Mire'*, in being located on the North Moor, and this tends to remove any justification for drawing a connection between this Northern Hound Tor or Little Hound Tor and the book. The other Hound Tor which can be found on modern maps, located between Manaton and Widecombe-in-the-Moor, is the one which has, too-frequently, been used to make claims for a link with the book. There are two problems with the suggestion that this Tor is associated with *The Hound*: firstly, there is no suitable great mire or other candidate Houndian location in the area, and secondly, this tor was recorded on the Ordnance Survey map used by ACD as Hounter Tor, not Hound Tor. In other sources of the time, however, it does appear as Houndtor, Houndtorre or Hound Tor. There is a further

Bellever Tor and Moor Ponies. Dr Watson mentions seeing *'Belliver Tor'* from the summit of a hill which is almost certainly North Hessary Tor. This photograph by Chpman & Sons was taken before the area around Bellever Tor was planted with conifers, which is how it would have been seen by Dr Watson in 1889 and by ACD in 1901. Interestingly, given the way in which ACD was fooled by photographs of the Cottingley Fairies, this photograph is a similar fake, in that the ponies were added to make the view of the Tor more picturesque. [56]

Hound Tor – Kistvaen. Robert Burnard's handwritten caption for this photograph, taken on 13 August 1889, records the location as being Hounter Tor, and not under its modern name of Hound Tor, and this Victorian name is shown on the Ordnance Survey maps of the time, which detracts from any suggestions that this Tor provided any sort of inspiration for The Hound. The very large kistvaen, or granite burial chamber, here is surrounded by a cairn part-circle of stones. [58]

point which seems to have been ignored by those who would like to be able to justify their claims for any of the Hound Tors being associated with the book, and that is the fact that had ACD shown any interest in these real Tors from an artistic viewpoint, then he would surely have used them in naming a Tor in the book, in the way in which he used the real Bellever and Vixen Tors.

NON-DARTMOOR REAL LOCATIONS

The Royal Links Hotel in Cromer. Unfortunately, the Royal Links Hotel, where ACD and BFR were staying when *The Hound* was conceived, was burned to the ground in a fire in 1970. A holiday complex has been built on the site, and the main clubhouse is situated on the exact point where the hotel had been located, with some of the foundations and supports of the hotel being incorporated into the new building. Potential guests at the holiday complex are welcomed by the management staff, and one can enjoy much the same view as that seen by ACD, over the golf course and along the sea cliffs.

Cromer Hall. Close to the site of the Royal Links Hotel is what may have been the main candidate for the inspiration for the description of *'Baskerville Hall'*, Cromer Hall. This is a strictly private residence, but the full frontage of the Hall can be seen from the adjacent public road, Hall Road, as can some of the adjoining grounds. From the public viewpoint one can see many of the features of *'Baskerville Hall'* which are described in the book, in that we have the trees on either side of Hall Road forming a *"...sombre tunnel..."* leading to the gates of the Hall and the driveway which opens out onto *"...a broad expanse of turf..."* in front of the Hall. The main part of the Hall fits the description of a *"...heavy block of building from which a porch projected..."* and it has *"...two wings..."*. Part of the front of the building was *"...draped in ivy..."*, with patches which were *"...clipped bare here and there where a window or a coat of arms..."* break through *"...the dark veil."*. The Hall has *"...two towers..."*, although only one of them rises from the central block, but that block is *"...crenellated..."*. It has *"...heavy mullioned windows..."*, there are *"...high chimneys..."* and there are *"...high-angled..."* roofs over the wings. Although the wings are not lined with black granite, they are faced with black flint blocks. It obviously cannot be seen from outside, but the main staircase is lined with a continuous succession of family portraits. Sadly, the *"...Yew Alley..."* is concealed behind the Hall, but on the moorland behind the Hall, which this alley leads out onto, via a *"...wicket-gate..."*, one can see *"...stunted oaks and firs which had been twisted and bent by the fury of years of storm..."*. There is no house on Dartmoor which fits the description of *'Baskerville Hall'* given in the book anywhere near as well as does Cromer Hall, but that does not mean, as some eccentric Sherlockian scholars with a penchant for such geographical transpositions might suggest (one of them once moved the Dartmoor race-horse case, 'Silver Blaze', to Hampshire!), that the dramatic events of *The Hound* took place in Norfolk, with Dr Watson moving them to Devonshire to disguise the location. What is missing in Norfolk is the atmosphere and geographical features which exist on Dartmoor and nowhere else in the world, proving that Dartmoor is essential to everything which happens in *The Hound*.

The Shipley Connection. There is an interesting London link with Dartmoor, in that the place from which the cabman in the story, John Clayton, operates is *'Shipley's Yard'*, near Waterloo Station. There was no such yard anywhere in London, but there is a Shipley Bridge and a Shipley Tor on Dartmoor in the very area which is closely associated with *The Hound*, and ACD may well have visited this area, in that he describes elements of the Moor which might be seen there.

Other London Locations. There are other London locations mentioned in the book which are more-easily identified, such as *Waterloo Station*, where Sir Henry arrives from Southampton, and *Paddington Station*, from which Dr Watson, Sir Henry and Mortimer depart for Devonshire. Some locations are reasonably easy to find, in that the building of the *Charing Cross Hospital* which Dr Watson mentions can still be seen, just off The Strand, although it has now been converted into a police station. Other locations will be mentioned within the Annotations which follow the main text of *The Hound*.

INVENTED HOUNDIAN LOCATIONS

Key Locations. The two most important Dartmoor locations mentioned in *The Hound* are both invented: *'Baskerville Hall'* and the *'great Grimpen Mire'*. This is almost inevitable with the first location, in that it would certainly have caused problems for the occupants of a real building if they were constantly pestered by tourists wanting to see *'Baskerville Hall'*. Indeed, this actually happened with the new residents at one of the main candidate locations for *'Baskerville Hall'*, who knew nothing about the sort of interest taken by Holmesians in such places, and who were sitting at breakfast one morning when they noticed a group of Japanese Holmesians filming them through their kitchen window! It may seem less understandable that someone should want to try to disguise the location of a mire on the Moor, but a similar problem occurs in making anything certain with such an important location, in that this would attract attention to the private buildings associated in the story with that mire, with *'Merripit House'*, for example, being described as being adjacent to the *'great Grimpen Mire'*. This section of the Investigation will consider some identificational details for several of the more important invented locations of *The Hound*, and discuss some of the candidates which have been proposed as having been significant in influencing ACD in his descriptions of the invented locations.

'BASKERVILLE HALL'

General Points. *'Baskerville Hall'* is, of course, absolutely vital to the identification of most of

Cromer Hall. Located close to the Royal Links Hotel in Cromer, the Hall may have inspired parts of the description of *Baskerville Hall*. [59]

COURTESY OF THE CROMER MUSEUM

61

Shipley Bridge. Robert Burnard's photograph was taken looking South, or downstream, on the River Avon (or Aune). The name of the bridge, and of the nearby Shipley Tor, is echoed in that of the yard from which the London cabman, John Clayton, worked. The bridge and Tor are also overlooked by Black Tor, with Watson mentioning *"...the black tor..."* upon which he had seen the mysterious figure outlined against the moon. [60]

the other important sites on the Moor which are associated with the story, since descriptions of their locations are mostly given in relative terms, based on journeys made to and from 'Baskerville Hall'. The description of 'Baskerville Hall' given in the story is extensive, and parts of this description have already been discussed above, in terms of its descriptive relationship to Cromer Hall and of the road approaches leading to 'Baskerville Hall'. There are other major points of identification, however, such as the fact that there is a track leading from 'Baskerville Hall' directly across the Moor for nine miles to the farm of the yeoman whose daughter was abducted by the

wicked Hugo Baskerville. This must have been a fairly large, clear and solidly-based track, in that horsemen galloped along it at night. Given that 'Baskerville Hall' lay on the East-South-Eastern rim of the Moor, and the distance involved, the suggestion is that this track must have run towards somewhere on the South-Western rim of the Moor, with the village of Sheepstor being a good candidate, and with the track being along part of the Southern extremity of what is now known as The Abbot's Way. This might conveniently have been reached from the Lud Gate area, over the major East-West track below the summit of Puper's Hill, then over or around

Huntingdon Warren to meet The Way. The Abbot's Way might then have been left in the area of the upper River Plym, onto the major tracks passing the old Eylesbarrow mine complex. The road which runs to *'Baskerville Hall'* from *'Coombe Tracey'* and from the *'…wayside railway station…'*, along the edge of the high Moor, might be one of those running from Newton Abbot or Totnes, through the Ashburton or Buckfastleigh areas towards the Holne or Scorriton areas. The continuation from *'Baskerville Hall'* to *'Grimpen'* could be that leading to Hexworthy, with that hamlet having many similarities to the *'Grimpen'* of the story, including a good track which leads to a true mire, through the valley of the River Swincombe. The author of these notes has, over several decades, investigated every single large house on Dartmoor in terms of its potential for being *'Baskerville Hall'*, and none of them fit the requirements perfectly. Some have excellent physical elements which match, but then do not have the relative locational requirements. With others the reverse is true. Some of the most important of the many candidates which have been proposed by Holmesian scholars, some by those with a commercial interest in suggesting that their building has some connection with *The Hound*, are considered below.

Brook Manor. This large country house, some-times recorded as 'Brooke Manor', is situated in the valley of the River Mardle near Buckfastleigh and it is the candidate which has most frequently been proposed as being an inspiration for *'Baskerville Hall'*. It is certainly old enough, with a major re-building having taken place in 1656, with *'Baskerville Hall'* being described as existing at the time of the Civil War. Brook Manor actually has very few of the required physical attributes, however, in that it is an L-shaped building, rather than having a central block with two wings. There are no towers, although the two very tall chimney stacks do give the appearance of being narrow towers. It is not located in a hollow, but in a sharply V-shaped valley. There are no yew trees close to the house, and there has certainly never been a yew alley. It has been sug-

gested that there is a long, tunnel-like driveway, which opens out into a grassy area in front of the porch of the house, but in the Nineteenth Century this driveway did not exist, in that the approach to the house was then made along an open driveway nearer the bottom of the valley. Perhaps the most devastating problem with Brook Manor is the fact that one cannot actually see the high Moor from any of its windows, and it would take a walk of at least four miles, passing through the lands of several farms, to get to the high Moor from the house, whereas the yew alley at *'Baskerville Hall'* led directly out onto the open Moor. One might well ask what it is that makes this house a popular candidate for being *'Baskerville Hall'*, and the answer lies in the hound legends which are attached to it. These are discussed in the Section on the possible legendary inspirations for *The Hound*. It has been seen that the legends associated with Brook Manor are not similar to that contained in the story, but then neither are any of the other hound legends on Dartmoor. One important association which has been discovered by The Baskerville Hounds, is that there is a family connection between Brook Manor and Cromer Hall, in that the family which built Brook Manor was the Cabell family (pronounced with a long 'A' as in 'cable'), and the family which resided at Cromer Hall when ACD and BFR visited Cromer was the Bond-Cabbell family (second half pronounced with a short 'A' as 'ka-bell'). There is a remarkable resemblance between the owner of Cromer Hall at the time of ACD's visit to Cromer, Benjamin Bond-Cabbell, and Sir Charles Baskerville, in that both had inherited estates which had been neglected or where little had been done to develop those estates for many years, and Sir Charles and Benjamin both set about rectifying this situation. One of Benjamin's developments lead to the creation of the golf course where ACD and BFR played, and its adjoining hotel, the Royal Links Hotel, where the two men stayed. Another Devonshire link is that SBG was related to the Bond family branch of the Bond-Cabbell family. It may well have been connections such as these, as well as the coincidence of fiery hound legends between

Waterloo Station. This is the London terminus station at which Sir Henry Baskerville arrived from Southampton, and from which Stapleton may have reached Dartmoor with The Hound. [60]

Cromer and Dartmoor, which so excited ACD in Cromer, and which encouraged him to dash down to Dartmoor to work on his new story. One should note that Brook Manor is private, but it can be seen clearly, over the hedge, from the Buckfastleigh to Holne road which runs along the upper edge of the valley to the East of the house, although one needs to park carefully to avoid obstructing the narrow road.

Hayford Hall. This large block-like building is located near Buckfastleigh, in a hollow sheltering under the rim of the high Moor, close to the source of the little Dean Burn, about which there is a solitary black hound legend. The house is in an almost perfect location as far as the relative locational details of other sites from the story are concerned, and it is possible to walk out of the grounds of the house, through an old yew alley, an extremely important link with *'Baskerville Hall'*, directly onto the high Moor. The yew alley was almost destroyed at some time, but the

present owner is restoring it. The house is surrounded by trees, like *'Baskerville Hall'*, and from a Western window one can just see a suitable rock outcrop for sending candle signals to the house from an adjacent hill, Pupers Hill. As well as the outcrop, known as Outer Pupers, one can see the rim of the Moor, partially obstructed by trees, exactly as one can from the window at *'Baskerville Hall'*. Although Pupers Hill obviously does not bear the name of a Tor, as does *'Cleft Tor'* in the story, it is, geologically, a classic Tor, in being a rounded hill with outcrops of granite on and around the summit. The construction of the house is, however, very dissimilar to that of *'Baskerville Hall'*, and it is known that at the time of the story it was an active farmhouse. There are crenellations, but these were added after the time of the story. There is a large gateway and a tunnel-like driveway through the trees, but the latter curves dramatically and one cannot see the gateway from the house. It should be noted that the house is a strictly private resi-

Paddington Station. This is the London terminus station of the Great Western Railway from which Dr Watson travelled to Dartmoor in the company of Sir Henry Baskerville and Mortimer. The photograph is of the last broad gauge train, pulled by *Bulkeley*, departing on 20 May 1892. [60]

dence, but a rather limited view of the house can be obtained, over the hedge, from the lane which leads from the entrance gate of Hayford Hall to Lud Gate, and a good view of its location can be seen from Pupers Hill. There is, in fact, a family link with Brook Manor and thus with Cromer Hall, and with hounds on Dartmoor, as will be seen with the next candidate, Fowelscombe.

Fowelscombe. The member of the Cabell family who lived at Brook Manor and who was responsible for the hound legends associated with the house, was the third Richard Cabell, who died in 1672 (almost certainly not 1677 as SBG suggests). In 1656 he married Elizabeth Fowells, a member of an ancient and powerful Devonshire family (William Fowell was MP for Totnes in 1455) which later fell upon hard times, thanks largely to excessive involvements in litigation, which raises echoes of Mr Frankland of *'Lafter Hall'* in *The Hound*. The Fowell family home was a magnificent mansion, Fowelscombe, which lies to the South-East of Ugborough, some three and

a half miles from the edge of the high Moors. This is possibly the best Devonshire candidate for *'Baskerville Hall'* in terms of its external appearance, in having a central block, two large wings, two towers, crenellations, mullioned windows, and a porch. It is certainly old enough, in having been built in 1537, and its frontage was almost doubled at some time between 1792 and 1865 by the extension of the wings, but in 1889 it belonged not to the Baskervilles, but to the Reverend Gordon Walters. Its setting, however, being in the lowlands well away from the Moor, is totally unsuitable. Some distance from the main house there are the remains of an extensive set of kennels for hounds, where a full hunting pack was once kept. Being at such an inconvenient distance from the high Moor, these hounds were, in the hunting season, moved up to temporary kennels at Hayford Hall, emphasising once again the way in which one could move directly onto the Moor from that location. The large outdoor clock which was once set in the main block of Fowelscombe has recently been rescued, restored

THE HOUND OF THE BASKERVILLES

and installed at Hayford Hall, thus maintaining the connection with Fowelscombe. Sadly, the latter is now in an advanced state of decay, and it cannot be visited, not only because of the danger of parts of the building collapsing, but because it is in the grounds of an active farm.

Lew House. This building, in the hamlet of Lewtrenchard, possesses many of the elements of the description of *'Baskerville Hall'*, with its central block, wings, porch, and its steeply-angled roofs, but there is no tree-lined driveway leading to the house. It was certainly old enough, in that the original Lew House is mentioned in the *Domesday Book* of 1086, although it has been suggested that the original house stood some distance from the present one. Lew House was the home of the great Devonshire squarson, novelist, historian, antiquarian, music-collector and writer of *Onward Christian Soldiers*, SBG, at the time of the events in *The Hound*, with Sabine having completed the reconstruction of the house to its near-present form in 1885. It became a candidate for *'Baskerville Hall'* largely at the instigation of Sabine's American-born grandson, William Stuart Baring-Gould, a well-known Sherlockian who wrote a 'biography' of Sherlock Holmes. In that biography, Baring-Gould attributed many aspects of the family history of the Baring-Goulds to Sherlock Holmes, lifting whole sections from real biographies written about SBG, and inventing many new 'facts' to support his biography. There may well be links between SBG and *The Hound*, but not those proposed by his over-imaginative descendant! Lew House, for example, is not only located on the wrong side of Dartmoor but it is also not even located on Dartmoor, being sited some five miles from the high Moor, to the North-West of the Moor, and there are no mires anywhere near Lew House. One cannot actually see Dartmoor from Lew House if one were to look from any of the windows in the West wing of the house, as Dr Watson and Sir Henry did from the window in the West wing of *'Baskerville Hall'*. One would, in fact, be looking towards Cornwall, with the border being located only seven miles away. Lew House is currently a splendid hotel, where guests are made very welcome.

Heatree House. This building bears very little resemblance to *'Baskerville Hall'*, either in its outward appearance or in its relationship to anything else connected with the Moor locations of *The Hound*. It is totally the wrong shape and it has almost none of the other physical attributes of *'Baskerville Hall'*. There is no tunnel-like driveway, and it is located in one of the softer and sheltered parts of Dartmoor, off the high Moor, in spite of its relatively high altitude. One can see almost nothing from its Western windows, and one cannot see any of the wild Moor. There are no mires in the vicinity. Its candidacy arose primarily from the suggestion which it has been claimed that Harry Baskerville made, that it was the inspiration for *'Baskerville Hall'*. It has also been suggested that Harry claimed that this house did once belong to the Baskerville family, but the current occupants can find no evidence for this. It is currently a private educational establishment, and it is not open to casual visitors.

Other Candidates. There are many more houses on Dartmoor which have been claimed by Holmesian enthusiasts, or by owners (especially owners of commercial establishments!) anxious to increase the reputation of their properties, to have been the original *'Baskerville Hall'*, but none of them have good justifications for such a claim. There has been the claim, for example, that Moretonhampstead Manor House, which matches the architectural description of *'Baskerville Hall'* in many ways, is *'Baskerville Hall'*. This claim, however, is largely based upon the fact that the Moretonhampstead Manor House was used, very briefly, in a film in 1931 as *'Baskerville Hall'*, but this splendidly Gothick building was not built until 1906, more than four years after the story was written. Other Dartmoor buildings for which there has been support include (in purely alphabetical order): Bagpark (or Widecombe Manor), Blackaton Manor, Buckland Abbey (the former home of Sir Francis Drake), Hannaford Manor, Holne Chase Hotel, Leighon, Lukesland, Lustleigh Hall, Natsworthy Manor, Prince Hall, Spitchwick Manor, Tor Royal and Wooder Manor. Most of these are private residences, with no public access, but all of them can, fortunately, be ignored as serious candidates for providing the inspiration for *'Baskerville Hall'*. There have also been proposals for the candidacy of buildings other than Cromer Hall which are not on Dartmoor, such as Crowsley Park in Shiplake, near Henley-on-Thames, and Clyro Court near Hay-on-Wye, with both of these houses having been seats of the Baskerville family, but with neither having any of the structural or locational requirements of *'Baskerville Hall'*, although both do have yew alleys. It has also been suggested that ACD's Jesuit school, Stonyhurst College, may have influenced the description of *'Baskerville Hall'*, in that it has towers and a yew alley with a gate, but one would actually see six towers if one looked down on Stonyhurst in the way that Watson first looks down on *'Baskerville Hall'* (the fact that one cannot look down upon Stonyhurst in a hollow also tells against it), and the yew alley there is totally different in nature to that described in *The Hound*.

'GREAT GRIMPEN MIRE'

General Points. Apart from *'Baskerville Hall'*, the other crucial location mentioned in the story is that of the *'great Grimpen Mire'*. Once again, there is no such mire on the Moor, and although there are many boggy places on the Moor which are named on the map as mires, there are very few places fitting the true meaning of that word. Land drainage associated with agriculture and with providing water for the rapidly growing port of Plymouth accounted for the drying up of many of the mires on the Moor during the Nineteenth Century, and those which remained were nowhere near as dangerous as the description of the *'great Grimpen Mire'* suggests. It is, in fact, almost impossible for a man to be sucked down completely beneath the surface anywhere on the Moor. This is not to say that one cannot sink in one of the very small and isolated bog holes on the Moor, but these are mostly filled with water, and if one falls in one can fairly easily get out again. It is also not to suggest that one cannot get stuck, or 'stugged' or 'stigged' as the Moormen say, in a mire, but it is extremely diffi-

cult to sink more than waist deep in these places, and one tends to get plenty of warning that this is liable to happen as one ploughs increasingly deeper into those parts of a mire. Members of The Baskerville Hounds have frequently and actively attempted to find areas in the wettest seasons of the year where one can sink beneath the surface of a true mire, thankfully without success. The great danger of being 'stugged', of course, is that it can be almost impossible to get out unaided, and one can easily die of exposure if stuck in such a position on the Moor in bad weather for even just a few hours. In fact, the truly great mires on the Moor can be reduced to only a handful.

Raybarrow Pool and Other Great North Moor Mires. One of the great 'mires' on the Northern Moor might seem to be very attractive as being the original of the *'great Grimpen Mire'*, in that it is located close to a Hound Tor and to Little Hound Tor, but the 'pool' element of the name of this 'mire' is indicative of its nature being different to that of most of the other great mires on the Moor, in that it contains far more surface water than do the majority of true mires. It is, in fact, the 'mire' which is involved in the interesting, anonymous short story already mentioned, about an escaped prisoner, fog, and someone disappearing into a mire, 'The Tale of a Dartmoor Fog', which was published in *Chambers's Journal* on 22 April 1893 and which may have had an influence on ACD. Raybarrow Pool is, however, far too close to the North Devon line, even if Stapleton travelled as far as Okehampton before starting his long walk across the Moor, and, very significantly, no suitable candidate for *'Merripit House'* lies in its close vicinity, or, even more significantly, no old tin mine workings lie within its boundaries. Some of the other great mires on the North Moor, located around the sources of most of the rivers which originate in that part of the Moor, are less watery in their constitution, but they all suffer from the other problems associated with Raybarrow Pool, and can thus be dismissed.

Head of Aune Mire. This mire has the alternative name of Head of Avon Mire, with Aune being an older version of the name Avon, with the source of the River Aune being located in this mire. It has the essential attribute of lying close to the South-Eastern rim of the Moor, and is the nearest of the great mires to the best locational candidates for 'Baskerville Hall'. It does not, however, have any houses adjacent to it to act as candidates for 'Merripit House', and it has no old tin mine workings within its boundaries. In addition, it does not have a path leading from it to a nearby hamlet or village, when there is such a path leading from the 'great Grimpen Mire' to 'Grimpen'. One advantage which it does have over other mires is that ACD and BFR may have walked near it, in that it is of Aune Head Mire that the story is usually told of 'The Hat on the Mire', and BFR did record that he told ACD this story whilst walking around a mire on the Moor. BFR's version of the story runs as follows:

> A moor man (who) on one occasion saw a hat near the edge of the morass and poked at it with a long pole he carried. 'You leave my hat alone!' came a voice from beneath it. 'Whoi! Be there a man under the 'at?' cried the startled rustic. 'Yes, you fool, and a horse under the man!'

This is, of course, typical of the sort of exaggeration which occurs over the depths to which one can sink in a mire, as well as of the depth to which humour can sink! It might be noted, however, that the story had already been recorded in connection with Aune Head Mire by SBG in his *A Book of Dartmoor*, published in 1900.

Sheepstor. Robert Burnard's photograph was taken on 9 May 1891, and shows the heart of the village, with the hill to the left of the church tower being the Tor after which the village is named. The farm of the yeoman whose daughter was kidnapped by the wicked Hugo Baskerville may have been inspired by one of those on the Moor side of the village. [62]

'Grimspound Bog'. This location, with its very obvious name association with the word *'Grimpen'* has been claimed to have been the inspiration for the *'great Grimpen Mire'* in scores of articles and books. The main influence here seems to be Baring-Gould, but once again it is not Sabine but his American grandson who is at fault, with no less an authority than the *Oxford English Dictionary* quoting him in defining the only English word which it accepts as being invented by ACD, 'Grimpen': "As is well known, Watson's 'great Grimpen Mire' is *Grimspound Bog*, three miles north and west of Widecombe-in-the-Moor." It should firstly be noted that a bog is, technically, not quite the same as a mire, although the differences are truly minor, and ACD does refer to part of the *'great Grimpen Mire'* as being a bog in *The Hound*, and BFR referred to Fox Tor Mires as being a bog. There are, however, several major problems with 'Grimspound Bog', with the first and most important being the fact that it does not exist, as is indicated by the quotation marks which are assigned to it here, which are absent in the arguments raised in its favour by misguided Holmesians and Sherlockians. There is a slightly boggy area surrounding the Grimslake stream, upstream of the Grimspound enclosure. Jeremy Butler refers to it as the Grimslake Mire, but it would be difficult to get one's calves wet in that small area, and the word 'small' is massively significant here, in that the great Grimpen Mire is, as its adjective suggests, meant to be large. BFR, in describing the mire which he visited with ACD, wrote, according to HJW Dam's 1905 interview: "...I took Doyle to see the mighty bog, a thousand acres of quaking slime..." The marshy area around the upper Grimslake occupies only a few dozen acres, even though it is an area which has never been artificially drained, and it could certainly never have been called 'mighty'. BFR mentions the mighty bog which he saw with ACD in order to suggest that it provided inspiration for the *'great Grimpen Mire'*, and his account continues: "From the bog we tramped eastward to the stone fort of Gromspound...". Allowing for the mis-spelling of Grimspound by the recorder of this account, and the mistaken idea that Grimspound was a fort, the mighty bog which they visited is clearly to the West of the Grimspound enclosure, whereas the small marsh on the Grimslake is to the East of the enclosure.

Fox Tor Mires. Although the name here is multiple, there is, in fact, merely one interlinked series of mires, located in a natural water-collecting landscape bowl, surrounded by hills on every side, some three miles to the South-East of Princetown. We know that ACD and BFR took a walk from the old Duchy Hotel in Princetown, and that they travelled around the edge of one of the great mires, and we also know, from the letter which ACD sent to his mother from the hotel, that he and BFR carried out one walk of some fourteen miles in length. If we add to this the fact that we know that ACD and BFR visited the Bronze Age enclosure of Grimspound, we can see that a very interesting walk can be inferred, with the whole walk taking place over good tracks. The walk starts at the hotel in Princetown and heads South to Nun's Cross Farm, overlooking Fox Tor Mires. The track then heads Eastwards, along the ridge between Fox Tor Mires and Aune Head Mire, then down the valley of the River Swincombe to Hexworthy. It continues over Laughter Tor, close to the old Laughter Hole Farm, to the hamlet of Bellever. Several tracks are then available for a fairly straight walk to Grimspound. The distance involved here is some fourteen miles, if the walkers were met at the enclosure by Harry Baskerville for the return journey to the hotel to be carried out by carriage, with a good access road for carriages to reach Grimspound having been built from the main Moor-crossing road, the Moretonhampstead to Tavistock road, in 1887. Dam concluded his interview with an anecdote of ACD and BFR sitting down inside one of the stone hut circles at Grimspound, to smoke their pipes out of the wind. Another tourist arrived, and he, startled to find two troglodytes inside the hut, ran off into the mist. From such incidents legends arise.

Further Points on Fox Tor Mires. The suggested walk described above involves numerous relevant points. Nun's Cross Cottage fits the description of *'Merripit House'* in many ways, in being truly desolate in nature, and in that it is adjacent to a great mire, although it is rather smaller than the description given in the story. It can be reached by carriage, by a roundabout route (through Princetown) from the best candidates for *'Baskerville Hall'* on the South-Eastern rim of the Moor, exactly as happens in the story. It can also be reached, on foot only, by a track from the hamlet or village of *'Grimpen'* on the Eastern rim of the Moor, exactly as happens in the story, with Hexworthy providing a convenient candidate for *'Grimpen'*. There are other, much more difficult, and more-direct, walking routes from the best candidates for *'Baskerville Hall'* to Nun's Cross Cottage, across the Moor, passing to the South of Fox Tor Mires exactly as the *'great Grimpen Mire'* is passed in the story. There are several references to *'Lafter Hall'*, the home of Frankland, in the story, and whilst there is no *'Lafter Hall'* on the Moor, there is, on the walk from Fox Tor Mires described above, the ancient Laughter Hole Farm. The *'Belliver Tor'* mentioned in the story is almost certainly Bellever Tor, with this Tor being located next to Laughter Tor, and over-looking the hamlet of Bellever, all of which are on the walk route from Fox Tor Mires. Finally, the local pronounciation of Grimspound is 'Grimspun', and this suggests a possible name with which to disguise the mire in which the villain may have perished. The *'great Grimpen Mire'* is described in the story as having the remains of an old tin mine within its boundaries, and there are the remains of old tin mine workings not only all around Fox Tor Mires but within it, including the remains of the water-wheel which is in the *'great Grimpen Mire'* mine-workings but absent from most mine-working areas on the Moor. Finally, the story suggests that there are paths which lead to the very heart of the *'great Grimpen Mire'* which can be followed only by those who know the special markings, and this too is the situation with Fox Tor Mires.

'MERRIPIT HOUSE'

General Points. The home of the Stapletons is obviously closely linked to the location of the *'great Grimpen Mire'*, in that the mire is seen to be near to the house and The Hound is also kept close to the house, and it is near to *'Baskerville Hall'*, in that Sir Charles was described as being a neighbour by Jack Stapleton and one might reasonably walk from *'Merripit House'* to *'Baskerville Hall'* at night, as Sir Henry is instructed to do at the climax of the story. One must be able to reach *'Merripit House'* on a track which starts at a junction with the road which runs from *'Baskerville Hall'* to the hamlet of *'Grimpen'*, and also reach it, by a longer route, by carriage. In passing along the track from the *'Grimpen'* road junction, one must pass a large hill which has been quarried to leave a cliff-like appearance, and pass to the South of the *'great Grimpen Mire'*, and one must head Westwards, since the road runs along the Eastern rim of the high Moor and the track heads into the wilder part of the Moor. Finally, and most importantly, *'Merripit House'* must be in a desolate location.

Higher, Middle and Lower Merripit. Each of these private houses, located in the village of Postbridge appear to have had an entirely suitable name to make them candidates for *'Merripit House'*, but although they did exist at the time of the story, they were all far too close to one of the major roads which cross Dartmoor, and too close to the other houses in the village, to have been described as being "...desolate...". From each of these houses the lights of other houses in the village could easily have been seen in 1889. There is also no true mire close to the area, in that with the mires marked on the map as such, like Stannon Mire, it would be difficult to get one's knees wet. For those who do support the Merripit area, there is an association with spectral animals, but they are not black hounds, and *'The Sow of the Stapletons'* does not have quite the right ring to it!

Merrivale. The name of this hamlet also suggests a source for the inspiration of the Merripit element of *'Merripit House'*, and there is a very dramatic quarry cut into the side of a hill in the hamlet which gives the appearance of being a cliff. Unfortunately, the houses in this hamlet lie close to one of the major roads which cross

Dartmoor. The water from this area is also well-drained into the River Walkman which flows through the heart of it, and so once again there is no suitable mire.

Fox Tor Farm. This farm was certainly in a suitable area, being located on a slope overlooking Fox Tor Mires, and it has the advantage that one can at least see Merripit Hill from the summit of the hill behind the farm, Ter Hill. Although it had been built in 1807, it was abandoned in 1863, and it would almost certainly have been in a state of collapse by 1889. It also fails in being reached on the track from the only suitable 'Grimpen' (Hexworthy) before one reaches Fox Tor Mires, and there is also no way in which one could have reached it by carriage. From its location the lights of the houses at Whiteworks could easily have been seen across the Mire, and it is thus not suitably remote. It does, however, have a connection with a literary escaped prisoner, in that Eden Phillpotts used it in his book *The American Prisoner*, although that was published two years after ACD's book. The farm no longer exists as a structure, but many of the remains can still be found.

Nun's Cross Cottage. This is certainly the best candidate for 'Merripit House' yet found, in that it lies on the Western edge of a good candidate for the 'great Grimpen Mire' (Fox Tor Mires), and yet it is concealed in a hollow so that it cannot be seen until the last minute when approaching it from the track from a suitable candidate for 'Grimpen' (Hexworthy), or on the good track over which a carriage could have travelled in 1889, with this latter track being a slight divergence from the excellent sandy road which ran from Princetown to Whiteworks. That road is at the end of what might be considered to be a lengthy road route from 'Baskerville Hall' (Hayford Hall), through 'Grimpen' (Hexworthy) to 'Merripit House' (Nun's Cross Cottage), with there being no shorter route from one to the other for a carriage. The cottage was, however, rather small for the description given in the story, although it would certainly have seemed to have been a reasonably large residence in 1889 in com-

parison with most of the other buildings in the area. There are the remains of a wall surrounding the house, exactly as described in the story, and even a few, small, stunted trees, as the remnants of the orchard at 'Merripit House'. There is even a choice of tracks passing to the South of the Mire towards 'Grimpen' (Hexworthy), which could have provided Beryl Stapleton with the short-cut which she used to overtake Watson. There are paths from the nearest of these tracks which enable one to reach the very heart of Fox Tor Mires, and to reach the remains of the tin mine which exist within that Mire. The cottage was built in 1871, and it was occupied at the time of the story by a tenant farmer, John Hooper. A new building was erected close to the old building in 1901, and the original building no longer exists, with the new building now being an expedition training base. One can walk around the outside of the cottage, but there is no public access and there is no longer any public vehicular access on the track.

Swallerton Gate & Yellowmeade Farm. These two large cottages, the first at the foot of Hound Tor and the second near Foggintor Quarries, were used to represent 'Merripit House' in separate films of *The Hound*. Although they are both old enough, neither of them is located in an area which matches the description in the story. Swallerton Gate had, in fact, once been The Hound Tor Inn, but it had become a private residence long before the events of *The Hound*. Both are now private residences, with no public access, although each can easily be viewed from the adjacent public track and road.

OTHER INVENTED DARTMOOR LOCATIONS

'Fernworthy'. This is a location where we cannot be sure whether it should be in the 'invented' or the 'real' sections of the Dartmoor locations, since there was, at the time of the events in *The Hound*, a hamlet called Fernworthy on the Moor. What little is left of this hamlet can now only be seen during drought conditions, since the valley in which it existed was flooded between 1936 and 1942 to form the Fernworthy Reservoir. As has

been mentioned above, in the literary and historical sources sections, this hamlet may have provided an influence on ACD in terms of it being the best candidate for the farm which plays a major rôle in 'A Tale of a Dartmoor Fog', and in the way in which the Fernworthy stone circle was found to have contained large quantities of charcoal. The hamlet was located on the Eastern rim of the high Moor, within a reasonable distance of good candidates for 'Lafter Hall', although there is no crucial reason why it need be close to the home of the man who was burnt in effigy by the Fernworthy folk, Mr Frankland. The latter might, however, quite rightly be annoyed by those who nowadays imitate the Fernworthy folk of the story by leaving "...their papers and their bottles..." scattered around the official picnic site which now overlooks the artificial lake at Fernworthy.

'Lafter Hall'. The residence of Mr Frankland is another where the misunderstanding of the Dartmoor accent may have had an influence. There are many names associated with the area near the presently-named Bellever Tor and Laughter Tor which is now known as Laughter Hole, and these include "Laster Hall", recorded in 1702. It might relevantly be noted that the long 's', looking like an 'f', was still in use at that time, and it is specifically mentioned by Holmes when he dates the Baskerville Legend document, and the name may therefore actually have been spelled Lafter Hall at that time. On 1 June 1872 the Duchy of Cornwall advertised "Lafter Hole" to be let by private contract from Michaelmas, and the first tenant, who was still there at the time of the events of *The Hound* was a Mr Holmes (no, sadly, not Sherlock but Joseph!). One can walk past the old farmhouse of Laughter Hole Farm, but there is no public access to the farmhouse itself. Locationally, as far as the best candidates for 'Baskerville Hall' are concerned, the best candidate for 'Lafter Hall' would be somewhere like White-Oxen Manor (no public access), being some four miles to the South of those 'Baskerville Hall' candidates, but there is no view of the Moor from there, or of the approaches to stone huts. For this, one of the houses on the road from

Buckfastleigh to Cross Furzes, in the region of Greendown (no public access), might be more appropriate.

Holmes's 'Stone Hut'. The stone hut circles at Grimspound are an obvious possible influence, since we know that ACD visited them. Grimspound is, however, rather a long way from the best candidates for 'Baskerville Hall' and the other Moor sites, and as there are many stone hut circles on the Moor there are many more locationally-appropriate candidates. Given the association between a Black Tor on the Moor and Holmes's stone hut, there are two good candidates. The first would be one of the many huts which can be seen from the Black Tor which overlooks the river Meavy, near Princetown. The second, and better, candidate would be one of the stone huts in Rider's Rings, overlooking the River Aune. This very large enclosure has the advantages of being closer to the best 'Baskerville Hall' candidates, to the route from those candidates to the Western side of the Moor, and to the London-associated sites of the nearby Shipley Tor and Shipley Bridge. In addition, one of the stone huts at Rider's Rings is known to have been roofed and used as accommodation in Victorian times, probably by a shepherd.

'Coombe Tracey'. There are two major candidates for this town, which should be located well off the South-Eastern edge of the Moor, at a distance of approximately 12 miles from 'Baskerville Hall', to allow for a two-hour carriage drive, with a final approach road onto the high Moor from the South. It should also have a railway station where express trains from London would have stopped. In the original, handwritten manuscript for *The Hound*, ACD wrote "Newton Abbott" at the start of the chapter entitled 'The Man on the Tor', then changed it to 'Coombe Tracey' in the manuscript. ACD himself arrived at Newton Abbot railway station from London in 1901. There is, however, another town with a station where express trains stopped which may have inspired 'Coombe Tracey', which is in an appropriate location, and that is Totnes. William S Baring-Gould ludicrously suggested that

Princetown. This photograph, taken by Robert Burnard on 1 June 1889, was taken from the track which leads to Tor Royal, Peat Cot, Nun's Cross Farm, the Whiteworks Tin Mine and Fox Tor Mires. In the centre foreground is The Plume of Feathers, with the Railway Inn to the right, and just beyond the former is the dark side and high chimney of Rowe's Duchy Hotel. In the middle distance, and slightly to the right of centre is Dartmoor Prison. The hill forming the left horizon leads to North Hessary Tor, and from there one can see both Vixen Tor and Bellever Tor, the two Tors which Dr Watson sees from the summit of the hill he climbs. [15]

Widecombe-in-the Moor was *'Coombe Tracey'*, when it does not have the main requirement, a railway station, let alone one at which London expresses stopped!

'Grimpen'. Once again the similarity in sound of Grimspound, especially when pronounced in the Dartmoor fashion as "Grimspun", suggests that the hamlet or village of *'Grimpen'* is located somewhere near Grimspound, but there are no other suitable candidate sites in the area of Grimspound. The nearby large village of Widecombe-in-the-Moor is totally unsuitable in terms of its location and surroundings, in spite of the fact that there is a William Henry Baskerville buried in the churchyard. There is, as has been indicated in connection with good candidates for other sites, an excellent candidate for *'Grimpen'* in Hexworthy. That village might appear to be something of a by-passed location these days, but the road from Buckfastleigh to Princetown was far more important in status in 1889. There is an inn at Hexworthy, The Forest

Inn, as required by the story, although it is no longer the one mentioned in *The Hound*, since that thatched building was almost completely destroyed by fire in 1913. There are several houses which fit the description of Mortimer's house, in terms of it overlooking the village. There is no combined post office and grocery shop, as required by the story, but letters were sent and collected from the inn and supplies were also sold there in the last century. Most significantly, just after leaving the village when heading towards the best candidates for *'Baskerville Hall'*, there is a track which leaves the road which runs along the edge of the high Moor and heads West towards the best candidates for the *'great Grimpen Mire'* and *'Merripit House'*.

'Foulmire'. This needs to be a farmhouse on the Moor, almost certainly within five miles of *'Baskerville Hall'*, in such a position that Mortimer would pass Watson whilst driving in his trap, whilst Watson was walking back from the *'Black Tor'* to *'Baskerville Hall'*. There are

farmhouses in the region of Cross Furzes which might fit, like Forder (no public access) or Greendown (no public access), or alternatively it might be seen to be some miasmic location, such as one of the cottages at Peat Cot (no public access individually). William S Baring-Gould, in his inimitable manner, gets things totally wrong by suggesting that *'Foulmire'*, a building, is Fox Tor Mires!

'The Railway Stations'. There are almost certainly three different Devonshire railway stations involved in *The Hound*, and although good candidates can be found, it must be accepted that there may be an invented element attached to one or all of them. The first is the North Devon Line station where Jack Stapleton arrived with The Hound. This is almost certainly one of the stations dotted around the Northern rim of the Moor, with Okehampton being the best candidate, in that one could quickly get from the station onto the Moor there without passing through any inhabited areas where The Hound might have attracted attention, since there is a short lane leading from the station directly onto the Moor. The second is the *"…wayside station…"* where Dr Watson, Sir Henry and Mortimer arrived near the Moor, and this is clearly on a branch line, rather than on the main line from Exeter to Plymouth, with the best candidate being Buckfastleigh, with the party having changed trains at Totnes. It is possible that this could have been a station like Bovey Tracey or Lustleigh, with the party having changed trains at Newton Abbot, but this would not have allowed the approach to have been made onto the high Moor from the South. Watson's party may have used Totnes because of a more-convenient connection on the branch line for reaching the Moor there, with the *"…wayside station…"* then being Staverton or Buckfastleigh, with Ashburton being discounted in being a terminus and not a wayside station. The final railway station is the one where the London express arrives, at *'Coombe Tracey'*, with the best candidate in this case being Newton Abbot. This location is, on only one occasion, and only in *The Strand Magazine* version of the text, referred to as *"…Templecombe…"*, which is

a real and important railway junction where London expresses very much thundered in. It is, however, located some 70 miles from Dartmoor! Totnes is an alternative for this express station, but South Brent must be ignored, in spite of it being a main-line station, in that expresses did not normally stop there.

INVENTED NON-DARTMOOR LOCATIONS

'221B Baker Street'. The Baskerville case does, of course, begin in London, in what has been suggested as being the most famous address ever created in fiction, *'221B Baker Street'*. In a survey amongst foreign tourists some years ago, it was found that more of the visitors knew the address of Sherlock Holmes than knew the address of the British Prime Minister; which is entirely appropriate, given the transient fame of most of the incumbents at the latter's residence. There is, however, a problem with locating the very precisely addressed home of Holmes, for although 221 Baker Street does exist, and there is at present a plaque on the building commemorating the Sherlock Holmes association with that address, it is not where Sherlock Holmes lived. Holmes resided at *'221B Baker Street'* from 1881 until about 1904, and throughout that period there was no number 221 in Baker Street. Until the 1930s, Baker Street was much shorter than it is at present, with two thirds of the present Baker Street being named York Place and Upper Baker Street, and with the present No 221 being located in the latter thoroughfare. The highest number in Baker Street itself at that time was 92, so here we have a clear case of Dr Watson (assisted by ACD) disguising the real location. There is an enormous amount of disagreement amongst Holmesians about the actual location of *'221B'*, but the most-scholarly opinion, originated by the greatest of all the Holmesian London locational scholars, Bernard Davies, suggests that it was sited in Victorian times at what was No 31 Baker Street. Sadly, No 31 is now part of a block of modern buildings, but a better indication of what the house originally looked like can be seen at what is now No 239 Baker Street, which is still the original Victorian building, and which has been converted into the Sherlock Holmes Museum, with replicas of the rooms as they might have been in Holmes's time, complete with all of the paraphernalia mentioned in the stories, or with displays of Holmesian incidents. This Museum could not, however, have been '221B', in that it was in what was Upper Baker Street.

The 'Northumberland Hotel'. The hotel where Sir Henry stayed in London, the 'Northumberland Hotel', where he vitally lost one of his boots, is also difficult to identify. There was a Northumberland Arms in the appropriate area of Charing Cross, which is now the Sherlock Holmes pub and which has a re-creation of Sherlock Holmes's study built into its restaurant and many items of Holmesian memorabilia on display. This establishment claims that it was the 'Northumberland Hotel', in spite of the fact that at the time of the case it was only a small drinking and lodging establishment, which catered pri-

marily for the labourers who shoveled coal from ships and barges on the nearby River Thames - hardly the sort of place at which a near-millionaire would stay! It may be noted that one of the three grand hotels which did exist in Northumberland Avenue at the time was, originally, to have been called The Northumberland Hotel, but the name was changed, two years before the Baskerville case took place, to the Hotel Victoria. Probably the best candidate is what was formerly the Hôtel Métropole, in that it was the highest class of hotel in the area, being the only one which had a royal suite. Internally it is the only one which matches the drawing which Sidney Paget produced showing Sir Henry in his hotel, although the evidence of Paget is never totally reliable. Unfortunately, much of the interior has been ruined by sub-division into offices by the Ministry of Defence, and public access is not readily available. ACD frequently stayed at the Hôtel Métropole.

THE AUTHORSHIP CONTROVERSY

Earlier Studies. As has been mentioned above, claims have been made that BFR wrote part of *The Hound*, with the level of his contribution varying from only the first chapter of the book to almost the whole of the book. Others, including ACD, have claimed that BFR contributed only some initial inspiration and practical assistance. There is clearly a requirement for a broader, but more directed, investigation of the association of BFR with the story. We will here firstly examine what ACD and BFR had to say in connection with the writing of the story, and then examine the pronouncements of the two major proponents of the case for BFR's greater involvement, before proceeding to look at remarks made by various other commentators.

The Major Pronouncements. ACD made several announcements about his being the sole author of *The Hound*, and BFR never made any claims that he was the author, but there have been two major instigators of claims that BFR made an extensive contribution to *The Hound*. One case came from the USA at the beginning of the Twentieth Century, primarily through a journalist, Arthur Bartlett Maurice, and the other came from Ashburton, on the South-Eastern fringe of the Moor, in the middle of the same century, through a retired labourer, Henry Baskerville, ably assisted and encouraged by journalists and other scandal-mongers. These suggestions have been revived at regular intervals, as new generations of commentators have 'rediscovered' the controversy.

ARTHUR CONAN DOYLE'S STATEMENTS

The Origins. It will be recalled that ACD and BFR initially decided to produce a book entitled *"The Hound of the Baskervilles"* as a collaborative effort, although the proposed co-written story with that title did not, at that time, include Sherlock Holmes. This original, non-Holmes story, the "Proto-Hound", was, in fact never written or published, although it will here be suggested that a short story might have been produced from part of it. As previously mentioned, and repeated here because of its importance within this different context, ACD had written to the Editor of *The Strand Magazine*, Herbert Greenhough Smith, from Cromer, with reference to the "Proto-Hound", saying:

> I have the idea for a real creeper for "The Strand". It is full of surprises, breaking naturally into good lengths for serial purposes. There is one stipulation. I must do it with my friend Fletcher Robinson, and his name must appear with mine. I can answer for the yarn being all my own in my own style without dilution, since your readers like that. But he gave me the central idea and the local colour, and so I feel his name must appear. I shall want my usual £50 per thousand words for all rights if you do business.

It must be noted that ACD says that "**I have** the idea for a real creeper for "The Strand"" [emphasis added], not 'We have', and he indicates that BFR only gave him the central idea and the local colour, as opposed to the idea for the book as a whole. This confirms the way in which J E Hodder Williams later said that it was agreed between the two men that ACD would write the story. This letter to Greenhough Smith was clearly written before Holmes was introduced to the story, as ACD subsequently wrote to Greenhough Smith to ask for the higher rate of £100 per thousand words for a story containing Sherlock Holmes:

> The price I quoted *[the £50 figure quoted above, and then referred to below as 'my old figure']* has for years been my serial price not only for you but with other journals. Now it is evident that this is a

Whiteworks Tin Mine. The waterwheel and its ore-crushing machinery were still almost complete on 1 June 1889 when Robert Burnard photographed them, and when Holmes visited here just over four months later, although the mine had been abandoned for more than a decade at that time, and they have now almost completely disappeared. They were located in what is currently the heart of Fox Tor Mire. It will be recalled that Watson described the lair of The Hound as being on a bog-girt island in the heart of the great Grimpen Mire, where: *"A huge driving-wheel and a shaft half-filled with rubbish showed the position of an abandoned mine."* The hill behind the mine is Royal Hill, with Peat Cot, Tor Royal and Princetown lying beyond it, with the first two having possible connections, and the third having definite connections with *The Hound*. [69]

very special occasion since as far as I can judge the revival of Holmes would attract a great deal of attention. If put up to open competition I could get very particular terms for this story. Suppose I gave the Directors the alternative that it should be without Holmes at my old figure or with Holmes at £100 per thou. which would they choose?

We thus already have the situation, even for the "Proto-Hound", that ACD had stated that the idea for the book was his own. The "…central idea…" which BFR contributed was, primarily, the Dartmoor hound legend which inspired the story, not the story itself, although BFR's contribution to the "Proto-Hound" may have been stronger than it was with the final version of *The Hound*, although it was also agreed that ACD would have written the whole of the "Proto-Hound", according to J E Hodder Williams. On Dartmoor, ACD wrote to his mother from Rowe's Duchy Hotel in Princetown (now the High Moorland Visitor Centre):

Dearest of Mams

Here I am in the highest town in England. Robinson and I are exploring the moor over our Sherlock Holmes book. I think it will work out splendidly - indeed I have already done nearly half of it. Holmes is at his very best, and it is a highly dramatic idea which I owe to Robinson.

It should be noted particularly that this is not a reference to the "Proto-Hound", since it refers to Holmes being included. ACD still refers to this new book as "…**our** Sherlock Holmes book…", but he goes on to say "…I have done nearly half of it." [emphases added], not '.. we have done nearly half of it.' It might be suggested that perhaps BFR wrote the other half, but it is clear that the book could not at that stage have been anywhere near complete, in that it was only on that day that ACD and BFR had visited the area of Dartmoor which plays such a crucial part in the story, Fox Tor Mires. In addition, we do also have ACD's guarantee to Greenhough Smith that even the "Proto-Hound" work was to have been "...all my own and in my own style without dilution...". With the inclusion of Sherlock Holmes, this would inevitably have been even more the case with the final version of *The Hound*. To suggest that BFR wrote any of *The Hound* in the face of ACD's clear statement on the matter is, in fact, a staggering accusation about ACD's integrity.

ARTHUR CONAN DOYLE'S ACKNOWLEDGEMENTS

The Strand Magazine. Various commentators have mentioned the dedications to BFR which ACD made in different editions of the story, but there are, in fact, no dedications. Most editions of the story do, however, include an acknowledgement made by ACD in connection with BFR's contribution to the production of the

story. The first appeared as a footnote to the title of the story, in the first instalment of the serialised edition of the story, in *The Strand Magazine* in August 1901. It reads:

This story owes its inception to my friend, Mr. Fletcher Robinson, who has helped me both in the general plot and in the local details - A.C.D.

There is no necessary indication here that ACD accepted that BFR provided the whole, or even a major part of the plot of the story. It can be suggested that the main, and possibly only, contribution to the general plot which BFR made was the provision of the legend of a Dartmoor hound which inspired ACD to produce the hound legend which eventually appeared in the story. The contribution which BFR made to the collection of local colour for the story is not here ques-

Higher Merripit. Burnard's photograph of the ancient longhouse farm of Higher Merripit, taken on 4 August 1892, indicates the rather ramshackle and organic nature of many of the farms on Dartmoor. The name of the farm obviously suggests a source for the name of the residence of Beryl and Jack Stapleton, *Merripit House*, in *The Hound*, as does the adjacent Merripit Hill, although the farm is too close to the village of Postbridge to be described as *"...lonely and desolate..."* [70]

tioned, in that BFR certainly accompanied ACD in exploring the Moor, but the way in which ACD transformed what he was told and what he saw is entirely in accordance with his earlier statement that "I can answer for the yarn being all my own in my own style without dilution…" There are some indications of the possible influence of BFR in the writing, but it is, fortunately, minimal in extent, and it might be identified as having encouraged the production of the worst parts of the story, but this will be discussed further below.

The Newnes First Edition. The first book edition of the story, published by Newnes on 25 March 1902, contained the following acknowledgement:

My Dear Robinson:

It was to your account of a West-Country legend that this tale owes its inception. For this and for your help in the detail all thanks.

Yours most truly,

A. Conan Doyle

It has frequently been claimed by those who support the case for BFR's authorship that ACD was here reducing the level of his acknowledge-ment to BFR, in that there is no longer any refer-ence to help with the general plot, but then this later acknowledgement needs to be seen within the context of an ill-informed and ignorant public accusation which had been made earlier, in October 1901 in the USA, to the effect that ACD had provided little more than permission for Sherlock Holmes to be used in a story which had been written almost entirely by BFR, an accusa-tion which will shortly be examined in depth. In reflection of such an accusation, ACD's March 1902 acknowledgement might better be seen as a clarifying of the real extent of BFR's contribution.

The McClure, Phillips & Co Edition. The first American book edition of the story, published by McClure, Phillips & Co on 15 April 1902, included the following acknowledgement:

My Dear Robinson:

It was your account of a west country legend which first suggested the idea of this little tale to my mind. For this and for the help which you have given me in its evolution, all thanks.

Yours most truly.

A. Conan Doyle

Some critics, again mostly American, have claimed that this was a third step in a process on the part of ACD, whereby he gradually decreased his acknowledgement of the contribution of BFR to the story. This suggestion is, in fact, nonsense, in that the McClure, Phillips & Co acknowledge-ment was actually written before the Newnes acknowledgement, in that exactly this wording was used by ACD in writing a letter to BFR from 'Undershaw' on 26 January 1902. Once again, the McClure, Phillips and Co acknowledgement can best be seen as a clear explication of the true situ-ation with regards to BFR's contribution to the textual content of the story.

The Murray Omnibus Edition. A fourth and final Doylean acknowledgement appeared in an omnibus edition of the four Holmes novellas, in the Preface to *Sherlock Holmes - The Complete Long Stories*, published by Murray on 14 September 1929. The Preface is actually dated 'June 1929' by ACD, and the relevant part reads:

Then came The Hound of the Baskervilles. It arose from a remark by that fine fellow, whose premature death was a loss to the world, Fletcher Robinson, that there was a spectral dog near his home on Dartmoor. That remark was the inception of the book, but I should add that the plot and every word of the actual narrative was my own.

This indicates that, according to ACD, BFR's primary contribution was the legend which inspired the story, and whilst it is a shame that

Nun's Cross Farm. The best candidate for *Merripit House*, located remotely beside Fox Tor Mires *('Grimpen Mire')*. [70]
COURTESY OF THE TAYLOR COLLECTION

there is no longer any reference to the assistance in gathering local colour, this acknowledgement is obviously intended to establish clearly that the plot and the writing were the product of ACD's mind, and it is equally clearly a statement made in reaction to the accusations that ACD had written little, if any, of the story.

BERTRAM FLETCHER ROBINSON'S STATEMENT

The 'Eventuation' of *The Hound*. Although claims were made that BFR was the major author of *The Hound* before *The Hound* had finished publication in *The Strand Magazine*, BFR appears to have made only one direct statement in connection with the authorship of *The Hound*. In his November 1905 article in the *Sunday Magazine* of the *New York Tribune* about ACD, H J W Dam indicates that BFR had recently written:

One of the most interesting weeks that I ever spent was with Doyle on Dartmoor.

He made the journey in my company shortly after I had told him, and he had accepted from me, the plot which eventuated in "The Hound of the Baskervilles." Dartmoor, the great wilderness of bog and rocks that cuts Devonshire into two parts, appealed to his imagination. He listened eagerly to my stories of the ghost hounds, of the headless riders and of the devils that lurked in the hollows - legends upon which I had been reared, for my home lay on the borders of the moor. How well he turned to account his impressions will be remembered by all readers of the "Hound."

Absence of Pertinent Claims. There is no reference here to BFR being the author, or even the co-author, of *The Hound*, in that BFR is commenting on what ACD did with his impressions of what BFR made available to him. BFR does not claim that the plot which he gave to ACD was actually used by ACD, and the plot which he gave to ACD may well have been that upon which the "Proto-Hound" was to have been based, for it will be noted that BFR indicates that it was shortly before ACD travelled to Dartmoor that he had given ACD this plot. It will also be noted that the legends which BFR implies that he told ACD on Dartmoor, concerning ghostly hounds (not a singular, spectral hound), headless riders, and devils that lurk in the hollows, are not like the legend which appears in *The Hound*. *The Hound* which "…eventuated…" may thus have almost no connection with the plot or the legends which BFR gave to ACD, and they may merely have provided exactly what ACD says that they provided, inspiration. We will now go back in time some four years from when BFR made this statement, which he allowed to be published in the USA, to see what had intervened on the literary front in the USA since *The Hound* first started to appear there, and what it was that he might easily have commented upon more fully if there were any real substance in it.

THE USA *BOOKMAN* ACCUSATIONS

The First Major Accusation. In the October 1901 issue of the American literary magazine, *The Bookman*, there appeared a news item in the editorial "Chronicle and Comment" section, under the title 'The New Sherlock Holmes Story'. The author of this item, although it is accredited to both of the editors, was almost certainly only one of the editors, Arthur Bartlett Maurice, in that he later produced a fuller review in the same magazine under his own name, containing similarly erroneous comments on the story and similar phraseology. The initial comments read:

> Every one who reads the opening chapter of the resuscitation of Sherlock Holmes in the September number of the *Strand Magazine* must have come to the conclusion that Dr. Doyle's share in the collaboration was a very small one. *The Hound of the Baskervilles* opens very dramatically, and promises to be a rousing good tale. But the Sherlock Holmes to whom

we are introduced is a totally different personage from the Sherlock Holmes of *The Study in Scarlet* [sic], *The Sign of the Four, The Adventures and The Memoirs.* Of course all the little superficial tricks and mannerisms have been worked in, but there it ends. In a brief note Dr. Doyle, whose name alone is at the head of the story, acknowledges the collaboration of Mr. Fletcher Robinson. Of course the matter is one which concerns primarily only the two authors and their publishers; but we have very little hesitation in expressing our conviction that the story is almost entirely Mr. Robinson's, and that Dr. Doyle's only important contribution to the partnership is the permission to use the character of Sherlock Holmes.

The magazine containing this diatribe should not be confused with the English literary magazine with the same title, which had begun publication several years before the American magazine. Although the American magazine was a copy of the British one, the two magazines were independent and differed markedly in their content and their style, with the American copy often including what can only be described as literary gossip and unsubstantiated rumour, particularly in connection with European matters.

It is not just the expectation that the portrayal of Sherlock Holmes, a character rejected in despair by ACD in 1893, would not have changed after an absence of almost eight years, or the mistitling of the first Sherlock Holmes novella, which indicates ignorance in the American attack on ACD's integrity. Nor is it the way in which the editorial's author fails to appreciate that Sherlock Holmes is not resurrected in the story. It is a lack of awareness of the different writing styles of ACD and BFR which totally condemns this ill-informed commentary. The editorial judgement is made on the basis of only the first episode of *The Hound*, since the American edition of *The Strand Magazine* was published a month after the English edition. That first episode is considered by most knowledgeable Holmesian scholars to be a classic piece of Doylean writing. That episode ends with the stunning dialogue between Holmes and Mortimer:

> *"Footprints?"*
> *"Footprints."*
> *"A man's or a woman's?"*
> *Dr. Mortimer looked strangely at us for an instant, and his voice sank almost to a whisper as he answered: -*
> *"Mr. Holmes, they were the footprints of a gigantic hound."*

BFR never wrote anything as good as that in his whole life!! Most of his dialogues were absolutely appalling, and although his plots were frequently ingenious, his plot development was usually extremely poor. If one were to pick a part of *The Hound of the Baskervilles* which one might reasonably claim, on the grounds of style and plot development, to be similar to that of BFR, it could only be the final chapter, 'A Retrospection'. Most of BFR's detective stories leave far too much to be explained in the closing stages, and the explanations are often dubious in nature. It is for these very reasons that 'A Retrospection' is generally considered by most Holmesian scholars to be the least satisfactory of the chapters in *The Hound*, and one of ACD's worst story endings. It is not suggested here that 'A Retrospection' was written by BFR, but the way in which it has to include so many explanations, and in which so many of those explanations are unsatisfactory, may be an indication of the influence of BFR on the shaping of the general plot; possibly as a result of the presence of remnants of unsuitable content from the original, non-Holmes plot for the *Hound of the Baskervilles*, the "Proto-Hound". It will be seen shortly that BFR may have used some of these remnants, both in terms of plot and actual text, in stories which he wrote himself several years after the publication of *The Hound*.

It is all too apparent that very few of those who have commented upon the question of the authorship of *The Hound* have ever read any of

BFR's work, and some of the 'authorities' on the subject were all too obviously not even aware of all that BFR had produced which might be relevant to the discussion. This was to some extent understandable, in that until recently BFR's two adventure books have been very difficult to obtain. That in itself might be seen as a literary commentary on the value of his work, in that few readers had considered that copies of these books were worth preserving. An inexpensive, and slightly corrupted, combined version of these two books was published in 1998 to meet the suggestion of a few serious Doylean scholars that these books should be made more-readily available, so that BFR's style might more-easily be compared with that of ACD. What is ridiculous in the claim made by *The Bookman* is the fact that the editors of that magazine had nothing from BFR with which to compare *The Hound*, since BFR did not publish his first book of fiction until 1905 (1904 in magazine format).

The Second Major Accusation. In the February 1902 issue of *The Bookman*, the editors introduced a theory from a correspondent in connection with the clue of the missing boots (or 'shoes' as they insist), to the effect that the pregnant wife (who does not exist in the story), saw the death of her husband (called 'Sir Hugh Baskerville' in the editorial), and gave birth to a child with feet shaped like those of a hound! Further developments of this theory were to be aired in *The Bookman* after the full story had been published. In the April 1902 issue, the two editors admitted the enthusiasm with which they had read each episode, and also admitted that they differed over their ideas about the book. Amongst the questions which they raised and left unanswered was that of the contribution of BFR to the story. For the May 1902 issue, with the full story having been published in the USA the previous month, Maurice wrote a review which summarised much of the early plot, and which again included numerous factual errors. He describes Holmes and Watson, for example, as living in 'Upper Baker Street', which at that time was separated from the Baker Street where Holmes lived by the whole length of York Place, and he has 'Baskerville Hall' located in North Devon rather than South Devon. He refers to 'Sir Hugo', when neither of the Hugos was knighted; to 'Roger Baskerville' instead of Rodger; and the body of Sir Charles is found in the wrong place. This is a man who clearly does not know his Baskervilles, or his *Hound of the Baskervilles*! On the authorship controversy he was slightly less positive in his accusation against ACD:

> When the subject of this story was first discussed in literary and publishing circles in London there prevailed the idea that Mr. Fletcher Robinson had in hand a story to which Dr. Doyle was lending some assistance, his name, and the character of Sherlock Holmes. A little later it was being said that Dr. Doyle and Mr. Robinson were in collab-oration on this new Sherlock Holmes story. Finally, the first instalment of the tale itself appeared as being the work of Dr. Doyle alone. Allusion to Mr. Fletcher Robinson was made only in a foot-note, in which the reputed writer courteously, but rather vaguely, thanked Mr. Robinson for one or two hints and suggestions that had been of some value to him in the writing of the story. Just what the meaning of all this was, just how much Mr. Robinson did contribute to the inception and the working out of *The Hound of the Baskervilles*, the reviewer is neither inclined nor prepared to say.

Although Maurice claims that there were dis-cussions on the authorship question in London, nothing seems to be available in print from the time, and when J E Hodder Williams published his article on ACD in the English version of *The Bookman*, in April 1902, there was no reference whatsoever to controversies over authorship, nor was there any suggestion of controversy in Andrew Lang's book review in *The Times Literary Supplement* of 11 April 1902. Maurice

Nun's Cross. This photograph by Robert Burnard, taken on 14 April 1888, shows the granite cross, over 7 feet in height, located near the cottage which is named after it, to the South of Princetown and adjacent to Fox Tor Mires, which lies in the hollow beyond the wall. The cross is mentioned in a charter of 1240, and the other side of it bears the name of Syward or Siward, who may have been a Saxon Earl of Westmoreland, and it will be recalled that the next member of the Baskerville family in line for the estate after Sir Henry was from Westmoreland. [70]

unfairly changes the nature of the acknowl-edgement which ACD gave to BFR in the various editions of the story. His account of the process by which the nature of the collabo-ration changed might, however, be seen to be a good one, if one notes the fact, which Maurice does not seem to appreciate, that the initial story, the "Proto-Hound", was one which did not include Sherlock Holmes. One of the short detective stories which BFR published in 1904, 'The Terror in the Snow', indicates that BFR may well have had a family-haunting canine story in mind when he met up with ACD in Cromer, or developed it whilst with ACD in Cromer, with the dramatic events of that story taking place only a few miles along the coast from the hotel where ACD and BFR stayed. This short story does contain some minor elements of similarity with *The Hound*, but if it was the primary story behind the "Proto-Hound" it clearly had to be changed dramatically once Sherlock Holmes was introduced, and the eventual *Hound of the Baskervilles* is superior in every possible way. If, however, BFR already had the concept of his inferior detective, Addington Peace, developed when he

got to Cromer, it was a concept which he had very much taken from ACD's Sherlock Holmes, whilst introducing some obvious differences.

Maurice continues his May 1902 review by saying that:

> …there is in this book much that is materially different from the former work of Dr. Doyle in his detective stories, and the methods of Sherlock Holmes here are not entirely the methods of the astute intellectual reasoner…

Here he clearly fails to appreciate that a writer's style of depicting a character can change, and he was, of course, unable to see that the accusa-

Fernworthy – The Clapper Bridge. The bridges over the stream which now forms part of the Fernworthy Reservoir can occasionally still be seen, when drought dries up the reservoir. Clapper bridges were popular on the Moor, in being easily constructed from the readily available slabs of granite lying on the Moor. Although they were very narrow, the lack of abutments caused no problems for heavily-laden pack animals carrying side panniers. [71]

tion that Holmes was never so good as he had been prior to his 'death' at the Reichenbach Falls was to be raised, very often with good justification, against ACD with many of the 33 Holmes stories which he was to write after *The Hound*. Certainly, the only Holmes novella which ACD wrote after *The Hound*, *The Valley of Fear*, is by far the worst of the four Holmes long cases, with its dreary and overextended American flashback sequence not involving Holmes in any way. Maurice concludes his review by saying that:

> As a story of mystery and horror, *The Hound of the Baskervilles* is a success; for Sherlock Holmes, the Master of the Science of Deduction, whose creator has proclaimed him the peer of Dupin and of Lecoq, it is a *débâcle*.

Here we have an indication of the slightly anti-British attitude which Maurice recurringly expressed in print against ACD and others, as well as a further example of his own ignorance. Maurice seems to have objected to the way in which 'ACD' had suggested that Dupin, created by Maurice's countryman, Edgar Allan Poe, was *"...a very inferior fellow..."* [*A Study in Scarlet*]. He similarly objected to the way in which 'ACD' had said that Lecoq, created by a writer from the land which gave Maurice's homeland its philosophy of law and independence in the face of British imperialism, Emile Gaboriau, was a *"...miserable bungler..."* [*A Study in Scarlet*]. Maurice fails to appreciate that the fact that ACD put these words into the mouth of Holmes did not mean that he agreed with them, and in other works ACD expressed his admiration for Poe and Gaboriau. ACD frequently had to respond to those who could not tell the difference between the puppet and the puppeteer, as he put it. Although ACD certainly owed a very great debt of influence to these two writers, Maurice's criticism of *The Hound* in comparison with their works is ludicrous, in that neither of them ever wrote a detective story as good as *The Hound*. Perhaps one might best summarise the situation by suggesting that ACD's debt was anterior,

whereas Maurice's comments were posterior! In the August 1902 issue of *The Bookman*, there seems to have been a change of attitude, or, more probably, a change of predominating editor. In a rather foolish and ill-informed item on the British honours system, responding to ACD having been knighted earlier that month, it is suggested that *The Hound* was such a good story that ACD deserved to be made a Baron for producing it, rather than a mere Knight Bachelor. If Maurice had led in this article, with his conception of the degree of BFR's contribution to the book, he would surely have had to suggest that BFR should have been made an Earl!

HARRY BASKERVILLE'S COMMENTS

Harry's Late Rise to Fame. The second main proponent of the claims that BFR wrote much, if not all, of *The Hound* was the one-time carriage driver of the Fletcher Robinson family, Harry Baskerville. Harry was later to admit that although he could read, he had throughout his life followed his father's advice by being a non-reader, although, in his typically contradictory way, he did also confess that he had read *The Hound* several times. Exactly why a minimally educated domestic servant's opinion should be accepted so readily as being valid in a literary discussion is not clear, unless it is because it nicely met the requirements of those who wanted to regenerate the controversy over the authorship question well over half a century after it had first arisen. There was a rapid growth in public enthusiasm for Sherlock Holmes following the re-creation of Holmes's sitting room in Baker Street, at the head offices of the Abbey National Building Society which were located at No 221, as part of the Festival of Britain celebrations of 1951, when Harry was 80 years old. Harry was increasingly interviewed by newspaper reporters, rumour-mongers, Holmesians and Sherlockians, after his picture was included in the Abbey National exhibition, and he seems to have become more extravagant in his claims as time went by. In 1951 he claimed that ACD had asked for permission for his name to be used in the book, which is nonsense, when we know that

Laughter Hole Farm. Robert Burnard's handwritten caption for this photograph, records the name of the site as being Laugh Tor Hole, which closely resembles the name of the *'Lafter Hall'* residence of Frankland in *The Hound*, and the name of the real location may thus have influenced the fictional one. Earlier records do, in fact, indicate that this ancient farm was at some time called Lafter Hall, and in 1889 there was a Mr Holmes in residence! [72]

ACD had chosen to call the book *The Hound of the Baskervilles* before he ever met Harry. Harry repeatedly supported this suggestion with a copy of *The Hound* which he owned which contained the inscription: 'To Harry Baskerville, with apologies for using the name'. This actually suggests that the name had been used without permission, but it must be noted that it came from BFR, not from ACD. ACD may, of course, have heard of Harry's name from BFR whilst they were at Cromer, and he would almost certainly have been aware of the main branch of the family living on the Welsh border, but he clearly never asked for Harry's permission before using the name. Some have suggested that such an unusual name must have been associated with this man, but there were more than 200 people called Baskerville living in Devonshire at the time of the case, with most of them living on the fringes of Dartmoor.

Further Claims to Fame. A rich American Sherlockian, James Montgomery, stimulated interest in the authorship controversy. He had a reputation for making startling discoveries, and after touring England on a Sherlockian pilgrimage in the mid-1950s he hinted that he had 'discovered' something startling about which he was going to write a monograph. He died within three weeks of returning to the USA, and his notes were never found. In 1959 it was suggested by one of those who knew him that he had interviewed Harry Baskerville, and that his revelations might have been connected with the authorship of *The Hound*. In 1957 Harry was interviewed by a local newspaper reporter, from *The Western Times and Gazette*, in his 'Dorncliffe' home, in West Street, Ashburton, close to St Andrew's Church where he was buried in 1962. He claimed that Heatree House and Spitchwick Manor, both on Dartmoor, had once belonged to his family, and that the former, which he should have inherited, was the model for 'Baskerville Hall', even though it bears no resemblance whatsoever to the building described in the story, and even though it is in country which is totally different in nature to that which surrounds 'Baskerville Hall'. He said that BFR became closely associated with ACD in connection with the Boer War, and that it was at about that time, between 1900 and 1901, that BFR discussed his idea about a story involving the mysterious hound of the Moor with that well-known literary advisor, Harry Baskerville! On this occasion, it was recorded that Harry had a copy of the first edition of the book of *The Hound* with the inscription: "To Harry Baskerville from B. Fletcher Robinson, with apologies for using **your** name." [emphasis added]. Harry mentioned that he had been visited by several American Sherlockians, who had lionised him, and that he had been made a member of one of the American societies, The Musgrave Ritualists. Although Harry's carriage driving days were long over by the 1950s, he does seem to have taken many other people for a ride in connection with Dartmoor in the years which followed, in what might well be called a new form of "Gullible Travels"!

Controversy with Adrian Conan Doyle. Harry's opinions on the authorship question reached a climax in 1959, and he created a massive amount of new interest in the problem when he was interviewed at 'Dorncliffe' by Peter Evans for *The Daily Express*, the newspaper for which BFR had once been an editor. The interview was connected with the then shortly to be released Hammer Films version of *The Hound of the Baskervilles*. Harry was reported as saying that:

> Doyle didn't write the story himself. A lot of the story was written by Fletcher Robinson. But he never got the credit he deserved.

> They wrote it together at Park Hill, over at Ipplepen. I know because I was there.

Harry claimed that BFR had confided in him:

> Harry, I'm going to write a story about the moor and I would like to use your name.

He continued:

> Shortly after his return from the Boer War, Bertie told me to meet Mr. Doyle at the station. He said that they were going to work on the story he had told me about.

> Mr. Doyle stayed for eight days and nights. I had to drive him and Bertie about the moors. And I used to watch them in the billiard room in the old house, sometimes they stayed long into the night, writing and talking together.

> Then Mr. Doyle left and Bertie said to me: "Well, Harry, we've finished that book I was telling you about. The one we're going to name after you."

ACD's youngest son, Adrian Conan Doyle, responded to these statements in no uncertain terms. Adrian was then living in Switzerland, and when told of Harry Baskerville's claims by Peter Evans on the telephone he responded:

> Fletcher Robinson played no part whatsoever in the writing of *The Hound*. He refused my father's offer to collaborate and retired at an early stage of the project.

> Furthermore, my father never stayed with Robinson. He stayed at the Duchy Hotel, Princetown. He accepted Robinson's offer of a coach and went riding with him on the moors simply to get the atmosphere of the place.

> In fact, I have letters from Robinson proving this. It was Robinson who told my father about a West Country legend,

but that was just about the extent of his contribution.

This is a rather typical example of Adrian's tendency to mix fact with misunderstanding or deliberate misinformation to suit his own ends. BFR may, indeed, have played no part whatsoever in the actual writing of the story, but he certainly did contribute more than just giving a West Country legend to ACD, since ACD acknowledged help with the plot and with the local colour. We know that ACD stayed at Rowe's Duchy Hotel with BFR, and ACD's letter to his mother indicates that he was due to visit BFR's parents in Ipplepen on 10th June 1901. The letters from BFR which apparently prove Adrian's case would certainly be most helpful with this current discussion, but they have, sadly, never been produced. Adrian did attempt to make an excuse for Harry, when he responded to the attempts of Dennis Thornton, the publicity supervisor for Hammer Films, to use Harry's statements to generate further interest in the film. In a letter to Thornton, copied in the April 1959 issue of *The Baker Street Journal*, the journal of the world's oldest Sherlock Holmes society, The Baker Street Irregulars, Adrian repeated his above-quoted remarks, and prefaced them with the remark that:

> … I cannot … allow Mr. Harry Baskerville's marvellous piece of fiction to pass un-remarked, though one must excuse slips of the memory in a man of 88 …

It might be noted that Adrian Conan Doyle had, in 1955, when introducing a selection of Sherlock Holmes stories, published as *A Treasury of Sherlock Holmes*, indicated that it was not in Cromer that BFR had first mentioned the legend of a hound to ACD, and he further claimed that his father had given BFR's legend a different cultural basis. In discussing *The Hound* he wrote:

> When my father wrote this book, his Celtic nature was reacting strongly to the legend of the phantom hound that his

friend Fletcher Robinson had mentioned to him during their homeward voyage from the Boer War, and perhaps even more to those lonely days that he had spent tramping the moors or sitting on the tors, consuming Holmesian quantities of pipe tobacco while he jotted down in a notebook his impressions of that bleak yet wonderful landscape. The Hound - the very word is enough. A lesser man might have called it the Dog. What a horrible thought!

If in nothing else, Adrian was certainly right that 'The Dog of the Baskervilles' would have been a far lesser creation. The suggestion that ACD first heard BFR's hound legend on the way home from South Africa in 1900 had already been made by other writers, as will be seen shortly.

OTHER COMMENTATORS

Bertram Fletcher Robinson's Publishers. Although BFR himself never published anything to suggest that he was dissatisfied with ACD claiming the full authorship of *The Hound*, his first short detective story to be published, 'The Terror in the Snow', appeared in the USA in August 1904, in *The Lady's Home Magazine of Fiction*, under the series title of "The Chronicles of Addington Peace", with the author's name followed by the words: 'Joint Author with Sir A. Conan Doyle in his best Sherlock Holmes Story, "The Hound of the Baskervilles."' When a bastardised version of this story appeared in *The Penny Magazine* on 4 May 1907, shortly after BFR's death, under the series title of "Addington Peace of the 'Yard'", that series title was followed by the words: "These clever stories, starting to-day, are by the author who collaborated with Sir A. Conan Doyle in 'The Hound of the Baskervilles.'" This is a far more accurate claim, provided that the word 'author' is here associated with the writing of the Addington Peace series, and not with the writing of *The Hound*. Interestingly, the name of the 'author' mentioned in this statement, is not given anywhere in the magazine, which is perhaps a kindness, in view of the way in which the original text was mangled in these versions of the stories. However, in 1905, whilst BFR was still alive, the six short stories which had been published in *The Lady's Home Magazine of Fiction* were published in book form by Harper & Brothers, with two new stories being added, under the title of *The Chronicles of Addington Peace*. One of the new stories was inserted before 'The Terror in the Snow' to give a better introduction to the series characters, and this necessitated some minor re-writing of the start of 'The Terror in the Snow'. Although BFR clearly had the opportunity to claim co-authorship of *The Hound* in this book version of his own detective stories, there is no reference whatsoever to any literary connection between BFR and ACD.

Charlton Andrews. It might be thought that the American campaign against ACD was purely the invention of Maurice, but there was another early reference to the points raised by Maurice. As this item appeared in the June 1902 issue of *The Bookman*, Maurice's influence may, of course, have come to bear upon its selection, for it is one of the worst examples of Holmesian parody in existence, in that it makes no sense whatsoever. The item is entitled 'The Bound of the Astorbilts', and it has the sub-title of 'A Modern Detective Story'. Within the outrageous exaggerations of Holmes's craft, there is the following sentence:

> Sherlock Holmes donned his dressing gown and slippers and stood before the fireplace, a copy of *Monsieur Lecoq* in one hand and one arm resting affectionately about the portrait of Edgar Allan Poe.

Is there a hint here of Maurice's animosity over ACD's supposed slighting of Gaboriau (the

The Forest Inn at Hexworthy. The best candidate for the Village of *'Grimpen'*. [63]

Hexworthy Bridge. Looking South from the West bank of the West Dart River, with the road to the Ashburton to Two Bridges road off to the left and the road to the main village of Hexworthy to the right. The large house is Huccaby House, the Summer residence of the Burnard family. Robert Burnard took the photograph in May 1892. His son, Lawrence, is seen fishing from the East bank of the river, and Robert described this large house as a 'fishing-box'. [63]

author of *Monsieur Lecoq*) and Poe? The story concludes with a paragraph which bears no relationship to anything which has gone before:

> As I gazed, from far out upon the moor there came the deep, unearthly baying of a gigantic hound. Weirdly it rose and fell in blood-curdling intensity until the inarticulate sound gradually shaped itself into this perfectly distinguishable wail: "I wonder how much of it Robinson wrote?"

Maybe one of the editors of *The Bookman* was being honest enough to accept that the emphasis on the question of the contribution of BFR to *The Hound* had been taken too far? Perhaps the fact that the distinguishable part of the wail had come out of something which had been inarticu-

late was lost upon the editor against whom it was actually aimed? One hopes so!

Herbert Greenhough Smith. Neither ACD nor BFR raised the topic in public, other than with ACD's published acknowledgements. With the death of BFR in 1907 and that of ACD in 1930, the opportunity arose for various commentators to lay claim to having been involved in the inspiration for *The Hound*, or for having inside information on the question of the authorship. In the October 1930 issue of *The Strand Magazine*, published only three months after the death of ACD, the editor, Herbert Greenhough Smith, supported ACD over the controversy. After reproducing the letter in which ACD first mentioned the story, and in which he had suggested that BFR's name should appear, Greenhough Smith wrote:

As readers of the story are aware, Fletcher-Robinson's [sic] name was fully acknowledged. His share in the transaction was to draw the attention of Conan Doyle to the tradition of the fiery hound in a Welsh guide-book.

The erroneous suggestion of the primacy of the Welsh hound legend is discussed elsewhere, but the important point here is that Greenhough Smith considered that this was BFR's only major involvement, and he indicated that BFR had received a full acknowledgement.

Edmund Pearson. In the August 1932 issue of *The Bookman*, Edmund Pearson suggested that ACD had treated the theoretical solutions of readers of *The Bookman* from 1901 and 1902, sent to ACD by Maurice, with an entirely appropriate literary contempt, by suggesting that they were worthy of Gregson and Lestrade, the generally dim-witted professionals from Scotland Yard.

Archibald Marshall. In 1933, almost a quarter of a century after the death of BFR, his friend, Archibald Marshall, published a series of random reminiscences entitled *Out and About*. In this he wrote, of BFR, referring to him by his nickname:

> He gave Conan Doyle the idea and plot of *The Hound of the Baskervilles*, and wrote most of its first instalment for the *Strand Magazine*. Conan Doyle wanted it to appear under their joint names, but his name alone was wanted, because it was worth so much more. They were paid £100 a thousand words, in the proportion of three to one. As I put it to Bobbles at the time, "Then if you write 'How do you do?' Doyle gets six shillings and you get two." He said that he had never been good at vulgar fractions, but it sounded right, and anyhow what he wrote was worth it.

One should be wary of Marshall's claimed familiarity with BFR, for in the same chapter as the above quotation Marshall associated BFR's death with the curse of a mummy upon which BFR had been working, which is a ridiculous story generated by journalists. He went on to write that BFR "…had gone over to Paris, caught pneumonia, and died in a few days at the age of thirty-six or seven." The uncertainty about BFR's age was something which had again been gleaned from newspaper accounts, since even *The Times* included this uncertainty. BFR was actually 35 years old at death, and he had been ill at home in London for three weeks, suffering from enteric fever, before dying of peritonitis. As has been mentioned elsewhere, an examination of BFR's style reveals that he was incapable of writing anything as good as the first instalment of *The Hound*. At the rates suggested, BFR would have received some £1,500 as his share of the fee for the UK edition of *The Strand Magazine*, but ACD's literary agency, A P Watt Ltd, has formally informed this present commentator that they have no record of any such payment arrangement.

Walter Klinefelter. Klinefelter, an American Sherlockian, wrote on the subject of BFR's provision of the hound legend in 1938 and in 1983, in two separate books, *Ex Libris A. Conan Doyle - Sherlock Holmes*, and *Origins of Sherlock Holmes*:

> Its source is partly indicated in the dedication. *My Dear Robinson* was one Fletcher of that surname with whom Conan Doyle formed a lasting friendship on their return from South Africa in 1899. From him he must have had the legend at that time or a little while thereafter…there are no tenable grounds that Doyle had read or heard of it prior to his friendship with Fletcher Robinson.

This was supplemented, 46 years later, with the '1899' date corrected, as follows:

> The two men had met and formed a lasting friendship while returning in 1900 on the steamship Briton from service in

the Boer War...And so far as is known, this was the first time the legend had come to Doyle's attention.

Christopher Morley. This very well-known Sherlockian also suggested that BFR had provided ACD with the hound legend prior to Adrian Conan Doyle's statement to that effect, in *Sherlock Holmes and Dr. Watson: A Textbook of Friendship*, published in 1944:

> One believes that it was in the long voyage back from Capetown that his friend B. Fletcher Robinson, a war correspondent, told him the "West Country Legend" that became The Hound of the Baskervilles.

Morley then proceeds to diminish the credibility of his evidence somewhat by repeating rumours of BFR's death from the Mummy's Curse.

Christopher Frayling. In one part of a four-part BBC TV series, entitled *Nightmare - The Birth of Horror*, Professor Christopher Frayling examined *The Hound* as an example of Gothick horror fiction. In connection with the authorship controversy Frayling concentrated primarily on sources which had argued in favour of BFR contributing far more to the writing of *The Hound* than ACD indicated. Some of the information which he presented in the programme was factually incorrect, or misleadingly presented, and many of his quotations were mis-quotations. Although it may not have been Frayling's intention, this programme created the impression that BFR wrote most, if not all, of *The Hound*, amongst many of the non-Doyleans in his audience. This emphasis was less pronounced in the book which accompanied the series, and in his subsequent Introduction to the Penguin Classics edition of *The Hound* there is a more-balanced discussion of the situation.

Rodger Garrick-Steele. In 1995, Rodger Garrick Steele, who was at that time living in part of the Fletcher Robinson family's former home, announced in the *Western Morning News* that he

had been researching the authorship of *The Hound* since 1991, and he indicated that he had produced a manuscript which showed that ACD was not the author. Mr Garrick-Steele is unknown in Holmesian and Doylean scholarly circles, but on 2 September 2000, again in the *Western Morning News*, and after claiming that he had by then been researching the authorship of *The Hound* since 1989, he announced that not only had BFR written most of *The Hound*, but that ACD had had an affair with BFR's wife and had persuaded her to assist him in murdering BFR with poison to cover up his plagiarism. These claims were, unfortunately, taken up by many other newspapers in the UK and overseas, with these newspapers recording scores of statements which can easily be shown to be factually false or misleading, and with Garrick-Steele being recorded as admitting that some of his evidence was circumstantial. The newspaper accounts also stated that Garrick-Steele had a book by BFR, entitled *An Adventure on Dartmoor*, and whilst the discovery of any new book by BFR would be welcome in its own right, it could only indicate further, as has been discussed above, that he was incapable of writing anything as good as *The Hound*. Garrick-Steele was quoted as saying that his manuscript had been turned down by 100 publishers, and that may well be a pertinent commentary on its historical and literary value. Although this manuscript might well contain valuable new information about ACD and BFR, its general aim and conclusion certainly seem to indicate a gross misunderstanding of the character of ACD and of the literary talents of BFR.

Collaborationists. It must be pointed out that there is an example of ACD publishing a book in 1926, *The History of Spiritualism*, in collaboration with another author, Leslie Curnow, where Curnow made a major contribution to the writing, with ACD merely changing Curnow's text only slightly to coincide with his own ideas, and where ACD once again wanted the book to appear under both names. The publishers, Cassell, within which organisation BFR's friend Max Pemberton had a powerful influence,

Hexworthy – Jolly Cot Lane. This was the last cottage built on Dartmoor under the law which allowed the builder to own the moorland upon which it was built, if it could be built in one day. It is not the sort of accommodation which would have been occupied by Dr Mortimer in *'Grimpen'* village, as that residence would have been more like the grand houses which occupy the heights of Hexworthy. This photograph was taken by Robert Burnard in June 1889. [63]

decided that ACD's name alone should be used, and Curnow received no acknowledgement whatever, but there are clear records of Curnow and his heirs receiving a share of the royalties. In a personal interview querying this subject, ACD's last descendant, Dame Jean Conan Doyle, informed the present commentator that she had seen no indication in the family papers that BFR and his heirs had ever received any payments from ACD or his estate in connection with *The Hound*. She recalled that there had been some trivial payments to BFR which were clearly not commercial in nature. There is no reference to such an arrangement in BFR's will, drawn up in November 1906, although that document is rather generalised in nature. It should, to the contrary, be noted that although ACD wrote a

considerable amount of the actual text of the last two chapters of *Hilda Wade* in 1899, following the death-bed request of his friend Grant Allen, from plot notes left by the latter, ACD did not insist upon his name being included in the book. BFR, in comparison, does not seem to have had any problems in having his name included on the many other works which he co-wrote, including, just a few days before his death, the release of a dreadful little play entitled *The Progressive's Progress*, written with P G Wodehouse.

SOME TENTATIVE SPECULATIONS AND A CONCLUSION

Bertram Fletcher Robinson's "Hound Story". If BFR did intend publishing a story about a family-haunting hound, prior to that published by ACD, one might ask whether we have any information about its nature. BFR certainly does not seem to have published any such story before *The Hound* appeared, and he produced nothing like it until 1904, when he published the short story 'The Terror in the Snow'. This does contain a spectral canine, or more-specifically, a spectral wolf, which haunts a family, and it also involves a large country house with an alley of hedges behind it. This story takes place, however on the cliffs of the Norfolk coast, near Cromer. Perhaps this later story, which BFR may have wanted to write before the Boer War, was the basis of the non-Holmes story which ACD and BFR were initially going to write together, the "Proto-Hound", for it certainly could be described using the words which ACD used when he was in Cromer to describe the "Proto-Hound" - "...a real creeper." Once ACD decided to include Sherlock Holmes in the story, much of this early material may have had to be rejected. It should be noted that if BFR's idea of a spectral giant wolf did exist when he met up with ACD in Cromer, it would not have been something original to ACD. The latter had, in fact, written a lengthy short story about a spectral, giant wolf, entitled 'The King of the Foxes', which had appeared in the *Windsor Magazine* in July 1898. It might be thought that BFR decided to use the rejected 'wolf' material in his 1904 short story. He may similarly have used other material which had been rejected by ACD, or used by him in an altered form, in at least one of the other Addington Peace stories, 'The Tragedy of Thomas Hearne'. This was an untypical Peace story, in that the detective plays no active part, merely repeating a narrative given him by someone else, and it is also untypical in being better written than the other BFR stories. It involves a convict escaping from Dartmoor Prison and two visitors to the Moor, one of whom is named Mortimer, staying at an hotel in Princetown which remarkably has a "...wicket-gate that opened on to the moor...". Another phrase that certainly rings a Houndian bell, occurs when the narrator mentions "...the clink of a boot striking a stone...", with the Doylean

version having Watson hear Holmes approach the stone hut through: *"...the sharp clink of a boot striking upon a stone."* Do we have a simple case of BFR copying some of ACD's phrases here, deliberately or unwittingly recalling ACD's phrases, or do we have a gentle hinting by BFR that ACD had used phrases which BFR had contributed to the "Proto-Hound"? There are other references in *The Hound* which might be identified as being from BFR, such as when Holmes recognises that the warning note sent to Sir Henry in London had been cut from an article on tariff reform. BFR wrote the words of a song entitled *John Bull's Store*, which was concerned with tariff reform, but then ACD had raised the subject himself during his campaigning for Parliament, prior to writing *The Hound*.

Friends to the End. In 1905 ACD and BFR were amongst the six people who were invited to double the original membership of a rather mysterious organisation known as Our Society. This society, which still exists, gathered to discuss various aspects of crime, and as the membership included eminent lawyers and judges, it was quickly decided that the matters discussed at the meetings should remain secret, although the titles of the topics for discussion have since been published. ACD presented papers on three occasions, covering his attempts at proving the innocence of George Edalji and Oscar Slater, and with his most controversial presentation being on the use of the paranormal in solving crime. BFR does not seem to have presented any papers, but the fact that both men readily joined such an intimate discussion group suggests that there was no animosity between them. Mrs Georgina Doyle has kindly informed this commentator that the diary of Innes Doyle (the brother of ACD) records that on 20 October 1906, only three months before he died, BFR travelled by car with ACD to stay with the latter at 'Undershaw'. When they arrived at Hindhead they immediately set off to do exactly what they had met to do during that momentous holiday which resulted in the creation of *The Hound*, which was to play golf. Whatever the arrangement was that they had made over the authorship of *The Hound*, it certainly seems to have been an amicable one, and there appears to have been no question of BFR feeling that ACD had slighted him with the minor variations in the acknowledgements which accompanied the different editions of the story. When BFR died in London, his body was removed to Ipplepen for burial in the village churchyard, and amongst the wreaths was one from ACD with a card which read: "In loving memory of an old and valued friend."

The True Author of *The Hound of the Baskervilles*. There is no need for speculation in connection with the question of the writing of *The Hound*. It was, quite simply, all written by Arthur Conan Doyle. What remains in question is the degree and type of contribution made by Bertram Fletcher Robinson. The provision of inspiration, and even help with the plot does not mean that someone deserves to be referred to as the co-author of a work, for we do have examples of other Sherlock Holmes stories where ACD admitted that he had been provided with the central plot, by his wife and by his mother, but there is no suggestion that their names should appear with his. We also know that ACD bought plots from others, with the intention of possibly using those plots in one of his own works. Unless some substantial documentary evidence is produced, we will probably never fully know the answer to the question of how much BFR contributed to *The Hound*, but the indications are that ACD's acknowledgements to BFR are probably appropriate. Those acknowledgements may not, however, fully reflect the contribution derived from literary intercourse during the production of a book, but this may not reflect any deliberate intention on the part of ACD. We might usefully return to a point not yet resolved within this discussion, which is the way in which ACD initially insisted that BFR's name should appear with his on the book. The book which he was there referring to was not the version of *The Hound* which we now have, but the "Proto-Hound", which was never published. It must be recalled, however, that even for the "Proto-Hound", ACD had promised that it would be "...all my own in my own style without dilution...", and J E Hodder Williams' report suggests that even with that work, BFR had agreed that ACD would actually write it. The book which did appear must have been considerably different to the "Proto-Hound", since the whole structure of the original story must have been changed by the introduction of Holmes, and it may therefore be this fact, more than any other, which allowed ACD to drop BFR's name from the work with a clear conscience, other than in the acknowledgements which were published in the various editions of the final version of the story throughout his lifetime. ACD's intention that the book to be entitled *The Hound of the Baskervilles*, whether in the "Proto-Hound" form or in its eventual form, would be all his own work is clear throughout its development. We can only conclude by repeating ACD's final words on the subject, from 1929, just one year before his death:

"...I should add that the plot and every word of the actual narrative was my own."

Okehampton Railway Station. The best candidate for the station where the villain arrives with The Hound on Dartmoor. [74]

COURTESY OF DARTMOOR MUSEUM OF RURAL LIFE

Ivybridge Railway Station. Only part of the platform of this station remains, even though the main line over the magnificent viaduct is still in use on the Totnes to Plymouth route. It is possible that one of these stations on the Southern edge of the Moor provided the inspiration for the station where Inspector Lestrade arrived from London, with the ready access to the Moor being visible beyond the station in this photograph, although a better candidate is that at Newton Abbot. [74]

COURTESY OF THE TAYLOR COLLECTION

Buckfastleigh Railway Station. A possible candidate for the *"...wayside station..."* where Watson, Mortimer and Sir Henry arrived on the edge of the Moor. [74]

Totnes Railway Station (c.1910). It is possible that Watson, Mortimer and Sir Henry arrived here and changed onto the branch line train to Buckfastleigh here. It is also possible that Inspector Lestrade arrived here. [74]

Newton Abbot Railway Station. The best candidate for the station where Inspector Lestrade arrives. Arthur Conan Doyle arrived here, according to some, to stay with Bertram Fletcher Robinson in 1901. [74]

COURTESY OF THE TAYLOR COLLECTION

Princetown Railway Station. This photograph is of a station which no longer exists, and which is not mentioned in *The Hound*, although the Yelverton to Princetown line was used in a 1931 film version of the story, with a distant shot of a train rounding King's Tor. To make matters worse, that train then arrived at Lustleigh station, on the Newton Abbot to Moretonhampstead line! Bertram Fletcher Robinson pointed out in his short story, 'The Tragedy of Thomas Hearne', that this station would have been well-guarded in the event of a convict escape. [74]

COURTESY OF THE TAYLOR COLLECTION

THE HOUND ON SCREEN

Popularity and Adaptability. Sherlock Holmes is claimed to be the most frequently filmed character in the history of cinema and television, with over two hundred Holmes films having been made, not counting documentaries and advertisements involving Holmes. Details on all of the Holmes films are not readily available or always reliable, so an inevitable degree of uncertainty exists in some cases. The first Holmes film, entitled *Baffled*, is claimed to have been made in 1900, although it was released in 1903, but many of the films which have since appeared have, like *Baffled*, not been directly linked with any of the 60 Holmes stories written by ACD. Many of the early films included no Dr Watson, as his rôle was mistakenly seen to be redundant when he was not needed to describe what was going on, and other key characters have sometimes been removed, including a truly startling one in the first film version of *The Hound*! In the first seven film versions of this story, it was acted in the then-modern costume, and it was not until 1939 that it was played as if taking place in 1889. All subsequent film performances of *The Hound* have been located in the Victorian period. The first four film versions of the story were silent. One way in which most of the films fail to follow the original story is in the way in which they graphically include Stapleton disappearing beneath the *'great Grimpen Mire'*, for it will be recalled that Stapleton's final fate is not actually revealed in ACD's text.

Availability. Most of the Holmes films have been made in English, but several of the other major languages have been used, and many films have been dubbed or sub-titled in other languages to make this a truly international sub-genre. Amongst the Doylean based films, the most popular has always been *The Hound of the Baskervilles*, with at least 19 versions having been produced, in six different original languages,

although one might also say seven languages in consideration of the latest version. The 'at least' caveat is included because it is possible that other versions have existed, or do exist, since some supposedly 'lost' versions have been found in recent years. For many years, Holmesian film histories suggested that the first English sound version of *The Hound* existed only with the sound track in one country and the film track in another country, with the two owners refusing to combine the separated parts, but a near-perfect copy was then found to exist in the British Film Institute's archives. Where a film is definitely known to be still in existence, the title in the listing below is followed by an asterisk. With Houndian, and other Holmesian, films, the game of hunting for the missing films is still afoot. Sadly, only four of the film versions of *The Hound* are known to have been shot on Dartmoor, although there is a possible fifth, but the most famous version was filmed entirely in a studio! As this is very much a book about Dartmoor, greater emphasis will be given here to those films made on the Moor.

1. *Den Grå Dame (The Grey Lady)* - Denmark 1909 - Nordisk Films

Most Holmesian film histories suggest that the first film version of *The Hound of the Baskervilles* was the 1914 German film, but this ignores a film which may not have the required title but which follows the text of *The Hound* far more closely than many of those which bear that title. There is a major change in the basic plot, however, in that there is no hound, as its rôle is taken over by the eponymous grey lady. Viggo Larsen played Holmes in this and five other Nordisk films (he repeated the rôle many times in films made in other countries), but in this one, as was later to occur with the most famous film version of *The Hound*, the actor playing Holmes was not billed as the leading star, with that credit going to Forrest Holger-Madsen, even though he played a character who is now not recalled in the filmographies.

2. *Der Hund von Baskerville (The Hound of the Baskervilles)* - Germany 1914 - Vitaskop

Here we have an example of a Watson becoming a Holmes, with Alwin Neuss having appeared in the former rôle in the Danish film version of *The Hound of the Baskervilles*. Perhaps it was because Neuss was not available to play Watson that The Good Doctor does not appear in this film! This film was partially based on the Doylean text, and it was followed by a series of six films which had some connection with *The Hound*, although this was often minimal. The second in the series (1914), *Das Einsame Haus (The Isolated House)*, had Stapleton escaping from prison to a remarkable submersible house. The fourth (1915) had a title which indicated a connection, *Wie Enstand der Hund von Baskerville (How the Hound of the Baskervilles Arose)*.

3. *The Hound of the Baskervilles* * - England 1921 - Stoll

It has frequently been claimed that this, the first English version, was filmed on Dartmoor, but a careful examination of the film has failed to reveal any firm evidence for this, and several of the outdoor scenes are filmed in locations which are very unlike the Dartmoor environment. It is a very dark film, with exciting shots of The Hound seen on skylines against the failing light, and it is often claimed that the flickering light which surrounds The Hound to represent his phosphorous daubing was produced by scratching the original film negative, although some film authorities suggest that this was achieved by painting the relevant frames. The star, Eille Norwood, is the actor who has played Holmes most frequently on film, with 47 performances. He was a master of make-up, and was sometimes filmed taking off his disguising make-up to reveal his Holmes make-up, which is a point later commemorated on screen by the man who is probably the most famous film Holmes, Basil Rathbone. Norwood's real surname was Brett, which was the stage surname later taken by another portrayer of Holmes in *The Hound of the*

Baskervilles, Jeremy Brett, who starred in the second largest number of Holmes films, with 41 screen performances. Norwood was the first film actor to devote a great deal of study to the original Holmes stories in order to improve his performance in the rôle, and he was followed very much in this practice by the other Brett.

4. *Mouken no Himitsu (The Mystery of the Ferocious Hound)* - Japan 1924 - Nikkatsu Kyoto Motion Picture Co

All is transferred to the Far East in this version of the story, and all of the character names change to Japanese ones. The 'Sir Charles' character lives in Kobe, and his nephew, the 'Sir Henry' character, returns from Shanghai. The 'Holmes' character, known as Hoshi Tatsuhiko and played by Mizushima Ryotaro, initiates his own investigation of the death of the 'Sir Charles' character. An assistant to the 'Jack Stapleton' character, locks 'Holmes' in a room at one point, to allow 'Stapleton' to disguise himself as a detective and try to kill 'Sir Henry'. 'Holmes' escapes and triumphs, of course. Possibly to remove any offensive intimations of an incestuous relationship, the 'Beryl' character becomes the sister-in-law of 'Stapleton'. References to The Hound in this film differed, in that in newspaper advertisements in Tokyo The Hound was referred to as 'Ban-ken' or 'Barbarian Hound', whereas in Yokohama newspaper advertisements it was 'Yo-ken' or 'Mysterious Hound'.

5. *Der Hund von Baskerville (The Hound of the Baskervilles)* - Germany 1929 - Erda Films

Although produced by a German company in Berlin, the cast was truly international, with an American Holmes, Carlyle Blackwell and a Russian Watson, Georges Seroff, accompanied by German and Italian actors. It stuck even more closely to the original text than its 1914 Vitaskop predecessor. As with all of the German versions, it was filmed in a very dark fashion, with starkly contrasting highlighted areas.

6. *The Hound of the Baskervilles* * - England 1931 - Gainsborough Pictures

This film is frequently listed as a 1932 film, but it was actually shot during the Winter of 1929-30 and released the following year. It was made as a result of a poll carried out amongst British cinemagoers as to which story they would most like to see filmed by Gainsborough. This film established several firsts: it was the first sound version of *The Hound of the Baskervilles*, it is the first which can definitely be identified as being made on Dartmoor, and it is also the only one to star a Holmes who was born on Dartmoor, with Robert Rendel coming from Lustleigh. Rendel was surprised when he returned to the village of his birth to find that the railway station had temporarily been renamed as 'Baskerville'! The train carrying Watson and, incorrectly, Holmes to Dartmoor arrives at Lustleigh station, which

is rather surprising, since a slightly earlier shot of the train shows it circling around King's Tor, which is on the Princetown line, rather than on the Moretonhampstead line which includes Lustleigh. There were problems with the filming, such as when shooting was stopped for bad light half-way through the Lustleigh station scenes, and when snow fell on the area overnight before filming could begin again. It has been claimed that the *'Baskerville Hall'* scenes were filmed at Lustleigh Hall, but the tiny dining hall in that building would barely have allowed a game of écarté to have taken place, and would certainly not have enabled the roistering of Hugo's companions which occurs in what is clearly a studio set. Some external scenes are shot at a *'Baskerville Hall'* which is definitely the 1906-built Moretonhampstead Manor House Hotel. Some of the filming took place near Bonehill Rocks and Chinkwell Tor, close to

'Baskerville' Railway Station. Robert Rendel (centre in Trilby hat) at Lustleigh Station, disguised for the 1931 film of *The Hound of the Baskervilles*. [101]

Lustleigh Railway Station. Generator set for filming *The Hound of the Baskervilles* stands on a Hydra D well-wagon at Lustleigh. [101]

Widecombe-in-the-Moor. The film has a very strong Art Deco atmosphere in its London settings, and young Cartwright dashing around the Moor on his motorbike just does not seem right. Although the main line of the book is followed, there are numerous diversions, and the film generally fails to create the required suspense and excitement.

7. *Der Hund von Baskerville (The Hound of the Baskervilles)* * - Germany 1937 - Ondra-Lamac-Film

This film has achieved a somewhat notorious association, in having been a favourite of Adolf Hitler, who had a private copy in his film library, and there is a rumour that it was the film which he watched the night before he committed suicide, although other sources suggest that the film was found at Berchtesgarten. Holmes,

played by Bruno Güttner, abandons the traditional film deerstalker and Inverness cape for a flat cap and leather coat, reflecting the way in which Holmes was sometimes described in Germany as a secret policeman, rather than a private detective. There are numerous changes to the original story, with Holmes solving the key problem of the case merely by asking the telephone operator who had called '*Baskerville Hall*'. Beryl Stapleton is actually staying at '*Baskerville Hall*', under her real name of Beryl Vandeleur. The film is, as might be expected with any German version of the story, very stark.

8. *The Hound of the Baskervilles* * USA 1939 - Twentieth Century Fox

The lead star billing in what has since become the most famous film version of *The Hound of the Baskervilles* went not to Basil Rathbone as

Holmes, but to Richard Greene as Sir Henry. The film follows the original story very closely, although there are some notorious changes, such as the introduction of a hokum seance, and Holmes's closing line becoming "Quick, Watson, the needle!", which Rathbone uncharacteristically gabbles off, clearly out of embarrassment. The filming was all done in a studio, with Daryl F Zanuck's production standards creating a set for the *great Grimpen Mire* which was large enough, reportedly, for the star, Greene, to get lost on it. For many enthusiasts this remains the best version of the story. The only major first which it achieved, however, was that it was the first *Hound of the Baskervilles* to be made in period costume. The low point of the film was the dreadful portrayal of poor old Watson as the ultimate "Buffoonicus Britannicus". Although Watson had been portrayed in this way before, Nigel Bruce ruined the reputation of Watson for many decades to come, although even he managed a few good scenes in this powerful story.

9. *The Hound of the Baskervilles* * - England 1959 - Hammer Films

Another *Hound of the Baskervilles* film first was achieved with this version, in that it was the first in colour. There was a problem with the very tall Sir Henry, Christopher Lee, in comparison with the average height Holmes (Peter Cushing). As Holmes is meant to be well over six feet in height, and as this Holmes had to look up to Sir Henry at a sharp angle when they got close together, Sir Henry must have been close to seven feet tall! Some dreadful liberties were taken with the plot, with rumours that the tarantula spider which stars was under contract to appear in every third Hammer Studios film! The character who proves to be the villain will be a total surprise to anyone who has only read the book! There are a couple of scanning views of Dartmoor, which are actually stock shots. One, where the carriage drops off Mortimer on the Moor is blended into the movie element with just a slight glitch (watch for the finger post sign which materialises beside the cross-road from nowhere!). This shot also reveals the sandy soil of the location where the outdoor

scenes of 'the Moor' were filmed, on the ridge above the Great Frensham Pond (which can be seen prominently in the background). This was on the border of Surrey and Hampshire just a few miles away from where the writing of the story was completed. Cushing deliberately produces a very quirky and nervous interpretation of Holmes, and he is well supported by an intelligent Watson, André Morell, for a change.

10. *The Hound of the Baskervilles* * - England 1968 - BBC TV

There are two firsts here, with this being the first film version of *The Hound of the Baskervilles* made for TV, and with it having the only example of an actor, Peter Cushing, having played Holmes twice in different versions of the story. It was made in colour, unlike the episodes in the earlier BBC TV Sherlock Holmes series, in two 50-minute episodes, first aired in the Autumn of 1968. Although it did not have anywhere near the vast budget devoted to the 1959 Hammer Films version, and in spite of it being shot in only a few weeks, this version surpassed Cushing's Hammer film in many ways, in spite of his Watson, Nigel Stock, being made to return slightly to the 'dumb-waiter' mode. Watson and his party arrive on Dartmoor at Staverton railway station, on the restored steam-operated Dart Valley Railway. They cross the River Dart in a wagonette, and then realistically have to dismount and push to get it up the steep hill leading towards Huxham's Cross, whilst the train which they have just left, which should have been heading towards Buckfastleigh, is unfortunately shown heading down the valley behind them, towards Totnes. They then arrive at the superbly Gothick Dartmoor house of Lukesland near Ivybridge, although it does not have many of the features associated with *'Baskerville Hall'*. Much of the Moor filming was done in the Foggintor Quarries area, with Yellowmeade Farm featuring nicely as *'Merripit House'*. Cushing appears on the Moor wearing the soft trilby hat which Holmes was shown to be wearing in the original version of the story, as illustrated by Sidney Paget. This version follows the original story very closely, with only minor diversions, and this, in conjunction with Cushing's performance, is one of the major reasons why it is a favourite amongst many serious Holmesians, including the present commentator.

11. *L'Ultimo dei Baskerville (The Last of the Baskervilles)* - Italy 1968 - RAI (State TV)

This made-for-TV film achieved a first, in being the first three-episode film version of *The Hound of the Baskervilles*, with an actor who is extremely well-known in Italy, Nando Gazollo, portraying Holmes. The episodes were initially transmitted, each a week apart, in November 1968. All of the studio work was done in Italy, but location filming was carried out in England, not far from Cromer, where the story saw its birth, with Blickling Hall acting as *'Baskerville*

Hall'. It is thought that the film might still exist, as the other Italian Holmes film, *La Valle della Paura (The Valley of Fear)*, made at the same time (including location filming for 'Birlstone Manor' at Oxburgh Hall in Norfolk), has been re-discovered recently.   The Italian Sherlock Holmes society, Uno Studio in Holmes, is actively pursuing the RAI in search of this 'lost' version. Mercifully, prehaps, nothing is known of the content of the 1915 Luna film, *La Pulce Dei Baskerville (The Flea of the Baskervilles)*!

12. *The Hound of the Baskervilles* * - USA 1972 - Universal

Almost unbelievably, as late as the 1970s, this film can claim a first, in being the first colour film version of *The Hound of the Baskervilles* to be

"If you can't shoot the Hound, Holmes, you can always beat it to death with your pipe!" A charming photograph of the only man to play Holmes twice on screen in *The Hound of The Baskervilles*. Peter Cushing and his good Watson, André Morell, at The Sherlock Holmes Pub Musuem. [103]

made in the USA. Rather ridiculously, the actor playing the part of the wicked Hugo Baskerville, William Shatner, is very clearly shown to be the same actor as is playing Jack Stapleton, thus giving away the largest film clue ever as to the identity of the villain, although he does, in the Hugo rôle, seem to have another actor's voice dubbed onto him. Once again, this film was not made on Dartmoor, and the only English scenes are stock films of British steam trains. Given the small and large screen rôle for which the actor playing Stapleton is best known, it is rather surprising that he did not manage to use his Scottish contacts to arrange for the whole cast to be moved to Dartmoor, especially as there is a location on the Moor, less than two miles from Dartmoor Prison, known as Holming Beam! Holmes, played rather stolidly by Stewart Granger, is encumbered with yet another bumbling Watson, Bernard Fox. One nice touch is that at its conclusion this film raises the point which is not only forgotten in all the other films, but in the original story itself, which is that nothing is said about The Hound which created the legend, as opposed to The Hound bought by Stapleton which is killed. As the 'Moor' activities end, one can hear what might be the sound of the 'real' legendary Hound floating across the Moor. Numerous less acceptable changes are made to the original story.

13. *The Hound of the Baskervilles* * - England 1978 - Hemdale

It was extremely tempting to leave this supposed version of *The Hound of the Baskervilles* out of this listing, as it is a total travesty, but it is included for the sake of completeness in name only. It does not even have the saving grace of being funny, in that it is filled with examples of schoolboy, lavatorial humour of the worst kind, and it obviously bears almost no relationship whatsoever to the original story. Given the vast array of talent available within the cast, with Peter Cook as 'Sherlock Holmes' and Dudley Moore as 'Watson', the opportunity was wasted for producing a truly humorous version of the story, which is clearly a possibility with any story involving such stark and

dramatic events, but it seems that everyone involved was too busy being self-indulgent to consider the requirements of an intelligent audience.

14. *Sobaka Baskervilej (The Hound of the Baskervilles)* * - USSR 1981 - Lens Films

This Russian language film version of *The Hound of the Baskervilles* has, sadly, been largely ignored by most Western Holmesians. Sherlock Holmes was always extremely popular in the former Soviet Union, but when a series of films was made starring Vasili Livanov as Holmes and Vitali Solomin as Watson as a regular, and superbly matched, partnership it quickly became the custom to include elements from more than one of the original Doylean cases in the adaptations. *The Hound of the Baskervilles* is an exception, in that it is one of the most faithful copies of the original story. What it includes, which is often missed in other versions of the story, is the element of humour which exists in this sometimes dark story, and which is well exploited by the personal relationship which had by then developed between the stars. One does not need to speak Russian to understand the joke played upon Watson by Holmes with the silver coffee pot in the opening scenes, and there is clearly a sense of unspoken understanding between the two actors. The film was made in and around part of the Leningrad area, now known as Stone Island, and locations in the Baltic States were used to add what the studio referred to as a 'Teutonic' atmosphere which does not quite match the environment of Dartmoor. Effective English Victorian props were obviously in limited supply, and one can have fun watching for the very mobile British Victorian Penfold pillar box which springs up on street corners throughout the film! Fortunately, this film is now available commercially on video in the West, so it may now become better appreciated.

15. *The Hound of the Baskervilles* * - England 1982 - BBC TV

This made-for-TV version of *The Hound of the Baskervilles* appeared as four 30-minute episodes in a Sunday Afternoon Classic Serial in the Autumn of 1982. It is the adaptation which most closely follows the original text, and it includes most of ACD's choicest phrases, but it is spoiled by its casting for Holmes, Tom Baker, and Watson, Terence Rigby. The former's performance is reasonable, but he was far too closely associated with having portrayed, for a long period, another cult TV hero of the time, Dr Who, and he carried over some of his mannerisms from that rôle. His Dr Watson looked exactly right, but proved to be appalling as soon as he spoke, or rather, mumbled! On the other hand, it includes by far the most chillingly convincing Stapleton, in Christopher Ravenscroft, and the very best Sir Henry, in Nicholas Woodeson, who is uniquely appropriate in more than just his correctly diminutive stature. It includes some good filming on Dartmoor, with Hound Tor playing a truly central part, complete with temporary 'stone huts', and with Swallerton Gate at its foot acting as *'Merripit House'*. Lestrade arrives at the Staverton restored steam railway station 'from London', although the train is, once again, travelling in the wrong direction, in that it is heading for Totnes, and it must be pointed out that London expresses never travelled on that line. Some filming was done at Lydford, beyond the Western rim of Dartmoor, with scenes inside the village pub, The Castle Inn.

16. *The Hound of the Baskervilles* * - USA 1983 - Mapleton

An American financed and released, made-for-TV, film version of *The Hound of the Baskervilles*, made in England, using a British cast, with Ian Richardson sometimes playing Holmes superbly and sometimes with too much tongue in his cheek. At times his Watson, Donald Churchill, out-Bruces Nigel Bruce! It is certainly the most glossy and glamorous version of the story which has been produced, but far too many changes are made to the original, with most of them being unnecessary and unsatisfactory, such as having Laura Lyons murdered in order to allow Lestrade to arrest her husband, Sir Henry seeing The Hound well before the *dénoue-*

ment, and Holmes in the ludicrously-thin disguise of a gypsy playing the fool on the Moor. At least the two actors playing Beryl and Sir Henry make more-plausible lovers than in many pairings, with the absolutely gorgeous Glynis Barber and the almost as pretty Martin Shaw, but one is left to wonder why Sir Henry's voice is dubbed, out of synchronisation, albeit with the voice of Martin Shaw! On the positive side it is the version which contains more filming on Dartmoor than any other, with some magnificently sweeping scenes on the Moor, mostly in bright sunshine, and with horizons ranging through Rippon Tor and Haytor, although the approach to the *'great Grimpen Mire'* is what Wordsworth would have called 'plashy' rather than frightening. Most of the filming is done in the Hound Tor area, especially on the ridge to the South of Hound Tor, with that Tor playing the part of the *'Cleft Tor'* of the story, although some of the close-up 'outdoor' scenes clearly use studio sets. Knightshayes Court, near Tiverton, is used for the exterior of *'Baskerville Hall'*.

17. *Sherlock Holmes and the Baskerville Curse* * - Australia 1983 - Burbank Films

The 'actors' in this 52-minute cartoon version of *The Hound of the Baskervilles* often produce far less wooden performances than the actors in many of the other film versions of the story, with the leading rôle being read by Peter O'Toole, although one might note the way in which Barrymore's accent changes from Welsh to that of Yorkshire. The film follows the original story fairly well, and might have acted as a good storyboard for the improvement of some of the other film versions.

18. *The Hound of the Baskervilles* * - England 1988 - Granada

Part of the long-running, frequently-superlative, often-definitive, and sometimes-dreadful Granada Sherlock Holmes series, with Jeremy Brett as Holmes. The excellent Edward Hardwicke, the best Watson yet seen, shines in what is, after all, Watson's finest case.

Unfortunately, this double-length episode probably caused more disappointment amongst serious Holmesians than did any other. Not because it was the worst, as there were several episodes vying for that dishonour towards the end of the run, but because it was the first which failed to meet its potential. It is actually far better than many other film versions of *The Hound of the Baskervilles*, but given the extremely high standards of performance and veracity of the earlier episodes it appeared at the time to be a disaster. There were many reasons for this, with the most significant being the adaptor, who managed to ruin the original story with his pointless changes. There are several very short stock shots of Dartmoor, without any actors, for the outdoor action was filmed on the North York Moors, with Heath Hall near Cheadle acting as *'Baskerville Hall'*, when financial cuts had to be made after a serious over-spend on an earlier episode, which may also explain the total absence of Lestrade.

19. *The Hound of the Baskervilles* * - Canada 2000 - CTV

This version, made in the land from which Sir Henry Baskerville returned to England, was produced for CTV in Canada, and it is, sadly, one of the worst versions of the story yet seen. The star of the film, Matt Frewer, can certainly be described as being a man of the right stature for the part, in that he is six foot three inches tall, with Holmes being described as being well over six foot in height, but he failed as Holmes in all other departments. The 'London' scenes were shot in Old Montreal, with 'Dartmoor' being Laval. Some stock scenes were filmed on the Moor, but the 'Baskerville Hall' external shots are of Montacute House near Yeovilton, some 70 miles from Dartmoor. The Director described that house as being "… built by some Tudor dude in 1590 …" which nicely sets the tone and inaccuracy (it was built in 1601) of the whole film, in that the Director encouraged far too many changes to the original text, in setting out with the aim of making this the scariest version yet, and in emphasising the supernatural elements of the story. The screenplay writer introduced numerous errors which revealed a limited understanding of the nature of the original and a poor grasp of English cultural and social history. His original script had Watson, who could never bring himself to call Holmes by his first name, calling Sir Henry 'Hank'. Our advice to remove this may have prevailed Given the essential canine aspects of the story, it is a shame that the Bloodhound-Mastiff cross-breed becomes a mundane German Shepherd Dog (the unfortunate 'star' in the latter case was called Eno, which some may remember was also the trade name for a stomach settling preparation, which might be useful after watching this travesty!).

Acknowledgements. Personal thanks are expressed here to: Uwe Sommerlad, Enrico Solito & Gianluca Salvatori, Hirayama Yuichi & Takahiko Endo, and Tanya & David Izzard for translations and information on the German, Italian, Japanese and Russian film versions of *The Hound of the Baskervilles*.

The lady sprang from her chair
Holmes is holding what looks like a soft cap.

We all three shook hands
Holmes is now wearing a soft Trilby, whilst Lestrade
and Watson are wearing bowlers.

He looked round him in surprise
Lestrade now seems to be wearing the soft cap which
Holmes had at Laura Lyon's house.

THE HOUNDIAN PHENOMENON

INTRODUCTION

Varied Activities. *The Hound* has created an enthusiasm which far exceeds that of any of the other Holmes stories. Its very precise association with Dartmoor has resulted in its commemoration on the Moor at various times and in various ways, and the strong individual elements within the story, with The Hound being paramount here, has enabled the story to be epitomised and caricatured very easily. Those who have wished to be associated with the story in some way have been given many opportunities to do so.

Dartmoor Commercial Enterprises. On numerous occasions those in business on the Moor have attempted to focus attention on their enterprises through the Hound connection, although not always with any true Doylean justification. This has often been the case with public houses, but as there is a tendency for such hostelries to change their names, close, re-open, and change management, any indication of the presence of something 'Holmesian' may quickly become out of date. A good example of all of these processes involves the East Dart Hotel in Postbridge. In the 1990s, the then-new landlady converted the restaurant of this establishment into a Victorianly-decorated room with a Holmesian theme, having lots of posters and pictures of Holmes, with the walls lined with his usual accoutrements from *'221B Baker Street'*. The opening night included a group of Holmesians dining in Victorian costume. The 'connection' with *The Hound* was that there was a 'hound' legend associated with the pub. There are various versions of this story from the mid-Nineteenth Century, with either the landlord returning to the pub after a day of heavy drinking elsewhere, or with the landlady having been to church and having heard a sermon on the evils of drink. The landlady decided that the pub should become a temperance hotel (which it

did in real history) and that all the beer should be poured into the East Dart River. A black dog (not a hound!) was at the time drinking at a downstream point and it ended up howling at the Moon. It is claimed that the ghost of the dog has since been seen on the road near the pub. When a new landlord arrived a few years later, all of the Holmesian material was removed. In the late 1990s, in Princetown, the Railway Inn changed its name to The Devil's Elbow, which is the name of what was once a notorious bend in the road between Princetown and Yelverton, close to Black Tor (a name mentioned in *The Hound*), where it was said that the Devil steered vehicles off the road. A portrayal of The Hound and a silhouette of Holmes were added to the pub sign, but no other Holmesian changes were introduced, and the 'connection' disappeared when the pub reverted to its previous name. At Easter 2000, a small but interesting museum of Holmesian material was opened at the rear of a café in Princetown, called The Sherlock Holmes Experience, but this also quickly folded. There have been several hotels and other public residences which have claimed that they have a connection with *The Hound*, but the only ones which have had any real justification have been Brook Manor, with its Richard Cabell legend association, and Heatree House, with Harry Baskerville having suggested, misleadingly, that it influenced the description of *'Baskerville Hall'*. For several years, the most charming of the commercial uses of the Hound association has been the superior quality snack and drinks van which is located for most of the year in the car park at Hound Tor. Although there is no real Doylean connection, this van provides excellent service under the title of "The Hound of the Basketmeals", with food being served in baskets. One can, almost inevitably, obtain a Houndburger!

The High Moorland Visitor Centre. The Dartmoor National Park Authority has created a

Baker Street. The street in which the residence of Sherlock Holmes was located. [74]

splendid information and interpretation centre in what was once Rowe's Duchy Hotel, in Princetown, and no trip to Dartmoor is complete without a visit to this centre, where there is a mass of information available about every aspect of the Moor, and where there are frequent temporary exhibitions on specialist Dartmoor matters. The centre was opened in 1993 by His Royal Highness Prince Charles, the Prince of Wales, in his capacity as the Duke of Cornwall, in which rôle he, rather paradoxically, owns much of Dartmoor. At the opening he was introduced to many of those who organise the multitude of activities which take place on the Moor, who had helped to present information on their activities in the Centre. In this way he was introduced to the present commentator, in the guise of Sherlock Holmes, and he showed a great deal of interest in the Doylean connection. The centre includes a life-size mannequin of Holmes on the staircase of the former hotel, looking as if he is setting out for the wild Moor, and there is a life-

size photograph of ACD at the head of the stairs watching his creation depart. This display, and the literary information presentation in one of the other halls, was designed by, and partially paid for, by the world's leading Sherlock Holmes correspondence study group, The Franco-Midland Hardware Company, which is an international literary society (named after a company set up in one of the Holmes short stories), and there is a plaque commemorating this in the Centre. The technical advice for all of this was provided primarily by The Baskerville Hounds, which is a locally-meeting, Dartmoor specialist sub-group of The Franco-Midland Hardware Company. More details on this group are given below.

HOUNDIAN SOCIETIES

A Worldwide Game. There are about 500 Sherlock Holmes societies around the world, with membership numbers varying from one (a 'group' appropriately entitled The Solitary Cyclist, comprising one lady in splendid isolation) to 1,500 (The Japan Sherlock Holmes Club). The oldest society is The Baker Street Irregulars, formed in 1934, named after Holmes's street urchin assistants in London, although the society is actually based in New York, whilst the oldest British society is The Sherlock Holmes Society of London, founded in 1951. As *The Hound* is by far the most popular of the Holmes cases, it is not surprising that there are numerous societies named after references taken from it. The oldest of these, being founded in 1943 in Chicago, is The Hounds of the Baskerville (sic), whereof this present commentator is a proud member, as he is of many of the others [yes, that '(sic)' is part of the formal title!]. There are, or have been, many other Houndian-named groups, such as: The Baskerville Hall Club of Sweden, The Bootmakers of Toronto, The Chester Baskerville Society, The Footprints of a Gigantic Hind [the last word is 'Hind' not 'Hound', in that this Kenyan society takes its title from a Kikuyu legend of a giant avenging antelope!], The Friends of the Great Grimpen Mire, The Grimpen Admirers of Sherlock Holmes [they deliberately planned those initials!], The Grimpen Post Office [they also deliberately planned their initials to match those of the UK's earlier General Post Office service], The Hansoms of John Clayton, Hugo's Companions, The Men on the Tor, The Merripit House Guests, The Mexborough Lodgers, The Poor Folk Upon The Moors, and The Sound of the Baskervilles [they are based around the Puget Sound in the USA].

"The Baskerville Hounds". This group was founded in 1989, by a gathering of Dartmoor and Holmesian enthusiasts, to celebrate the centenary of the dramatic events described in *The Hound*. The group has grown over the years, and now has hundreds of members, located in over 40 countries, having become the world's leading authority on the study of *The Hound*, and on other aspects of ACD's connections with Dartmoor. The group publishes an annual journal, entitled *The Hound*, produces specialist monographs on its researches, and re-publishes out of print works connected with *The Hound*. It arranges numerous meetings on Dartmoor, with one regular function being a five-day event over Easter each year, and another being The Pack Meet, which takes place over the weekend nearest to the date of the death of The Hound (19 October). The group also arranges meetings at other locations, outside of Devonshire, which have connections with ACD's Dartmoor stories, such as in Cromer, Herefordshire and that location which Dr Watson referred to as *"…that great cesspool into which all the loungers and idlers of the Empire are irresistibly drained."*, London. The group carries out occasional costumed events, but the wearing of costume is always optional. Those with an interest in Holmes or Dartmoor are all made welcome at the meetings of this group, where there are discussions of topics connected with ACD's Dartmoor stories, and explorations of the locations associated with them. There are two annual events which involve awards. The first is the BEAST (the Baskerville Écarté All-Stars Tournament), the world's premier championship for playing the popular Victorian card game enjoyed by Sir Henry Baskerville and Dr Mortimer in *The Hound*. The second is the Houndathon, which follows a different marathon-length route each year in linking together as many Houndian locations on the Moor as possible. Participants can follow only one short leg of this trek, but those who complete the full course receive the prestigious certificate for becoming a member of Mortimer's Moormen! Details of membership can be obtained – see the Conclusion Section.

CONCLUSION

Continuing Studies. There can, of course, never be a conclusion to Holmesian Studies on Dartmoor, but we will here attempt to provide something important upon which to focus, to draw this Investigation to a close. On the topic of continuing studies, however there is one major point to be made. It has been impossible to provide the full references required by formal scholarship within this Investigation. An attempt was made to do this, but it resulted in more than 500 footnotes, which badly disrupted the text and layout of the Investigation and the general appearance of the book. A very extensive bibliography has been provided, which should enable the identification of all of the source material used, although there has, of course, been a great deal of original research incorporated in this Investigation. For those with a specialist interest, and in order to aid the further development of Holmesian Studies on Dartmoor, more-detailed information can be obtained from "The Baskerville Hounds", in exchange for a contribution towards the costs involved in producing the information required. Initial contact should include three First Class stamps (from within the UK) or three International Reply Coupons or two US dollar bills in cash (from outside the UK). Alternatively, you can search for the latest e-mail contact address on the Internet under "The Baskerville Hounds". Further contributions, if necessary, will be requested on a cost-only basis. Details of membership of "The Baskerville Hounds" and the latest e-mail contact information will be sent with responses to initial contacts. All details from:

The Kennel Maid, 6 Bramham Moor, Hill Head, Fareham, Hampshire, PO14 3RU, England.

Further Activities. Some of the material in this Investigation has deliberately been presented in what may be seen as a highly critical and provocative manner, although it has all been based on sound principles of scholarship and fun. The fun element is intended to be very much in the same spirit as the way in which Holmes comments on Watson's deductions, derived from Mortimer's walking stick, when he says:

> *When I said that you stimulated me I meant, to be frank, that in noting your fallacies I was occasionally guided towards the truth.*

It is hoped that those who disagree with any of the comments made in this Investigation will be guided towards their own greater truth, and that they will be encouraged to develop their own arguments in response. It is also hoped that those who may have pertinent evidence which has not been made available to Holmesian scholars in the past will be persuaded to bring it into the light of open discussion. In both of these ways, it is intended that we might all be able to answer the question posed in the title of Mortimer's *Journal of Psychology* article, 'Do We Progress?', in the affirmative.

A Tentative Conclusion. Perhaps the best way in which to close this Investigation of *The Hound* is to concentrate on the character in the story who is so often forgotten, even though this character is essential to the story: The Hound himself. Much scholarship has gone into discussing exactly what sort of creature he was, with some of the candidates being absolutely outrageous - we will pass over The Chihuahua of the Baskervilles in silence! There is, in fact, no real problem about the identification of the breed of The Hound, or rather the breeds, in that he is what Watson clearly describes him as being, a mixture of a bloodhound and a mastiff, with first-cross breeding having been a popular pursuit in Britain at the end of the Nineteenth Century. Within "The Baskerville Hounds" he is commemorated every year, on the Saturday nearest to the date of his demise (19 October), on a grassy mound on the edge of Fox Tor Mires which overlooks the heart of the mire, with that mound being known within the group as 'The Hound Mound'. A commemorative piece of doggerel (sorry about that!) is read after a wreath made from local reeds is cast into the mire.

The Doggerel in the Night-Time

Ode To The Hound

Philip Weller

To become involved in Baskerville wrangles,
The Hound left his lair at old Ross and Mangles.

From then on the days would no longer be fine,
For the Hound which travelled the North Devon line.

No hound was worse-painted, not e'en by Landseer,
Than when this one was daubed from muzzle to ear.

Tied up and half-starved in a tin-mine's dank gloom,
His cries were mis-heard as the last bittern's boom.

Though many who heard said it curdled the blood,
There was one who claimed it was settling mud.

When let loose one night for a run in the fog,
He sought out a friend, as would any good dog.

As he ran with Sir Henry, over the bank,
'The Man on the Tor' put five shots in his flank.

If you go on the Moor, where spirits abound,
You may yet find prints from that gigantic Hound.

There is fire in his eyes, which still shine with pride,
As he crosses the Moor at night in full stride.

When the powers of evil are exalted,
The soul of that Hound should never be faulted.

It was not his own choice, to cause so much fright,
Or look like a beacon that glows in the night.

So do spare a thought for the Hound with no name,
And look to the Moor for his flickering flame.

A mist-shrouded Dartmoor Prison, with North Hessary Tor in the background. The hotel where ACD stayed, Rowe's Duchy Hotel is off to the left-hand side of the picture [15].

Brook Manor, between Buckfastleigh and Holne, the former home of Richard Cabell III, and a popular candidate for *'Baskerville Hall'*, even though one cannot see the open Moor from here. From a distance, the two chimneys give the appearance of the two towers of *'Baskerville Hall'* [63].

Hayford Hall, a good locational candidate for 'Baskerville Hall', seen from near the old yew alley which leads out onto the Moor. The old clock from Fowelscombe can clearly be seen in the central tower, thus combining two candidates for 'Baskerville Hall' [64].

The track beside the River Aune, from Huntingdon Cross towards the Erme and Plym Valleys, which is a candidate for part of the path to Sheepstor, along which the wicked Hugo Baskerville took his fateful ride [61].

Deadman's Bottom, near Plym Steps, a candidate for the *goyal* where the wicked Hugo Baskerville met the original Hound [61].

The massive tin works at Erme Head, on the route from Huntingdon Cross to the Plym Valley [61].

Black Tor [56] (left) and Shipley Tor [57], on the other side of the Aune Valley (right), with a *'Black Tor'* and *'Shipley's Yard'* being mentioned in *The Hound*.

Rider's Rings (central horizon) from Black Tor (right) above the River Aune. This massive Bronze Age enclosure includes a candidate for the stone hut where Holmes stayed on the Moor [72].

Fox Tor Mires, which is almost certainly the inspiration for the *'great Grimpen Mire'* [69], viewed from the South, which was Dr Watson's viewpoint on his first visit. The old mine workings and houses at Whiteworks [70] can be seen at middle-distance left, and North Hessary Tor [56] can be seen on the horizon above Whiteworks. Nun's Cross Cottage, a candidate for *'Merripit House'* [71], is just beyond the left edge of the picture.

The Bronze Age enclosure of Grimspound, containing 24 stone hut circles, as seen from Hameldown [35], where ACD and BFR sat inside one of the huts [69]. The name of Grimspound (pronounced 'Grimspun' on Dartmoor) may well have influenced the choice of the name 'Grimpen' [70].

Cleft Rock, a candidate for 'Cleft Tor' [29], viewed from the Holne Chase Hotel, with intervening trees, exactly as at 'Baskerville Hall', although Cleft Rock is not on the open Moor.

A closer view of Cleft Rock not normally available to the public, since the rock is located on private land.

Inside the cleft of Cleft Rock.

The view of Bellever Tor (the rocky hill between the trees in the mid-distance) from North Hessary Tor, with Watson having seen this Tor from a hill from which one could also see Vixen Tor. One can, indeed, see Vixen Tor from North Hessary Tor [56].

Hound Tor, near Manaton [58], used in several films, although there is no Hound Tor in *The Hound*.

A view of Vixen Tor [56], showing the 'face' of Vixiana, who lured unsuspecting travellers to a mire-bound death.

Bellever Tor [56] (left) with Laughter Tor (right) [72], with *'Belliver Tor'* and *'Lafter Hall'* being mentioned in *The Hound.*

A distant, atmospheric view of Hound Tor, with Hay Tor in the background [58].

The view onto the Moor from above Okehampton, showing Row Tor [74].

The River Swincombe flowing out of the *'great Grimpen Mire'* (Fox Tor Mires) [67].

The grave of Selden, the escaped convict? Princetown church with the gravestones of prisoners [56].

Various books and comics based on the story of The Hound.

Sherlock Holmes – The Bloodhound
From Country Companions

Holmes on the Tor
From The Sherlock Holmes Museum

Holmes and the Hound
From Role Models

The Northumberland Hotel
From The Sherlock Holmes Pub

Stones amongst the prehistoric Merrivale Stone Rows, looking like the *'fang-like'* rocks where the wicked Hugo Baskerville died [70].

THE HOUND
OF THE
BASKERVILLES

Arthur Conan Doyle

The text used is that of

The Strand Magazine

as published in

monthly episodes between

August 1901 and April 1902

The Hound of the Baskervilles
The 17th Century Hugo Baskerville wearing 18th Century costume.

The Hound of the Baskervilles.*

ANOTHER ADVENTURE OF

SHERLOCK HOLMES.

BY CONAN DOYLE.

CHAPTER I.

MR. SHERLOCK HOLMES.

 R. SHERLOCK HOLMES, who was usually very late in the mornings, save upon those not infrequent occasions when he was up all night, was seated at the breakfast table. I stood upon the hearth-rug and picked up the stick which our visitor had left behind him the night before. It was a fine, thick piece of wood, bulbous-headed, of the sort which is known as a "Penang lawyer." Just under the head was a broad silver band, nearly an inch across. "To James Mortimer, M.R.C.S., from his friends of the C.C.H.," was engraved upon it, with the date "1884." It was just such a stick as the old-fashioned family practitioner used to carry - dignified, solid, and reassuring.

"Well, Watson, what do you make of it?"

Holmes was sitting with his back to me, and I had given him no sign of my occupation.

"How did you know what I was doing? I believe you have eyes in the back of your head."

"I have, at least, a well-polished silver-plated coffee-pot in front of me," said he. "But, tell me, Watson, what do you make of our visitor's stick? Since we have been so unfortunate as to miss him and have no notion of his errand, this accidental souvenir becomes of importance. Let me hear you reconstruct the man by an examination of it."

"I think," said I, following as far as I could the methods of my companion, "that Dr. Mortimer is a successful elderly medical man, well-esteemed, since those who know him give him this mark of their appreciation."

"Good!" said Holmes. "Excellent!"

"I think also that the probability is in favour of his being a country practitioner who does a great deal of his visiting on foot."

"Why so?"

"Because this stick, though originally a very handsome one, has been so knocked about that I can hardly imagine a town practitioner carrying it. The thick iron ferrule is worn down, so it is evident that he has done a great amount of walking with it."

"Perfectly sound!" said Holmes.

"And then again, there is the 'friends of the C.C.H.' I should guess that to be the Something Hunt, the local hunt to whose members he has possibly given some surgical assistance, and which has made him a small presentation in return."

"Really, Watson, you excel yourself," said Holmes, pushing back his chair and lighting a cigarette. "I am bound to say that in all the accounts which you have been so good as to give of my own small achievements you have habitually underrated your own abilities. It may be that you are not yourself luminous, but you are a conductor of light. Some people without possessing genius have a remarkable power of stimulating it. I confess, my dear fellow, that I am very much in your debt."

• This story owes its inception to my friend, Mr. Fletcher Robinson, who has helped me both in the general plot and in the local details. – A. C. D.

He had never said as much before, and I must admit that his words gave me keen pleasure, for I had often been piqued by his indifference to my admiration and to the attempts which I had made to give publicity to his methods. I was proud too to think that I had so far mastered his system as to apply it in a way which earned his approval. He now took the stick from my hands and examined it for a few minutes with his naked eyes. Then with an expression of interest he laid down his cigarette and, carrying the cane to the window, he looked over it again with a convex lens.

"Interesting, though elementary," said he, as he returned to his favourite corner of the settee. "There are certainly one or two indications upon the stick. It gives us the basis for several deductions."

"Has anything escaped me?" I asked, with some self-importance. "I trust that there is nothing of consequence which I have overlooked?"

"I am afraid, my dear Watson, that most of your conclusions were erroneous. When I said that you stimulated me I meant, to be frank, that in noting your fallacies I was occasionally guided towards the truth. Not that you are entirely wrong in this instance. The man is certainly a country practitioner. And he walks a good deal."

"Then I was right."

"To that extent."

"But that was all."

"No, no, my dear Watson, not all - by no means all. I would suggest, for example, that a presentation to a doctor is more likely to come from an hospital than from a hunt, and that when the initials 'C.C.' are placed before that hospital the words 'Charing Cross' very naturally suggest themselves."

"You may be right."

"The probability lies in that direction. And if we take this as a working hypothesis we have a fresh basis from which to start our construction of this unknown visitor."

"Well, then, supposing that 'C.C.H.' does stand for 'Charing Cross Hospital,' what further inferences may we draw?"

"Do none suggest themselves? You know my methods. Apply them!"

"I can only think of the obvious conclusion that the man has practised in town before going to the country."

"I think that we might venture a little farther than this. Look at it in this light. On what occasion would it be most probable that such a presentation would be made? When would his friends unite to give him a pledge of their good will? Obviously at the moment when Dr. Mortimer withdrew from the service of the hospital in order to start in practice for himself. We know there has been a presentation. We believe there has been a change from a town hospital to a country practice. Is it, then, stretching our inference too far to say that the presentation was on the occasion of the change?"

"It certainly seems probable."

"Now, you will observe that he could not have been on the *staff* of the hospital, since only a man well-established in a London practice could hold such a position, and such a one would not drift into the country. What was he, then? If he was in the hospital and yet not on the staff he could only have been a house-surgeon or a house-physician - little more than a senior student. And he left five years ago - the date is on the stick. So your grave, middle-aged family practitioner vanishes into thin air, my dear Watson, and there emerges a young fellow under thirty, amiable, unambitious, absent-minded, and the possessor of a favourite dog, which I should describe roughly as being larger than a terrier and smaller than a mastiff."

I laughed incredulously as Sherlock Holmes leaned back in his settee and blew little wavering rings of smoke up to the ceiling.

"As to the latter part, I have no means of checking you," said I, "but at least it is not difficult to find out a few particulars about the man's age and professional career." From my small medical shelf I took down the Medical Directory and turned up the name. There were several Mortimers, but only one who could be our visitor. I read his record aloud.

"Mortimer, James, M.R.C.S., 1882 Grimpen, Dartmoor, Devon. House surgeon, from 1882 to 1884, at Charing Cross Hospital. Winner of the Jackson prize for Comparative Pathology, with essay entitled 'Is Disease a Reversion?' Corresponding member of the Swedish Pathological Society. Author of 'Some Freaks of Atavism' (*Lancet*, 1882). 'Do We Progress?' (*Journal of Psychology*, March, 1883). Medical Officer for the parishes of Grimpen, Thorsley, and High Barrow."

"No mention of that local hunt, Watson," said Holmes, with a mischievous smile, "but a country doctor, as you very astutely observed. I think that I am fairly justified in my inferences. As to the adjectives, I said, if I remember right, amiable, unambitious, and absent-minded. It is my experience that it is only an amiable man in this world who receives testimonials, only an unambitious one who abandons a London career for the country, and only an absent-minded one who leaves his stick and not his visiting-card after waiting an hour in your room."

"And the dog?"

"Has been in the habit of carrying this stick behind his master. Being a heavy stick the dog has held it tightly by the middle, and the marks of his teeth are very plainly visible. The dog's jaw, as shown in the space between these marks, is too broad in my opinion for a terrier and not broad enough for a mastiff. It may have been - yes, by Jove, it *is* a curly-haired spaniel."

He had risen and paced the room as he spoke. Now he halted in the recess of the window. There was such a ring of conviction in his voice that I glanced up in surprise.

"My dear fellow, how can you possibly be so sure of that?"

"For the very simple reason that I see the dog himself on our very door-step, and there is the ring of its owner. Don't move, I beg you, Watson. He is a professional brother of yours, and your presence may be of assistance to me. Now is the dramatic moment of fate, Watson, when you hear a step upon the stair which is walking into your life, and you know not whether for good or ill. What does Dr. James Mortimer, the man of science, ask of Sherlock Holmes, the specialist in crime? Come in!"

The appearance of our visitor was a surprise to me, since I had expected a typical country practitioner. He was a very tall, thin man, with a long nose like a beak, which jutted out between two keen, grey eyes, set closely together and sparkling brightly from behind a pair of gold-rimmed glasses. He was clad in a professional but rather slovenly fashion, for his frock-coat was dingy and his trousers frayed. Though young, his long back was already bowed, and he walked with a forward thrust of his head and a general air of peering benevolence. As he entered his eyes fell upon the stick in Holmes's hand, and he ran towards it with an exclamation of joy. "I am so very glad," said he. "I was not sure whether I had left it here or in the Shipping Office. I would not lose that stick for the world."

"A presentation, I see," said Holmes.

"Yes, sir."

"From Charing Cross Hospital?"

"From one or two friends there on the occasion of my marriage."

"Dear, dear, that's bad!" said Holmes, shaking his head.

Dr. Mortimer blinked through his glasses in mild astonishment.

"Why was it bad?"

"Only that you have disarranged our little deductions. Your marriage, you say?"

"Yes, sir. I married, and so left the hospital, and with it all hopes of a consulting practice. It was necessary to make a home of my own."

"Come, come, we are not so far wrong after all," said Holmes. "And now, Dr. James Mortimer - "

"Mister, sir, Mister - a humble M.R.C.S."

"And a man of precise mind, evidently."

"A dabbler in science, Mr. Holmes, a picker up of shells on the shores of the great unknown ocean. I presume that it is Mr. Sherlock Holmes whom I am addressing and not - "

"No, this is my friend Dr. Watson."

"Glad to meet you, sir. I have heard your name mentioned in connection with that of your friend. You interest me very much, Mr. Holmes. I had hardly expected so dolichocephalic a skull or such well-marked supra-orbital development. Would you have any objection to my running my finger along your parietal fissure? A cast of your skull, sir, until the original is available, would be an ornament to any anthropological museum. It is not my intention to be fulsome, but I confess that I covet your skull."

Sherlock Holmes waved our strange visitor into a chair. "You are an enthusiast in your line of thought, I perceive, sir, as I am in mine," said he. "I observe from your forefinger that you make your own cigarettes. Have no hesitation in lighting one."

The man drew out paper and tobacco and twirled the one up in the other with surprising dexterity. He had long, quivering fingers as agile and restless as the antennae of an insect.

Holmes was silent, but his little darting glances showed me the interest which he took in our curious companion.

"I presume, sir," said he at last, "that it was not merely for the purpose of examining my skull that you have done me the honour to call here last night and again to-day?"

"No, sir, no; though I am happy to have had the opportunity of doing that as well. I came to you, Mr. Holmes, because I recognise that I am myself an unpractical man, and because I am suddenly confronted with a most serious and extraordinary problem. Recognising, as I do, that you are the second highest expert in Europe - "

"Indeed, sir! May I inquire who has the honour to be the first?" asked Holmes, with some asperity.

"To the man of precisely scientific mind the work of Monsieur Bertillon must always appeal strongly."

"Then had you not better consult him?"

"I said, sir, to the precisely scientific mind. But as a practical man of affairs it is acknowledged that you stand alone. I trust, sir, that I have not inadvertently - "

"Just a little," said Holmes. "I think, Dr. Mortimer, you would do wisely if without more ado you would kindly tell me plainly what the exact nature of the problem is in which you demand my assistance."

CHAPTER II.

THE CURSE OF THE BASKERVILLES.

"I have in my pocket a manuscript," said Dr. James Mortimer.

"I observed it as you entered the room," said Holmes.

"It is an old manuscript."

"Early eighteenth century, unless it is a forgery."

"How can you say that, sir?"

"You have presented an inch or two of it to my examination all the time that you have been talking. It would be a poor expert who could not give the date of a document within a decade or so. You may possibly have read my little monograph upon the subject. I put that at 1730."

"The exact date is 1742." Dr. Mortimer drew it from his breast-pocket. "This family paper was committed to my care by Sir Charles Baskerville, whose sudden and tragic death some three months ago created so much excitement in Devonshire. I may say that I was his personal friend as well as his medical attendant. He was a strong-minded man, sir, shrewd, practical, and as unimaginative as I am myself. Yet he took this document very seriously, and his mind was prepared for just such an end as did eventually overtake him."

Holmes stretched out his hand for the manuscript and flattened it upon his knee.

"You will observe, Watson, the alternative use of the long *s* and the short. It is one of several indications which enabled me to fix the date."

I looked over his shoulder at the yellow paper and the faded script. At the head was written: "Baskerville Hall," and below, in large, scrawling figures: "1742."

"It appears to be a statement of some sort."

"Yes, it is a statement of a certain legend which runs in the Baskerville family."

"But I understand that it is something more modern and practical upon which you wish to consult me?"

"Most modern. A most practical, pressing matter, which must be decided within twenty-four hours. But the manuscript is short and is intimately connected with the affair. With your permission I will read it to you."

Holmes leaned back in his chair, placed his finger-tips together, and closed his eyes, with an air of resignation. Dr. Mortimer turned the manuscript to the light and read in a high, crackling voice the following curious, old-world narrative: -

"Of the origin of the Hound of the Baskervilles there have been many statements, yet as I come in a direct line from Hugo Baskerville, and as I had the story from my father, who also had it from his, I have set it down with all belief that it occurred even as is here set forth. And I would have you believe, my sons, that the same Justice which punishes sin may also most graciously forgive it, and that no ban is so heavy but that by prayer and repentance it may be removed. Learn then from this story not to fear the fruits of the past, but rather to be circumspect in the future, that those foul passions whereby our family has suffered so grievously may not again be loosed to our undoing.

"Know then that in the time of the Great Rebellion (the history of which by the learned Lord Clarendon I most earnestly commend to your attention) this Manor of Baskerville was held by Hugo of that name, nor can it be gainsaid that he was a most wild, profane, and godless man. This, in truth, his neighbours might have pardoned, seeing that saints have never flourished in those parts, but there was in him a certain wanton and cruel humour which made his name a by-word through the West. It chanced that this Hugo came to love (if, indeed, so dark a passion may be known under so bright a name) the daughter of a yeoman who held lands near the

Baskerville estate. But the young maiden, being discreet and of good repute, would ever avoid him, for she feared his evil name. So it came to pass that one Michaelmas this Hugo, with five or six of his idle and wicked companions, stole down upon the farm and carried off the maiden, her father and brothers being from home, as he well knew. When they had brought her to the Hall the maiden was placed in an upper chamber, while Hugo and his friends sat down to a long carouse, as was their nightly custom. Now, the poor lass upstairs was like to have her wits turned at the singing and shouting and terrible oaths which came up to her from below, for they say that the words used by Hugo Baskerville, when he was in wine, were such as might blast the man who said them. At last in the stress of her fear she did that which might have daunted the bravest or most active man, for by the aid of the growth of ivy which covered (and still covers) the south wall she came down from under the eaves, and so homeward across the moor, there being three leagues betwixt the Hall and her father's farm.

"It chanced that some little time later Hugo left his guests to carry food and drink - with other worse things, perchance - to his captive, and so found the cage empty and the bird escaped. Then, as it would seem, he became as one that hath a devil, for, rushing down the stairs into the dining-hall, he sprang upon the great table, flagons and trenchers flying before him, and he cried aloud before all the company that he would that very night render his body and soul to the Powers of Evil if he might but overtake the wench. And while the revellers stood aghast at the fury of the man, one more wicked or, it may be, more drunken than the rest, cried out that they should put the hounds upon her. Whereat Hugo ran from the house, crying to his grooms that they should saddle his mare and unkennel the pack, and giving the hounds a kerchief of the maid's, he swung them to the line, and so off full cry in the moonlight over the moor.

"Now, for some space the revellers stood agape, unable to understand all that had been done in such haste. But anon their bemused wits awoke to the nature of the deed which was like to be done upon the moorlands. Everything was now in an uproar, some calling for their pistols, some for their horses, and some for another flask of wine. But at length some sense came back to their crazed minds, and the whole of them, thirteen in number, took horse and started in pursuit. The moon shone clear above them, and they rode swiftly abreast, taking that course which the maid must needs have taken if she were to reach her own home.

"They had gone a mile or two when they passed one of the night shepherds upon the moorlands, and they cried to him to know if he had seen the hunt. And the man, as the story goes, was so crazed with fear that he could scarce speak, but at last he said that he had indeed seen the unhappy maiden, with the hounds upon her track. 'But I have seen more than that,' said he, 'for Hugo Baskerville passed me upon his black mare, and there ran mute behind him such a hound of hell as God forbid should ever be at my heels.' So the drunken squires cursed the shepherd and rode onwards. But soon their skins turned cold, for there came a galloping across the moor, and the black mare, dabbled with white froth, went past with trailing bridle and empty saddle. Then the revellers rode close together, for a great fear was on them, but they still followed over the moor, though each, had he been alone, would have been right glad to have turned his horse's head. Riding slowly in this fashion they came at last upon the hounds. These, though known for their valour and their breed, were whimpering in a cluster at the head of a deep dip or goyal, as we call it, upon the moor, some slinking away and some, with starting hackles and staring eyes, gazing down the narrow valley before them.

"The company had come to a halt, more sober men, as you may guess, than when they started. The most of them would by no means advance, but three of them, the boldest, or it may be the most drunken, rode forward down the goyal. Now, it opened into a broad space in which stood two of those great stones, still to be seen there, which were set by certain forgotten peoples in the days of old. The moon was shining bright upon the clearing, and there in the centre lay the unhappy maid where she had fallen, dead of fear and of fatigue. But it was not the sight of her body, nor yet was it that of the body of Hugo Baskerville lying near her, which raised the hair upon the heads of these three dare-devil roysterers, but it was that, standing over Hugo, and plucking at his throat, there stood a foul thing, a great, black beast, shaped like a hound, yet larger than any hound that ever mortal eye has rested upon. And even as they looked the thing tore the throat out of Hugo Baskerville, on which, as it turned its blazing eyes and dripping jaws upon them, the three shrieked with fear and rode for dear life, still screaming, across the moor. One, it is said, died that very night of what he had seen, and the other twain were but broken men for the rest of their days.

"Such is the tale, my sons, of the coming of the hound which is said to have plagued the family so sorely ever since. If I have set it down it is because that which is clearly known hath less terror than that which is but hinted at and guessed. Nor can it be denied that many of the family have been unhappy in their deaths, which have been sudden, bloody, and mysterious. Yet may we shelter ourselves in the infinite goodness of Providence, which would not forever punish the innocent beyond that third or fourth generation which is threatened in Holy Writ. To that Providence, my sons, I hereby commend you, and I counsel you by way of caution to forbear from crossing the moor in those dark hours when the powers of evil are exalted.

"[This from Hugo Baskerville to his sons Rodger and John, with instructions that they say nothing thereof to their sister Elizabeth.]"

When Dr. Mortimer had finished reading this singular narrative he pushed his spectacles up on his forehead and stared across at Mr. Sherlock Holmes. The latter yawned and tossed the end of his cigarette into the fire.

"Well?" said he.

"Do you not find it interesting?"

"To a collector of fairy tales."

Dr. Mortimer drew a folded newspaper out of his pocket.

"Now, Mr. Holmes, we will give you something a little more recent. This is the *Devon County Chronicle* of May 14th of this year. It is a short account of the facts elicited at the death of Sir Charles Baskerville which occurred a few days before that date."

My friend leaned a little forward and his expression became intent. Our visitor readjusted his glasses and began:-

"The recent sudden death of Sir Charles Baskerville, whose name has been mentioned as the probable Liberal candidate for Mid-Devon at the next election, has cast a gloom over the county. Though Sir Charles had resided at Baskerville Hall for a comparatively short period his amiability of character and extreme generosity had won the affection and respect of all who had been brought into contact with him. In these days of *nouveaux riches* it is refreshing to find a case where the scion of an old county family which has fallen upon evil days is able to make his own fortune and to bring it back with him to restore the fallen grandeur of his line. Sir Charles, as is well known, made large sums of money in South African speculation. More wise than those who go on until the wheel turns against them, he realized his gains and returned to England with them. It is only two years since he took up his residence at Baskerville Hall, and it is common talk how large were those schemes of reconstruction and improvement which have been interrupted by his death. Being himself childless, it was his openly-expressed desire that the whole countryside should, within his own lifetime, profit by his good fortune, and many will have personal reasons for bewailing his untimely end. His generous donations to local and county charities have been frequently chronicled in these columns.

"The circumstances connected with the death of Sir Charles cannot be said to have been entirely cleared up by the inquest, but at least enough has been done to dispose of those rumours to which local superstition has given rise. There is no reason whatever to suspect foul play, or to imagine that death could be from any but natural causes. Sir Charles was a widower, and a man who may be said to have been in some ways of an eccentric habit of mind. In spite of his considerable wealth he was simple in his personal tastes, and his indoor servants at Baskerville Hall consisted of a married couple named Barrymore, the husband acting as butler and the wife as housekeeper. Their evidence, corroborated by that of several friends, tends to show that Sir Charles's health has for some time been impaired, and points especially to some affection of the heart, manifesting itself in changes of colour, breathlessness, and acute attacks of nervous depression. Dr. James Mortimer, the friend and medical attendant of the deceased, has given evidence to the same effect.

"The facts of the case are simple. Sir Charles Baskerville was in the habit every night before going to bed of walking down the famous Yew Alley of Baskerville Hall. The evidence of the Barrymores shows that this had been his custom. On the 4th of May Sir Charles had declared his intention of starting next day for London, and had ordered Barrymore to prepare his luggage. That night he went out as usual for his nocturnal walk, in the course of which he was in the habit of smoking a cigar. He never returned. At twelve o'clock Barrymore, finding the hall door still open, became alarmed, and, lighting a lantern, went in search of his master. The day had been wet, and Sir Charles's footmarks were easily traced down the Alley. Half-way down this walk there is a gate which leads out on to the moor. There were indications that Sir Charles had stood for some little time here. He then proceeded down the Alley, and it was at the far end of it that his body was discovered. One fact which has not been explained is the statement of Barrymore that his master's footprints altered their character from the time that he passed the moor-gate, and that he appeared from thence onwards to have been walking upon his toes. One Murphy, a gipsy horse-dealer, was on the moor at no great distance at the time, but he appears by his own confession to have been the worse for drink. He declares that he heard cries, but is unable to state from what direction they came. No signs of violence were to be discovered upon Sir Charles's person, and though the doctor's evidence pointed to an almost incredible facial distortion - so great that Dr. Mortimer refused at first to believe that it was indeed his friend and patient who lay before him - it was explained that that is a symptom which is not unusual in cases of dyspnœa and death from cardiac exhaustion. This explanation was borne out by the post-mortem examination, which showed long-standing organic disease, and the coroner's jury returned a verdict in accordance with the medical evidence. It is well that this is so, for it is obviously of the utmost importance that Sir Charles's heir should settle at the Hall and continue the good work which has been so sadly interrupted. Had the prosaic finding of the coroner not finally put an end to the romantic stories which have been whispered in connection with the affair it might have been difficult to find a tenant for Baskerville Hall. It is understood that the next-of-kin is Mr. Henry Baskerville, if he be still alive, the son of Sir Charles Baskerville's younger brother. The young man when last heard of was in America, and inquiries are being instituted with a view to informing him of his good fortune."

Dr. Mortimer refolded his paper and replaced it in his pocket.

"Those are the public facts, Mr. Holmes, in connection with the death of Sir Charles Baskerville."

"I must thank you," said Sherlock Holmes, "for calling my attention to a case which certainly presents some features of interest. I had observed some newspaper comment at the time, but I was exceedingly preoccupied by that little affair of the Vatican cameos, and in my anxiety to oblige the Pope I lost touch with several interesting English cases. This article, you say, contains all the public facts?"

"It does."

"Then let me have the private ones." He leaned back, put his finger-tips together, and assumed his most impassive and judicial expression.

"In doing so," said Dr. Mortimer, who had begun to show signs of some strong emotion, "I am telling that which I have not confided to anyone. My motive for withholding it from the coroner's inquiry is that a man of science shrinks from placing himself in the public position of seeming to indorse a popular superstition. I had the further motive that Baskerville Hall, as the paper says, would certainly remain untenanted if anything were done to increase its already rather grim reputation. For both these reasons I thought that I was justified in telling rather less than I knew, since no practical good could result from it, but with you there is no reason why I should not be perfectly frank.

"The moor is very sparsely inhabited, and those who live near each other are thrown very much together. For this reason I saw a good deal of Sir Charles Baskerville. With the exception of Mr. Frankland, of Lafter Hall, and Mr. Stapleton, the naturalist, there are no other men of education within many miles. Sir Charles was a retiring man, but the chance of his illness brought us together, and a community of interests in science kept us so. He had brought back much scientific information from South Africa, and many a charming evening we have spent together discussing the comparative anatomy of the Bushman and the Hottentot.

"Within the last few months it became increasingly plain to me that Sir Charles's nervous system was strained to breaking point. He had taken this legend which I have read you exceedingly to heart - so much so that, although he would walk in his own grounds, nothing would induce him to go out upon the moor at night. Incredible as it may appear to you, Mr. Holmes, he was honestly convinced that a dreadful fate overhung his family, and certainly the records which he was able to give of his ancestors were not encouraging. The idea of some ghastly presence constantly haunted him, and on more than one occasion he has asked me whether I had on my medical journeys at night ever seen any strange creature or heard the baying of a hound. The latter question he put to me several times, and always with a voice which vibrated with excitement.

"I can well remember driving up to his house in the evening, some three weeks before the fatal event. He chanced to be at his hall door. I had descended from my gig and was standing in front of him, when I saw his eyes fix themselves over my shoulder, and stare past me with an expression of the most dreadful horror. I whisked round and had just time to catch a glimpse of something which I took to be a large black calf passing at the head of the drive. So excited and alarmed was he that I was compelled to go down to the spot where the animal had been and look around for it. It was gone, however, and the incident appeared to make the worst impression upon his mind. I stayed with him all the evening, and it was on that occasion, to explain the emotion which he had shown, that he confided to my keeping that narrative which I read to you when first I came. I mention this small episode because it assumes some importance in view of the tragedy which followed, but I was convinced at the time that the matter was entirely trivial and that his excitement had no justification.

"It was at my advice that Sir Charles was about to go to London. His heart was, I knew, affected, and the constant anxiety in which he lived, however chimerical the cause of it might be, was evidently having a serious effect upon his health. I thought that a few months among the distractions of town would send him back a new man. Mr. Stapleton, a mutual friend who was much concerned at his state of health, was of the same opinion. At the last instant came this terrible catastrophe.

"On the night of Sir Charles's death Barrymore the butler, who made the discovery, sent Perkins the groom on horseback to me, and as I was sitting up late I was able to reach Baskerville Hall within an hour of the event. I checked and corroborated all the facts which were mentioned at the inquest. I followed the footsteps down the Yew Alley, I saw the spot at the moor-gate where he seemed to have waited, I remarked the change in the shape of the prints after that point, I noted that there were no other footsteps save those of Barrymore on the soft gravel, and finally I carefully examined the body, which had not been touched until my arrival. Sir Charles lay on his face, his arms out, his fingers dug into the ground, and his features convulsed with some strong emotion to such an extent that I could hardly have sworn to his identity. There was certainly no physical injury of any kind. But one false statement was made by Barrymore at the inquest. He said that there were no traces upon the ground round the body. He did not observe any. But I did - some little distance off, but fresh and clear."

"Footprints?"

"Footprints."

"A man's or a woman's?"

Dr. Mortimer looked strangely at us for an instant, and his voice sank almost to a whisper as he answered:-

"Mr. Holmes, they were the footprints of a gigantic hound!"

CHAPTER III.

THE PROBLEM.

CONFESS that at these words a shudder passed through me. There was a thrill in the doctor's voice which showed that he was himself deeply moved by that which he told us. Holmes leaned forward in his excitement and his eyes had the hard, dry glitter which shot from them when he was keenly interested.

"You saw this?"

"As clearly as I see you."

"And you said nothing?"

"What was the use?"

"How was it that no one else saw it?"

"The marks were some twenty yards from the body and no one gave them a thought. I don't suppose I should have done so had I not known this legend."

"There are many sheep-dogs on the moor?"

"No doubt, but this was no sheep-dog."

"You say it was large?"

"Enormous."

"But it had not approached the body?"

"No."

"What sort of night was it?"

"Damp and raw."

"But not actually raining?"

"No."

"What is the alley like?"

"There are two lines of old yew hedge, 12ft. high and impenetrable. The walk in the centre is about 8ft. across."

"Is there anything between the hedges and the walk?"

"Yes, there is a strip of grass about 6ft. broad on either side."

"I understand that the yew hedge is penetrated at one point by a gate?"

"Yes, the wicket-gate which leads on to the moor."

"Is there any other opening?"

"None."

"So that to reach the Yew Alley one either has to come down it from the house or else to enter it by the moor-gate?"

"There is an exit through a summer-house at the far end."

"Had Sir Charles reached this?"

"No; he lay about fifty yards from it."

"Now, tell me, Dr. Mortimer - and this is important - the marks which you saw were on the path and not on the grass?"

"No marks could show on the grass."

"Were they on the same side of the path as the moor-gate?"

"Yes; they were on the edge of the path on the same side as the moor-gate."

"You interest me exceedingly. Another point. Was the wicket-gate closed?"

"Closed and padlocked."

"How high was it?"

"About 4ft. high."

"There's our man, Watson! Come along."
Paget's drawing of Holmes and Watson in Regent Street, infamously
reversed in *The Strand Magazine*.

"Then anyone could have got over it?"

"Yes."

"And what marks did you see by the wicket-gate?"

"None in particular."

"Good Heaven! Did no one examine?"

"Yes, I examined myself."

"And found nothing?"

"It was all very confused. Sir Charles had evidently stood there for five or ten minutes."

"How do you know that?"

"Because the ash had twice dropped from his cigar."

"Excellent! This is a colleague, Watson, after our own heart. But the marks?"

"He had left his own marks all over that small patch of gravel. I could discern no others."

Sherlock Holmes struck his hand against his knee with an impatient gesture.

"If I had only been there!" he cried. "It is evidently a case of extraordinary interest, and one which presented immense opportunities to the scientific expert. That gravel page upon which I might have read so much has been long ere this smudged by the rain and defaced by the clogs of curious peasants. Oh, Dr. Mortimer, Dr. Mortimer, to think that you should not have called me in! You have indeed much to answer for."

"I could not call you in, Mr. Holmes, without disclosing these facts to the world, and I have already given my reasons for not wishing to do so. Besides, besides - "

"Why do you hesitate?"

"There is a realm in which the most acute and most experienced of detectives is helpless."

"You mean that the thing is supernatural?"

"I did not positively say so."

"No, but you evidently think it."

"Since the tragedy, Mr. Holmes, there have come to my ears several incidents which are hard to reconcile with the settled order of Nature."

"For example?"

"I find that before the terrible event occurred several people had seen a creature upon the moor which corresponds with this Baskerville demon, and which could not possibly be any animal known to science. They all agreed that it was a huge creature, luminous, ghastly, and spectral. I have cross-examined these men, one of them a hard-headed countryman, one a farrier, and one a moorland farmer, who all tell the same story of this dreadful apparition, exactly corresponding to the hell-hound of the legend. I assure you that there is a reign of terror in the district and that it is a hardy man who will cross the moor at night."

"And you, a trained man of science, believe it to be supernatural?"

"I do not know what to believe."

Holmes shrugged his shoulders.

"I have hitherto confined my investigations to this world," said he. "In a modest way I have combated evil, but to take on the Father of Evil himself would, perhaps, be too ambitious a task. Yet you must admit that the footmark is material."

"The original hound was material enough to tug a man's throat out, and yet he was diabolical as well."

"I see that you have quite gone over to the supernaturalists. But now, Dr. Mortimer, tell me this. If you hold these views, why have you come to consult me at all? You tell me in the same breath that it is useless to investigate Sir Charles's death, and that you desire me to do it."

"I did not say that I desired you to do it."

"Then, how can I assist you?"

"By advising me as to what I should do with Sir Henry Baskerville, who arrives at Waterloo Station" - Dr. Mortimer looked at his watch - "in exactly one hour and a quarter."

"He being the heir?"

"Yes. On the death of Sir Charles we inquired for this young gentleman, and found that he had been farming in Canada. From the accounts which have reached us he is an excellent fellow in every way. I speak now not as a medical man but as a trustee and executor of Sir Charles's will."

"There is no other claimant, I presume?"

"None. The only other kinsman whom we have been able to trace was Rodger Baskerville, the youngest of three brothers of whom poor Sir Charles was the elder. The second brother, who died young, is the father of this lad Henry. The third, Rodger, was the black sheep of the family. He came of the old masterful Baskerville strain and was the very image, they tell me, of the family picture of old Hugo. He made England too hot to hold him, fled to Central America, and died there in 1876 of yellow fever. Henry is the last of the Baskervilles. In one hour and five minutes I meet him at Waterloo Station. I have had a wire that he arrived at Southampton this morning. Now, Mr. Holmes, what would you advise me to do with him?"

"Why should he not go to the home of his fathers?"

"It seems natural, does it not? And yet, consider that every Baskerville who goes there meets with an evil fate. I feel sure that if Sir Charles could have spoken with me before his death he would have warned me against bringing this the last of the old race, and the heir to great wealth, to that deadly place. And yet it cannot be denied that the prosperity of the whole poor, bleak country-side depends upon his presence. All the good work which has been done by Sir Charles will crash to the ground if there is no tenant of the Hall. I fear lest I should be swayed too much by my own obvious interest in the matter, and that is why I bring the case before you and ask for your advice."

Holmes considered for a little time.

"Put into plain words, the matter is this," said he. "In your opinion there is a diabolical agency which makes Dartmoor an unsafe abode for a Baskerville - that is your opinion?"

"At least I might go the length of saying that there is some evidence that this may be so."

"Exactly. But surely, if your supernatural theory be correct, it could work the young man evil in London as easily as in Devonshire. A devil with merely local powers like a parish vestry would be too inconceivable a thing."

"You put the matter more flippantly, Mr. Holmes, than you would probably do if you were brought into personal contact with these things. Your advice, then, as I understand it, is that the young man will be as safe in Devonshire as in London. He comes in fifty minutes. What would you recommend?"

"I recommend, sir, that you take a cab, call off your spaniel who is scratching at my front door, and proceed to Waterloo to meet Sir Henry Baskerville."

"And then?"

"And then you will say nothing to him at all until I have made up my mind about the matter."

"How long will it take you to make up your mind?"

"Twenty-four hours. At ten o'clock to-morrow, Dr. Mortimer, I will be much obliged to you if you will call upon me here, and it will be of help to me in my plans for the future if you will bring Sir Henry Baskerville with you."

"I will do so, Mr. Holmes." He scribbled the appointment on his shirt cuff and hurried off in his strange, peering, absent-minded fashion. Holmes stopped him at the head of the stair.

"Only one more question, Dr. Mortimer. You say that before Sir Charles Baskerville's death several people saw this apparition upon the moor?"

"Three people did."

"Did any see it after?"

"I have not heard of any."

"Thank you. Good morning."

Holmes returned to his seat with that quiet look of inward satisfaction which meant that he had a congenial task before him.

"Going out, Watson?"

"Unless I can help you."

"No, my dear fellow, it is at the hour of action that I turn to you for aid. But this is splendid, really unique from some points of view. When you pass Bradley's would you ask him to send up a pound of the strongest shag tobacco? Thank you. It would be as well if you could make it convenient not to return before evening. Then I should be very glad to compare impressions as to this most interesting problem which has been submitted to us this morning."

I knew that seclusion and solitude were very necessary for my friend in those hours of intense mental concentration during which he weighed every particle of evidence, constructed alternative theories, balanced one against the other, and made up his mind as to which points were essential and which immaterial. I therefore spent the day at my club and did not return to Baker Street until evening. It was nearly nine o'clock when I found myself in the sitting-room once more.

My first impression as I opened the door was that a fire had broken out, for the room was so filled with smoke that the light of the lamp upon the table was blurred by it. As I entered, however, my fears were set at rest, for it was the acrid fumes of strong coarse tobacco which took me by the throat and set me coughing. Through the haze I had a vague vision of Holmes in his dressing-gown coiled up in an arm-chair with his black clay pipe between his lips. Several rolls of paper lay around him.

"Caught cold, Watson?" said he.

"No, it's this poisonous atmosphere."

"I suppose it *is* pretty thick, now that you mention it."

"Thick! It is intolerable."

"Open the window, then! You have been at your club all day, I perceive."

"My dear Holmes!"

"Am I right?"

"Certainly, but how - ?"

He laughed at my bewildered expression.

"There is a delightful freshness about you, Watson, which makes it a pleasure to exercise any small powers which I possess at your expense. A gentleman goes forth on a showery and miry day. He returns immaculate in the evening with the gloss still on his hat and his boots. He has been a fixture therefore all day. He is not a man with intimate friends. Where, then, could he have been? Is it not obvious?"

"Well, it is rather obvious."

"The world is full of obvious things which nobody by any chance ever observes. Where do you think that I have been?"

"A fixture also."

"On the contrary, I have been to Devonshire."

"In spirit?"

"Exactly. My body has remained in this arm-chair, and has, I regret to observe, consumed in my absence two large pots of coffee and an incredible amount of tobacco. After you left I sent down to Stamford's for the Ordnance map of this portion of the moor, and my spirit has hovered over it all day. I flatter myself that I could find my way about."

"A large scale map, I presume?"

"Very large." He unrolled one section and held it over his knee. "Here you have the particular district which concerns us. That is Baskerville Hall in the middle."

"With a wood round it?"

"Exactly. I fancy the Yew Alley, though not marked under that name, must stretch along this line, with the moor, as you perceive, upon the right of it. This small clump of buildings here is the hamlet of Grimpen, where our friend Dr. Mortimer has his headquarters. Within a radius of five miles there are, as you see, only a very few scattered dwellings. Here is Lafter Hall, which was mentioned in the narrative. There is a house indicated here which may be the residence of the naturalist - Stapleton, if I remember right, was his name. Here are two moorland farmhouses, High Tor and Foulmire. Then fourteen miles away the great convict prison of Princetown. Between and around these scattered points extends the desolate, lifeless moor. This, then, is the stage upon which tragedy has been played, and upon which we may help to play it again."

"It must be a wild place."

"Yes, the setting is a worthy one. If the devil did desire to have a hand in the affairs of men - "

"Then you are yourself inclining to the supernatural explanation."

"The devil's agents may be of flesh and blood, may they not? There are two questions waiting for us at the outset. The one is whether any crime has been committed at all; the second is, what is the crime and how was it committed? Of course, if Dr. Mortimer's surmise should be correct, and we are dealing with forces outside the ordinary laws of Nature, there is an end of our investigation. But we are bound to exhaust all other hypotheses before falling back upon this one. I think we'll shut that window again, if you don't mind. It is a singular thing, but I find that a concentrated atmosphere helps a concentration of thought. I have not pushed it to the length of getting into a box to think, but that is the logical outcome of my convictions. Have you turned the case over in your mind?"

"Yes, I have thought a good deal of it in the course of the day."

"What do you make of it?"

"It is very bewildering."

"It has certainly a character of its own. There are points of distinction about it. That change in the footprints, for example. What do you make of that?"

"Mortimer said that the man had walked on tiptoe down that portion of the alley."

"He only repeated what some fool had said at the inquest. Why should a man walk on tiptoe down the alley?"

"What then?"

"He was running, Watson - running desperately, running for his life, running until he burst his heart and fell dead upon his face."

"Running from what?"

"There lies our problem. There are indications that the man was crazed with fear before ever he began to run."

"How can you say that?"

"I am presuming that the cause of his fears came to him across the moor. If that were so, and it seems most probable, only a man who had lost his wits would have run *from* the house instead of towards it. If the gipsy's evidence may be taken as true, he ran with cries for help in the direction where help was least likely to be. Then, again, whom was he waiting for that night, and why was he waiting for him in the Yew Alley rather than in his own house?"

"You think that he was waiting for someone?"

"The man was elderly and infirm. We can understand his taking an evening stroll, but the ground was damp and the night inclement. Is it natural that he should stand for five or ten minutes, as Dr. Mortimer, with more practical sense than I should have given him credit for, deduced from the cigar ash?"

"But he went out every evening."

"I think it unlikely that he waited at the moor-gate every evening. On the contrary, the evidence is that he avoided the moor. That night he waited there. It was the night before he made his departure for London. The thing takes shape, Watson. It becomes coherent. Might I ask you to hand me my violin, and we will postpone all further thought upon this business until we have had the advantage of meeting Dr. Mortimer and Sir Henry Baskerville in the morning."

CHAPTER IV.

SIR HENRY BASKERVILLE.

OUR breakfast-table was cleared early, and Holmes waited in his dressing-gown for the promised interview. Our clients were punctual to their appointment, for the clock had just struck ten when Dr. Mortimer was shown up, followed by the young Baronet. The latter was a small, alert, dark-eyed man about thirty years of age, very sturdily built, with thick black eyebrows, and a strong, pugnacious face. He wore a ruddy-tinted tweed suit, and had the weather-beaten appearance of one who has spent most of his time in the open air, and yet there was something in his steady eye and the quiet assurance of his bearing which indicated the gentleman.

"This is Sir Henry Baskerville," said Dr. Mortimer.

"Why, yes," said he, "and the strange thing is, Mr. Sherlock Holmes, that if my friend here had not proposed coming round to you this morning I should have come on my own. I understand that you think out little puzzles, and I've had one this morning which wants more thinking out than I am able to give to it."

"Pray take a seat, Sir Henry. Do I understand you to say that you have yourself had some remarkable experience since you arrived in London?"

"Nothing of much importance, Mr. Holmes. Only a joke, as like as not. It was this letter, if you can call it a letter, which reached me this morning."

He laid an envelope upon the table, and we all bent over it. It was of common quality, greyish in colour. The address, "Sir Henry Baskerville, Northumberland Hotel," was printed in rough characters; the post-mark "Charing Cross," and the date of posting the preceding evening.

"Who knew that you were going to the Northumberland Hotel?" asked Holmes, glancing keenly across at our visitor.

"No one could have known. We only decided after I met Dr. Mortimer."

"But Dr. Mortimer was no doubt already stopping there?"

"No, I had been staying with a friend," said the doctor. "There was no possible indication that we intended to go to this hotel."

"Hum! Someone seems to be very deeply interested in your movements." Out of the envelope he took a half-sheet of foolscap paper folded into four. This he opened and spread flat upon the table. Across the middle of it a single sentence had been formed by the expedient of pasting printed words upon it. It ran: "as you value your life or your reason keep away from the moor." The word "moor" only was printed in ink.

"Now," said Sir Henry Baskerville, "perhaps you will tell me, Mr. Holmes, what in thunder is the meaning of that, and who it is that takes so much interest in my affairs?"

"What do you make of it, Dr. Mortimer? You must allow that there is nothing supernatural about this, at any rate?"

"No, sir, but it might very well come from someone who was convinced that the business is supernatural."

"What business?" asked Sir Henry, sharply. "It seems to me that all you gentlemen know a great deal more than I do about my own affairs."

"You shall share our knowledge before you leave this room, Sir Henry. I promise you that," said Sherlock Holmes. "We will confine ourselves for the present with your permission to this very interesting document, which must have been put together and posted yesterday evening. Have you yesterday's *Times*, Watson?"

"It is here in the corner."

"Might I trouble you for it - the inside page, please, with the leading articles?" He glanced swiftly over it, running his eyes up and down the columns. "Capital article this on Free Trade. Permit me to give you an extract from it. 'You may be cajoled into imagining that your own special trade or your own industry will be encouraged by a protective tariff, but it stands to reason that such legislation must in the long run keep away wealth from the country, diminish the value of our imports, and lower the general conditions of life in this island.' "What do you think of that, Watson?" cried Holmes, in high glee, rubbing his hands together with satisfaction. "Don't you think that is an admirable sentiment?"

Dr. Mortimer looked at Holmes with an air of professional interest, and Sir Henry Baskerville turned a pair of puzzled dark eyes upon me.

"I don't know much about the tariff and things of that kind," said he; "but it seems to me we've got a bit off the trail so far as that note is concerned."

"On the contrary, I think we are particularly hot upon the trail, Sir Henry. Watson here knows more about my methods than you do, but I fear that even he has not quite grasped the significance of this sentence."

"No, I confess that I see no connection."

"And yet, my dear Watson, there is so very close a connection that the one is extracted out of the other. 'You,' 'your,' 'your,' 'life,' 'reason,' 'value,' 'keep away,' 'from the.' Don't you see now whence these words have been taken?"

"By thunder, you're right! Well, if that isn't smart!" cried Sir Henry.

"If any possible doubt remained it is settled by the fact that 'keep away' and 'from the' are cut out in one piece."

"Well, now - so it is!"

"Really, Mr. Holmes, this exceeds anything which I could have imagined," said Dr. Mortimer, gazing at my friend in amazement. "I could understand anyone saying that the words were from a newspaper; but that you should name which, and add that it came from the leading article, is really one of the most remarkable things which I have ever known. How did you do it?"

"I presume, Doctor, that you could tell the skull of a negro from that of an Esquimaux?"

"Most certainly."

"But how?"

"Because that is my special hobby. The differences are obvious. The supra-orbital crest, the facial angle, the maxillary curve, the -"

"But this is my special hobby, and the differences are equally obvious. There is as much difference to my eyes between the leaded bourgeois type of a *Times* article and the slovenly print of an evening halfpenny paper as there could be between your negro and your Esquimaux. The detection of types is one of the most elementary branches of knowledge to the special expert in crime, though I confess that once when I was very young I confused the *Leeds Mercury* with the *Western Morning News*. But a *Times* leader is entirely distinctive, and these words could have been taken from nothing else. As it was done yesterday the strong probability was that we should find the words in yesterday's issue."

"So far as I can follow you, then, Mr. Holmes," said Sir Henry Baskerville, "someone cut out this message with a scissors -"

"Nail-scissors," said Holmes. "You can see that it was a very short-bladed scissors, since the cutter had to take two snips over 'keep away.' "

"That is so. Someone, then, cut out the message with a pair of short-bladed scissors, pasted it with paste - "

"Gum," said Holmes.

"With gum on to the paper. But I want to know why the word 'moor' should have been written?"

"Because he could not find it in print. The other words were all simple and might be found in any issue, but 'moor' would be less common."

"Why, of course, that would explain it. Have you read anything else in this message, Mr. Holmes?"

"There are one or two indications, and yet the utmost pains have been taken to remove all clues. The address, you observe, is printed in rough characters. But the *Times* is a paper which is seldom found in any hands but those of the highly educated. We may take it, therefore, that the letter was composed by an educated man who wished to pose as an uneducated one, and his effort to conceal his own writing suggests that that writing might be known, or come to be known, by you. Again, you will observe that the words are not gummed on in an accurate line, but that some are much higher than others. 'Life,' for example, is quite out of its proper place. That may point to carelessness or it may point to agitation and hurry upon the part of the cutter. On the whole I incline to the latter view, since the matter was evidently important, and it is unlikely that the composer of such a letter would be careless. If he were in a hurry it opens up the interesting question why he should be in a hurry, since any letter posted up to early morning would reach Sir Henry before he would leave his hotel. Did the composer fear an interruption - and from whom?"

"We are coming now rather into the region of guess work," said Dr. Mortimer.

"Say, rather, into the region where we balance probabilities and choose the most likely. It is the scientific use of the imagination, but we have always some material basis on which to start our speculations. Now, you would call it a guess, no doubt, but I am almost certain that this address has been written in an hotel."

"How in the world can you say that?"

"If you examine it carefully you will see that both the pen and the ink have given the writer trouble. The pen has spluttered twice in a single word, and has run dry three times in a short address, showing that there was very little ink in the bottle. Now, a private pen or ink-bottle is seldom allowed to be in such a state, and the combination of the two must be quite rare. But you know the hotel ink and the hotel pen, where it is rare to get anything else. Yes, I have very little hesitation in saying that could we examine the waste-paper baskets of the hotels round Charing Cross until we found the remains of the mutilated *Times* leader we could lay our hands straight upon the person who sent this singular message. Halloa! Halloa! What's this?"

He was carefully examining the foolscap, upon which the words were pasted, holding it only an inch or two from his eyes.

"Well?"

"Nothing," said he, throwing it down. "It is a blank half-sheet of paper, without even a watermark upon it. I think we have drawn as much as we can from this curious letter; and now, Sir Henry, has anything else of interest happened to you since you have been in London?"

"Why, no, Mr. Holmes. I think not."

"You have not observed anyone follow or watch you?"

"I seem to have walked right into the thick of a dime novel," said our visitor. "Why in thunder should anyone follow or watch me?"

"We are coming to that. You have nothing else to report to us before we go into this matter?"

"Well, it depends upon what you think worth reporting."

"I think anything out of the ordinary routine of life well worth reporting."

Sir Henry smiled.

"I don't know much of British life yet, for I have spent nearly all my time in the States and in Canada. But I hope that to lose one of your boots is not part of the ordinary routine of life over here."

"You have lost one of your boots?"

"My dear sir," cried Dr. Mortimer, "it is only mislaid. You will find it when you return to the hotel. What is the use of troubling Mr. Holmes with trifles of this kind?"

"Well, he asked me for anything outside the ordinary routine."

"Exactly," said Holmes, "however foolish the incident may seem. You have lost one of your boots, you say?"

"Well, mislaid it, anyhow. I put them both outside my door last night, and there was only one in the morning. I could get no sense out of the chap who cleans them. The worst of it is that I only bought the pair last night in the Strand, and I have never had them on."

"If you have never worn them, why did you put them out to be cleaned?"

"They were tan boots, and had never been varnished. That was why I put them out."

"Then I understand that on your arrival in London yesterday you went out at once and bought a pair of boots?"

"I did a good deal of shopping. Dr. Mortimer here went round with me. You see, if I am to be squire down there I must dress the part, and it may be that I have got a little careless in my ways out West. Among other things I bought these brown boots - gave six dollars for them - and had one stolen before ever I had them on my feet."

"It seems a singularly useless thing to steal," said Sherlock Holmes. "I confess that I share Dr. Mortimer's belief that it will not be long before the missing boot is found."

"And, now, gentlemen," said the Baronet, with decision, "it seems to me that I have spoken quite enough about the little that I know. It is time that you kept your promise and gave me a full account of what we are all driving at."

"Your request is a very reasonable one," Holmes answered. "Dr. Mortimer, I think you could not do better than to tell your story as you told it to us."

Thus encouraged, our scientific friend drew his papers from his pocket, and presented the whole case as he had done upon the morning before. Sir Henry Baskerville listened with the deepest attention, and with an occasional exclamation of surprise.

"Well, I seem to have come into an inheritance with a vengeance," said he, when the long narrative was finished. "Of course, I've heard of the hound ever since I was in the nursery. It's the pet story of the family, though I never thought of taking it seriously before. But as to my uncle's death - well, it all seems boiling up in my head, and I can't get it clear yet. You don't seem quite to have made up your mind whether it's a case for a policeman or a clergyman."

"Precisely."

"And now there's this affair of the letter to me at the hotel. I suppose that fits into its place."

"It seems to show that someone knows more than we do about what goes on upon the moor," said Dr. Mortimer.

"And also," said Holmes, "that someone is not ill-disposed towards you, since they warn you of danger."

"Or it may be that they wish, for their own purposes, to scare me away."

"Well, of course, that is possible also. I am very much indebted to you, Dr. Mortimer, for introducing me to a problem which presents several interesting alternatives. But the practical point which we now have to decide, Sir Henry, is whether it is or is not advisable for you to go to Baskerville Hall."

"Why should I not go?"

"There seems to be danger."

"Do you mean danger from this family fiend or do you mean danger from human beings?"

"Well, that is what we have to find out."

"Which ever it is, my answer is fixed. There is no devil in hell, Mr. Holmes, and there is no man upon earth who can prevent me from going to the home of my own people, and you may take that to be my final answer." His dark brows knitted and his face flushed to a dusky red as he spoke. It was evident that the fiery temper of the Baskervilles was not extinct in this their last representative. "Meanwhile," said he, "I have hardly had time to think over all that you have told me. It's a big thing for a man to have to understand and to decide at one sitting. I should like to have a quiet hour by myself to make up my mind. Now, look here, Mr. Holmes, it's half-past eleven now and I am going back right away to my hotel. Suppose you and your friend, Dr. Watson, come round and lunch with us at two? I'll be able to tell you more clearly then how this thing strikes me."

"Is that convenient to you, Watson?"

"Perfectly."

"Then you may expect us. Shall I have a cab called?"

"I'd prefer to walk, for this affair has flurried me rather."

"I'll join you in a walk, with pleasure," said his companion.

"Then we meet again at two o'clock. Au revoir, and good morning!"

We heard the steps of our visitors descend the stair and the bang of the front door. In an instant Holmes had changed from the languid dreamer to the man of action.

"Your hat and boots, Watson, quick! Not a moment to lose!" He rushed into his room in his dressing-gown and was back again in a few seconds in a frock-coat. We hurried together down the stairs and into the street. Dr. Mortimer and Baskerville were still visible about two hundred yards ahead of us in the direction of Oxford Street.

"Shall I run on and stop them?"

"Not for the world, my dear Watson. I am perfectly satisfied with your company if you will tolerate mine. Our friends are wise, for it is certainly a very fine morning for a walk."

He quickened his pace until we had decreased the distance which divided us by about half. Then, still keeping a hundred yards behind, we followed into Oxford Street and so down Regent Street. Once our friends stopped and stared into a shop window, upon which Holmes did the same. An instant afterwards he gave a little cry of satisfaction, and, following the direction of his eager eyes, I saw that a hansom cab with a man inside which had halted on the other side of the street was now walking slowly onwards again.

"There's our man, Watson! Come along! We'll have a good look at him, if we can do no more."

At that instant I was aware of a bushy black beard and a pair of piercing eyes turned upon us through the side window of the cab. Instantly the trapdoor at the top flew up, something was screamed to the driver, and the cab flew madly off down Regent Street. Holmes looked eagerly round for another, but no empty one was in sight. Then he dashed in wild pursuit amid the stream of the traffic, but the start was too great, and already the cab was out of sight.

"There now!" said Holmes, bitterly, as he emerged panting and white with vexation from the tide of vehicles. "Was ever such bad luck and such bad management, too? Watson, Watson, if you are an honest man you will record this also and set it against my successes!"

"Who was the man?"

"I have not an idea."

"A spy?"

"Well, it was evident from what we have heard that Baskerville has been very closely shadowed by someone since he has been in town. How else could it be known so quickly that it was the Northumberland Hotel which he had chosen? If they had followed him the first day I argued that they would follow him also the second. You may have observed that I twice strolled over to the window while Dr. Mortimer was reading his legend."

"Yes, I remember."

"I was looking out for loiterers in the street, but I saw none. We are dealing with a clever man, Watson. This matter cuts very deep, and though I have not finally made up my mind whether it is a benevolent or a malevolent agency which is in touch with us, I am conscious always of power and design. When our friends left I at once followed them in the hopes of marking down their invisible attendant. So wily was he that he had not trusted himself upon foot, but he had availed himself of a cab, so that he could loiter behind or dash past them and so escape their notice. His method had the additional advantage that if they were to take a cab he was all ready to follow them. It has, however, one obvious disadvantage."

"It puts him in the power of the cabman."

"Exactly."

"What a pity we did not get the number!"

"My dear Watson, clumsy as I have been, you surely do not seriously imagine that I neglected to get the number? 2704 is our man. But that is no use to us for the moment."

"I fail to see how you could have done more."

"On observing the cab I should have instantly turned and walked in the other direction. I should then at my leisure have hired a second cab and followed the first at a respectful distance, or, better still, have driven to the Northumberland Hotel and waited there. When our unknown had followed Baskerville home we should have had the opportunity of playing his own game upon himself, and seeing where he made for. As it is, by an indiscreet eagerness, which was taken advantage of with extraordinary quickness and energy by our opponent, we have betrayed ourselves and lost our man."

We had been sauntering slowly down Regent Street during this conversation, and Dr. Mortimer, with his companion, had long vanished in front of us.

"There is no object in our following them," said Holmes. "The shadow has departed and will not return. We must see what further cards we have in our hands, and play them with decision. Could you swear to that man's face within the cab."

"I could swear only to the beard."

"And so could I - from which I gather that in all probability it was a false one. A clever man upon so delicate an errand has no use for a beard save to conceal his features. Come in here, Watson!"

He turned into one of the district messenger offices, where he was warmly greeted by the manager.

"Ah, Wilson, I see you have not forgotten the little case in which I had the good fortune to help you?"

"No, sir, indeed I have not. You saved my good name, and perhaps my life."

"My dear fellow, you exaggerate. I have some recollection, Wilson, that you had among your boys a lad named Cartwright, who showed some ability during the investigation."

"Yes, sir, he is still with us."

"Could you ring him up? - thank you! And I should be glad to have change of this five-pound note."

A lad of fourteen, with a bright, keen face, had obeyed the summons of the manager. He stood now gazing with great reverence at the famous detective.

"Let me have the Hotel Directory," said Holmes. "Thank you! Now, Cartwright, there are the names of twenty-three hotels here, all in the immediate neighbourhood of Charing Cross. Do you see?"

"Yes, sir."

"You will visit each of these in turn."

"Yes, sir."

"You will begin in each case by giving the outside porter one shilling. Here are twenty-three shillings."

"Yes, sir."

"You will tell him that you want to see the waste paper of yesterday. You will say that an important telegram has miscarried and that you are looking for it. You understand?"

"Yes, sir."

"But what you are really looking for is the centre page of the *Times* with some holes cut in it with scissors. Here is a copy of the *Times*. It is this page. You could easily recognise it, could you not?"

"Yes, sir."

"In each case the outside porter will send for the hall porter, to whom also you will give a shilling. Here are twenty-three shillings. You will then learn in possibly twenty cases out of the twenty-three that the waste of the day before has been burned or removed. In the three other cases you will be shown a heap of paper and you will look for this page of the *Times* among it. The odds are enormously against your finding it. There are ten shillings over in case of emergencies. Let me have a report by wire at Baker Street before evening. And now, Watson, it only remains for us to find out by wire the identity of the cabman, No. 2704, and then we will drop into one of the Bond Street picture galleries and fill in the time until we are due at the hotel."

CHAPTER V.

THREE BROKEN THREADS.

HERLOCK HOLMES had, in a very remarkable degree, the power of detaching his mind at will. For two hours the strange business in which we had been involved appeared to be forgotten, and he was entirely absorbed in the pictures of the modern Belgian masters. He would talk of nothing but art, of which he had the crudest ideas, from our leaving the gallery until we found ourselves at the Northumberland Hotel.

"Sir Henry Baskerville is upstairs expecting you," said the clerk. "He asked me to show you up at once when you came."

"Have you any objection to my looking at your register?" said Holmes.

"Not in the least."

The book showed that two names had been added after that of Baskerville. One was Theophilus Johnson and family, of Newcastle; the other Mrs. Oldmore and maid, of High Lodge, Alton.

"Surely that must be the same Johnson whom I used to know," said Holmes to the porter. "A lawyer, is he not, grey-headed, and walks with a limp?"

"No, sir, this is Mr. Johnson the coal-owner, a very active gentleman, not older than yourself."

"Surely you are mistaken about his trade?"

"No, sir; he has used this hotel for many years, and he is very well known to us."

"Ah, that settles it. Mrs. Oldmore, too; I seem to remember the name. Excuse my curiosity, but often in calling upon one friend one finds another."

"She is an invalid lady, sir. Her husband was once Mayor of Gloucester. She always comes to us when she is in town."

"Thank you; I am afraid I cannot claim her acquaintance. We have established a most important fact by these questions, Watson," he continued, in a low voice, as we went upstairs together. "We know now that the people who are so interested in our friend have not settled down in his own hotel. That means that while they are, as we have seen, very anxious to watch him, they are equally anxious that he should not see them. Now, this is a most suggestive fact."

"What does it suggest?"

"It suggests - halloa, my dear fellow, what on earth is the matter?"

As we came round the top of the stairs we had run up against Sir Henry Baskerville himself. His face was flushed with anger, and he held an old and dusty boot in one of his hands. So furious was he that he was hardly articulate, and when he did speak it was in a much broader and more Western dialect than any which we had heard from him in the morning.

"Seems to me they are playing me for a sucker in this hotel," he cried. "They'll find they've started in to monkey with the wrong man unless they are careful. By thunder, if that chap can't find my missing boot there will be trouble. I can take a joke with the best, Mr. Holmes, but they've got a bit over the mark this time."

"Still looking for your boot?"

"Yes, sir, and mean to find it."

"But, surely, you said that it was a new brown boot?"

"So it was, sir. And now it's an old black one."

"What! you don't mean to say - ?"

"That's just what I do mean to say. I only had three pairs in the world - the new brown, the old black, and the patent leathers, which I am wearing. Last night they took one of my brown

The driver pointed with his whip – "Baskerville Hall," said he.
The road to 'Baskerville Hall' clearly runs along a ridge on the high Moor.

ones, and to-day they have sneaked one of the black. Well, have you got it? Speak out, man, and don't stand staring!"

An agitated German waiter had appeared upon the scene.

"No, sir; I have made inquiry all over the hotel, but I can hear no word of it."

"Well, either that boot comes back before sundown or I'll see the manager and tell him that I go right straight out of this hotel."

"It shall be found, sir - I promise you that if you will have a little patience it will be found."

"Mind it is, for it's the last thing of mine that I'll lose in this den of thieves. Well, well, Mr. Holmes, you'll excuse my troubling you about such a trifle - "

"I think it's well worth troubling about."

"Why, you look very serious over it."

"How do you explain it?"

"I just don't attempt to explain it. It seems the very maddest, queerest thing that ever happened to me."

"The queerest, perhaps," said Holmes, thoughtfully.

"What do you make of it yourself?"

"Well, I don't profess to understand it yet. This case of yours is very complex, Sir Henry. When taken in conjunction with your uncle's death I am not sure that of all the five hundred cases of capital importance which I have handled there is one which cuts so deep. But we hold several threads in our hands, and the odds are that one or other of them guides us to the truth. We may waste time in following the wrong one, but sooner or later we must come upon the right."

We had a pleasant luncheon in which little was said of the business which had brought us together. It was in the private sitting-room to which we afterwards repaired that Holmes asked Baskerville what were his intentions.

"To go to Baskerville Hall."

"And when?"

"At the end of the week."

"On the whole," said Holmes, "I think that your decision is a wise one. I have ample evidence that you are being dogged in London, and amid the millions of this great city it is difficult to discover who these people are or what their object can be. If their intentions are evil they might do you a mischief, and we should be powerless to prevent it. You did not know, Dr. Mortimer, that you were followed this morning from my house?"

Dr. Mortimer started violently.

"Followed! By whom?"

"That, unfortunately, is what I cannot tell you. Have you among your neighbours or acquaintances on Dartmoor any man with a black, full beard?"

"No - or, let me see - why, yes. Barrymore, Sir Charles's butler, is a man with a full, black beard."

"Ha! Where is Barrymore?"

"He is in charge of the Hall."

"We had best ascertain if he is really there, or if by any possibility he might be in London."

"How can you do that?"

"Give me a telegraph form. 'Is all ready for Sir Henry?' That will do. Address to Mr. Barrymore, Baskerville Hall. Which is the nearest telegraph-office? Grimpen. Very good, we will send a second wire to the postmaster, Grimpen: 'Telegram to Mr. Barrymore, to be delivered into his own hand. If absent, please return wire to Sir Henry Baskerville, Northumberland Hotel.' That should let us know before evening whether Barrymore is at his post in Devonshire or not."

"That's so," said Baskerville. "By the way, Dr. Mortimer, who is this Barrymore, anyhow?"

"He is the son of the old caretaker, who is dead. They have looked after the Hall for four generations now. So far as I know, he and his wife are as respectable a couple as any in the county."

"At the same time," said Baskerville, "it's clear enough that so long as there are none of the family at the Hall these people have a mighty fine home and nothing to do."

"That is true."

"Did Barrymore profit at all by Sir Charles's will?" asked Holmes.

"He and his wife had five hundred pounds each."

"Ha! Did they know that they would receive this?"

"Yes; Sir Charles was very fond of talking about the provisions of his will."

"That is very interesting."

"I hope," said Dr. Mortimer, "that you do not look with suspicious eyes upon everyone who received a legacy from Sir Charles, for I also had a thousand pounds left to me."

"Indeed! And anyone else?"

"There were many insignificant sums to individuals and a large number of public charities. The residue all went to Sir Henry."

"And how much was the residue?"

"Seven hundred and forty thousand pounds."

Holmes raised his eyebrows in surprise. "I had no idea that so gigantic a sum was involved," said he.

"Sir Charles had the reputation of being rich, but we did not know how very rich he was until we came to examine his securities. The total value of the estate was close on to a million."

"Dear me! It is a stake for which a man might well play a desperate game. And one more question, Dr. Mortimer. Supposing that anything happened to our young friend here - you will forgive the unpleasant hypothesis! - who would inherit the estate?"

"Since Rodger Baskerville, Sir Charles's younger brother, died unmarried, the estate would descend to the Desmonds, who are distant cousins. James Desmond is an elderly clergyman in Westmorland."

"Thank you. These details are all of great interest. Have you met Mr. James Desmond?"

"Yes; he once came down to visit Sir Charles. He is a man of venerable appearance and of saintly life. I remember that he refused to accept any settlement from Sir Charles, though he pressed it upon him."

"And this man of simple tastes would be the heir to Sir Charles's thousands."

"He would be the heir to the estate, because that is entailed. He would also be the heir to the money unless it were willed otherwise by the present owner, who can, of course, do what he likes with it."

"And have you made your will, Sir Henry?"

"No, Mr. Holmes, I have not. I've had no time, for it was only yesterday that I learned how matters stood. But in any case I feel that the money should go with the title and estate. That was my poor uncle's idea. How is the owner going to restore the glories of the Baskervilles if he has not money enough to keep up the property? House, land, and dollars must go together."

"Quite so. Well, Sir Henry, I am of one mind with you as to the advisability of your going down to Devonshire without delay. There is only one provision which I must make. You certainly must not go alone."

"Dr. Mortimer returns with me."

"But Dr. Mortimer has his practice to attend to, and his house is miles away from yours. With all the good will in the world, he may be unable to help you. No, Sir Henry, you must take with you someone, a trusty man, who will be always by your side."

"Is it possible that you could come yourself, Mr. Holmes?"

"If matters came to a crisis I should endeavour to be present in person; but you can understand that, with my extensive consulting practice and with the constant appeals which reach me from many quarters, it is impossible for me to be absent from London for an indefinite time. At the present instant one of the most revered names in England is being besmirched by a blackmailer, and only I can stop a disastrous scandal. You will see how impossible it is for me to go to Dartmoor."

"Whom would you recommend, then?"

Holmes laid his hand upon my arm.

"If my friend would undertake it there is no man who is better worth having at your side when you are in a tight place. No one can say so more confidently than I."

The proposition took me completely by surprise, but before I had time to answer Baskerville seized me by the hand and wrung it heartily.

"Well, now, that is real kind of you, Dr. Watson," said he. "You see how it is with me, and you know just as much about the matter as I do. If you will come down to Baskerville Hall and see me through I'll never forget it."

The promise of adventure had always a fascination for me, and I was complimented by the words of Holmes and by the eagerness with which the Baronet hailed me as a companion.

"I will come, with pleasure," said I. "I do not know how I could employ my time better."

"And you will report very carefully to me," said Holmes. "When a crisis comes, as it will do, I will direct how you shall act. I suppose that by Saturday all might be ready?"

"Would that suit Dr. Watson?"

"Perfectly."

"Then on Saturday, unless you hear to the contrary, we shall meet at the 10.30 train from Paddington."

We had risen to depart when Baskerville gave a cry of triumph, and diving into one of the corners of the room he drew a brown boot from under a cabinet.

"My missing boot!" he cried.

"May all our difficulties vanish as easily!" said Sherlock Holmes.

"But it is a very singular thing," Dr. Mortimer remarked. "I searched this room carefully before lunch."

"And so did I," said Baskerville. "Every inch of it."

"There was certainly no boot in it then."

"In that case the waiter must have placed it there while we were lunching."

The German was sent for, but professed to know nothing of the matter, nor could any inquiry clear it up. Another item had been added to that constant and apparently purposeless series of small mysteries which had succeeded each other so rapidly. Setting aside the whole grim story of Sir Charles's death, we had a line of inexplicable incidents all within the limits of two days, which included the receipt of the printed letter, the black-bearded spy in the hansom, the loss of the new brown boot, the loss of the old black boot, and now the return of the new brown boot. Holmes sat in silence in the cab as we drove back to Baker Street, and I knew from his drawn brows and keen face that his mind, like my own, was busy in endeavouring to frame some scheme into which all these strange and apparently disconnected episodes could be fitted. All afternoon and late into the evening he sat lost in tobacco and thought.

Just before dinner two telegrams were handed in. The first ran:-

"Have just heard that Barrymore is at the Hall. - BASKERVILLE." The second:-

"Visited twenty-three hotels as directed, but sorry to report unable to trace cut sheet of *Times*. - CARTWRIGHT."

"There go two of my threads, Watson. There is nothing more stimulating than a case where everything goes against you. We must cast round for another scent."

"We have still the cabman who drove the spy."

"Exactly. I have wired to get his name and address from the Official Registry. I should not be surprised if this were an answer to my question."

The ring at the bell proved to be something even more satisfactory than an answer, however, for the door opened and a rough-looking fellow entered who was evidently the man himself.

"I got a message from the head office that a gent at this address had been inquiring for 2,704," said he. "I've driven my cab this seven years and never a word of complaint. I came here straight from the Yard to ask you to your face what you had against me."

"I have nothing in the world against you, my good man," said Holmes. "On the contrary, I have half a sovereign for you if you will give me a clear answer to my questions."

"Well, I've had a good day and no mistake," said the cabman with a grin. "What was it you wanted to ask, sir?"

"First of all your name and address, in case I want you again."

"John Clayton, 3, Turpey Street, the Borough. My cab is out of Shipley's Yard, near Waterloo Station."

Sherlock Holmes made a note of it.

"Now, Clayton, tell me all about the fare who came and watched this house at ten o'clock this morning and afterwards followed the two gentlemen down Regent Street."

The man looked surprised and a little embarrassed. "Why, there's no good my telling you things, for you seem to know as much as I do already," said he. "The truth is that the gentleman told me that he was a detective and that I was to say nothing about him to anyone."

"My good fellow, this is a very serious business, and you may find yourself in a pretty bad position if you try to hide anything from me. You say that your fare told you that he was a detective?"

"Yes, he did."

"When did he say this?"

"When he left me."

"Did he say anything more?"

"He mentioned his name."

Holmes cast a swift glance of triumph at me. "Oh, he mentioned his name, did he? That was imprudent. What was the name that he mentioned?"

"His name," said the cabman, "was Mr. Sherlock Holmes."

Never have I seen my friend more completely taken aback than by the cabman's reply. For an instant he sat in silent amazement. Then he burst into a hearty laugh.

"A touch, Watson - an undeniable touch!" said he. "I feel a foil as quick and supple as my own. He got home upon me very prettily that time. So his name was Sherlock Holmes, was it?"

"Yes, sir, that was the gentleman's name."

"Excellent! Tell me where you picked him up and all that occurred."

"He hailed me at half-past nine in Trafalgar Square. He said that he was a detective, and he offered me two guineas if I would do exactly what he wanted all day and ask no questions. I was glad enough to agree. First we drove down to the Northumberland Hotel and waited there until two gentlemen came out and took a cab from the rank. We followed their cab until it pulled up somewhere near here."

"This very door," said Holmes.

"Well, I couldn't be sure of that, but I dare say my fare knew all about it. We pulled up halfway down the street and waited an hour and a half. Then the two gentlemen passed us, walking, and we followed down Baker Street and along - "

"I know," said Holmes.

"Until we got three-quarters down Regent Street. Then my gentleman threw up the trap, and he cried that I should drive right away to Waterloo Station as hard as I could go. I whipped up the mare and we were there under the ten minutes. Then he paid up his two guineas, like a good one, and away he went into the station. Only just as he was leaving he turned round and said: 'It might interest you to know that you have been driving Mr. Sherlock Holmes.' That's how I come to know the name."

"I see. And you saw no more of him?"

"Not after he went into the station."

"And how would you describe Mr. Sherlock Holmes?"

The cabman scratched his head. "Well, he wasn't altogether such an easy gentleman to describe. I'd put him at forty years of age, and he was of a middle height, two or three inches shorter than you, sir. He was dressed like a toff, and he had a black beard, cut square at the end, and a pale face. I don't know as I could say more than that."

"Colour of his eyes?"

"No, I can't say that."

"Nothing more that you can remember?"

"No, sir; nothing."

"Well, then, here is your half-sovereign. There's another one waiting for you if you can bring any more information. Good-night!"

"Good-night, sir, and thank you!"

John Clayton departed chuckling, and Holmes turned to me with a shrug of the shoulders and a rueful smile.

"Snap goes our third thread, and we end where we began," said he. "The cunning rascal! He knew our number, knew that Sir Henry Baskerville had consulted me, spotted who I was in Regent Street, conjectured that I had got the number of the cab and would lay my hands on the driver, and so sent back this audacious message. I tell you, Watson, this time we have got a foeman who is worthy of our steel. I've been checkmated in London. I can only wish you better luck in Devonshire. But I'm not easy in my mind about it."

"About what?"

"About sending you. It's an ugly business, Watson, an ugly, dangerous business, and the more I see of it the less I like it. Yes, my dear fellow, you may laugh, but I give you my word that I shall be very glad to have you back safe and sound in Baker Street once more."

CHAPTER VI.

BASKERVILLE HALL.

SIR HENRY BASKERVILLE and Dr. Mortimer were ready upon the appointed day, and we started as arranged for Devonshire. Mr. Sherlock Holmes drove with me to the station and gave me his last parting injunctions and advice.

"I will not bias your mind by suggesting theories or suspicions, Watson," said he; "I wish you simply to report facts in the fullest possible manner to me, and you can leave me to do the theorizing."

"What sort of facts?" I asked.

"Anything which may seem to have a bearing however indirect upon the case, and especially the relations between young Baskerville and his neighbours, or any fresh particulars concerning the death of Sir Charles. I have made some inquiries myself in the last few days, but the results have, I fear, been negative. One thing only appears to be certain, and that is that Mr. James Desmond, who is the next heir, is an elderly gentleman of a very amiable disposition, so that this persecution does not arise from him. I really think that we may eliminate him entirely from our calculations. There remain the people who will actually surround Sir Henry Baskerville upon the moor."

"Would it not be well in the first place to get rid of this Barrymore couple?"

"By no means. You could not make a greater mistake. If they are innocent it would be a cruel injustice, and if they are guilty we should be giving up all chance of bringing it home to them. No, no, we will preserve them upon our list of suspects. Then there is a groom at the Hall, if I remember right. There are two moorland farmers. There is our friend Dr. Mortimer, whom I believe to be entirely honest, and there is his wife, of whom we know nothing. There is this naturalist Stapleton, and there is his sister, who is said to be a young lady of attractions. There is Mr. Frankland, of Lafter Hall, who is also an unknown factor, and there are one or two other neighbours. These are the folk who must be your very special study."

"I will do my best."

"You have arms, I suppose?"

"Yes, I thought it as well to take them."

"Most certainly. Keep your revolver near you night and day, and never relax your precautions."

Our friends had already secured a first-class carriage, and were waiting for us upon the platform.

"No, we have no news of any kind," said Dr. Mortimer, in answer to my friend's questions. "I can swear to one thing, and that is that we have not been shadowed during the last two days. We have never gone out without keeping a sharp watch, and no one could have escaped our notice."

"You have always kept together, I presume?"

"Except yesterday afternoon. I usually give up one day to pure amusement when I come to town, so I spent it at the Museum of the College of Surgeons."

"And I went to look at the folk in the park," said Baskerville. "But we had no trouble of any kind."

"It was imprudent, all the same," said Holmes, shaking his head and looking very grave. "I beg, Sir Henry, that you will not go about alone. Some great misfortune will befall you if you do. Did you get your other boot?"

"No, sir, it is gone forever."

"Indeed. That is very interesting. Well, good-bye," he added, as the train began to glide down the platform. "Bear in mind, Sir Henry, one of the phrases in that queer old legend which Dr. Mortimer has read to us, and avoid the moor in those hours of darkness when the powers of evil are exalted."

I looked back at the platform when we had left it far behind, and saw the tall, austere figure of Holmes standing motionless and gazing after us.

The journey was a swift and pleasant one, and I spent it in making the more intimate acquaintance of my two companions and in playing with Dr. Mortimer's spaniel. In a very few hours the brown earth had become ruddy, the brick had changed to granite, and red cows grazed in well-hedged fields where the lush grasses and more luxuriant vegetation spoke of a richer, if a damper, climate. Young Baskerville stared eagerly out of the window, and cried aloud with delight as he recognised the familiar features of the Devon scenery.

"I've been over a good part of the world since I left it, Dr. Watson," said he; "but I have never seen a place to compare with it."

"I never saw a Devonshire man who did not swear by his county," I remarked.

"It depends upon the breed of men quite as much as on the county," said Dr. Mortimer. "A glance at our friend here reveals the rounded head of the Celt, which carries inside it the Celtic enthusiasm and power of attachment. Poor Sir Charles's head was of a very rare type, half Gaelic, half Ivernian in its characteristics. But you were very young when you last saw Baskerville Hall, were you not?"

"I was a boy in my teens at the time of my father's death, and had never seen the Hall, for he lived in a little cottage on the south coast. Thence I went straight to a friend in America. I tell you it is all as new to me as it is to Dr. Watson, and I'm as keen as possible to see the moor."

"Are you? Then your wish is easily granted, for there is your first sight of the moor," said Dr. Mortimer, pointing out of the carriage window.

Over the green squares of the fields and the low curve of a wood there rose in the distance a grey, melancholy hill, with a strange jagged summit, dim and vague in the distance, like some fantastic landscape in a dream. Baskerville sat for a long time, his eyes fixed upon it, and I read upon his eager face how much it meant to him, this first sight of that strange spot where the men of his blood had held sway so long and left their mark so deep. There he sat, with his tweed suit and his American accent, in the corner of a prosaic railway-carriage, and yet as I looked at his dark and expressive face I felt more than ever how true a descendant he was of that long line of high-blooded, fiery, and masterful men. There were pride, valour, and strength in his thick brows, his sensitive nostrils, and his large hazel eyes. If on that forbidding moor a difficult and dangerous quest should lie before us, this was at least a comrade for whom one might venture to take a risk with the certainty that he would bravely share it.

The train pulled up at a small wayside station and we all descended. Outside, beyond the low, white fence, a wagonette with a pair of cobs was waiting. Our coming was evidently a great event, for station-master and porters clustered round us to carry out our luggage. It was a sweet, simple country spot, but I was surprised to observe that by the gate there stood two soldierly men in dark uniforms, who leaned upon their short rifles and glanced keenly at us as we passed. The coachman, a hard-faced, gnarled little fellow, saluted Sir Henry Baskerville, and in a few minutes we were flying swiftly down the broad, white road. Rolling pasture lands curved upwards on either side of us, and old gabled houses peeped out from amid the thick green foliage, but behind the peaceful and sunlit country-side there rose ever, dark against the evening sky, the long, gloomy curve of the moor, broken by the jagged and sinister hills.

The wagonette swung round into a side road, and we curved upwards through deep lanes worn by centuries of wheels, high banks on either side, heavy with dripping moss and fleshy hart's-tongue ferns. Bronzing bracken and mottled bramble gleamed in the light of the sinking sun. Still steadily rising, we passed over a narrow granite bridge, and skirted a noisy stream which gushed swiftly down, foaming and roaring amid the grey boulders. Both road and stream wound up through a valley dense with scrub oak and fir. At every turning Baskerville gave an exclamation of delight, looking eagerly about him and asking countless questions. To his eyes all seemed beautiful, but to me a tinge of melancholy lay upon the country-side, which bore so clearly the mark of the waning year. Yellow leaves carpeted the lanes and fluttered down upon us as we passed. The rattle of our wheels died away as we drove through drifts of rotting vegetation - sad gifts, as it seemed to me, for Nature to throw before the carriage of the returning heir of the Baskervilles.

"Halloa!" cried Dr. Mortimer, "what is this?"

A steep curve of heath-clad land, an outlying spur of the moor, lay in front of us. On the summit, hard and clear like an equestrian statue upon its pedestal, was a mounted soldier, dark and stern, his rifle poised ready over his forearm. He was watching the road along which we travelled.

"What is this, Perkins?" asked Dr. Mortimer.

Our driver half turned in his seat.

"There's a convict escaped from Princetown, sir. He's been out three days now, and the warders watch every road and every station, but they've had no sight of him yet. The farmers about here don't like it, sir, and that's a fact."

"Well, I understand that they get five pounds if they can give information."

"Yes, sir, but the chance of five pounds is but a poor thing compared to the chance of having your throat cut. You see, it isn't like any ordinary convict. This is a man that would stick at nothing."

"Who is he, then?"

"It is Selden, the Notting Hill murderer."

I remembered the case well, for it was one in which Holmes had taken an interest on account of the peculiar ferocity of the crime and the wanton brutality which had marked all the actions of the assassin. The commutation of his death sentence had been due to some doubts as to his complete sanity, so atrocious was his conduct. Our wagonette had topped a rise and in front of us rose the huge expanse of the moor, mottled with gnarled and craggy cairns and tors. A cold wind swept down from it and set us shivering. Somewhere there, on that desolate plain, was lurking this fiendish man, hiding in a burrow like a wild beast, his heart full of malignancy against the whole race which had cast him out. It needed but this to complete the grim suggestiveness of the barren waste, the chilling wind, and the darkling sky. Even Baskerville fell silent and pulled his overcoat more closely around him.

We had left the fertile country behind and beneath us. We looked back on it now, the slanting rays of a low sun turning the streams to threads of gold and glowing on the red earth new turned by the plough and the broad tangle of the woodlands. The road in front of us grew bleaker and wilder over huge russet and olive slopes, sprinkled with giant boulders. Now and then we passed a moorland cottage, walled and roofed with stone, with no creeper to break its harsh outline. Suddenly we looked down into a cup-like depression, patched with stunted oaks and furs which had been twisted and bent by the fury of years of storm. Two high, narrow towers rose over the trees. The driver pointed with his whip.

"Baskerville Hall," said he.

Its master had risen and was staring with flushed cheeks and shining eyes. A few minutes later we had reached the lodge-gates, a maze of fantastic tracery in wrought iron, with weather-bitten pillars on either side, blotched with lichens, and surmounted by the boars' heads of the

Baskervilles. The lodge was a ruin of black granite and bared ribs of rafters, but facing it was a new building, half constructed, the firstfruit of Sir Charles's South African gold.

Through the gateway we passed into the avenue, where the wheels were again hushed amid the leaves, and the old trees shot their branches in a sombre tunnel over our heads. Baskerville shuddered as he looked up the long, dark drive to where the house glimmered like a ghost at the farther end.

"Was it here?" he asked, in a low voice.

"No, no, the Yew Alley is on the other side."

The young heir glanced round with a gloomy face.

"It's no wonder my uncle felt as if trouble were coming on him in such a place as this," said he. "It's enough to scare any man. I'll have a row of electric lamps up here inside of six months, and you won't know it again, with a thousand candle-power Swan and Edison right here in front of the hall door."

The avenue opened into a broad expanse of turf, and the house lay before us. In the fading light I could see that the centre was a heavy block of building from which a porch projected. The whole front was draped in ivy, with a patch clipped bare here and there where a window or a coat-of-arms broke through the dark veil. From this central block rose the twin towers, ancient, crenellated, and pierced with many loopholes. To right and left of the turrets were more modern wings of black granite. A dull light shone through heavy mullioned windows, and from the high chimneys which rose from the steep, high-angled roof there sprang a single black column of smoke.

"Welcome, Sir Henry! Welcome, to Baskerville Hall!"

A tall man had stepped from the shadow of the porch to open the door of the wagonette. The figure of a woman was silhouetted against the yellow light of the hall. She came out and helped the man to hand down our bags.

"You don't mind my driving straight home, Sir Henry?" said Dr. Mortimer. "My wife is expecting me."

"Surely you will stay and have some dinner?"

"No, I must go. I shall probably find some work awaiting me. I would stay to show you over the house, but Barrymore will be a better guide than I. Good-bye, and never hesitate night or day to send for me if I can be of service."

The wheels died away down the drive while Sir Henry and I turned into the hall, and the door clanged heavily behind us. It was a fine apartment in which we found ourselves, large, lofty, and heavily raftered with huge balks of age-blackened oak. In the great old-fashioned fireplace behind the high iron dogs a log-fire crackled and snapped. Sir Henry and I held out our hands to it, for we were numb from our long drive. Then we gazed round us at the high, thin window of old stained glass, the oak panelling, the stags' heads, the coats-of-arms upon the walls, all dim and sombre in the subdued light of the central lamp.

"It's just as I imagined it," said Sir Henry. "Is it not the very picture of an old family home? To think that this should be the same hall in which for five hundred years my people have lived. It strikes me solemn to think of it."

I saw his dark face lit up with a boyish enthusiasm as he gazed about him. The light beat upon him where he stood, but long shadows trailed down the walls and hung like a black canopy above him. Barrymore had returned from taking our luggage to our rooms. He stood in front of us now with the subdued manner of a well-trained servant. He was a remarkable-looking man, tall, handsome, with a square black beard, and pale, distinguished features.

"Would you wish dinner to be served at once, sir?"

"Is it ready?"

"In a very few minutes, sir. You will find hot water in your rooms. My wife and I will be happy, Sir Henry, to stay with you until you have made your fresh arrangements, but you will understand that under the new conditions this house will require a considerable staff."

"What new conditions?"

"I only meant, sir, that Sir Charles led a very retired life, and we were able to look after his wants. You would, naturally, wish to have more company, and so you will need changes in your household."

"Do you mean that your wife and you wish to leave?"

"Only when it is quite convenient to you, sir."

"But your family have been with us for several generations, have they not? I should be sorry to begin my life here by breaking an old family connection."

I seemed to discern some signs of emotion upon the butler's white face.

"I feel that also, sir, and so does my wife. But to tell the truth, sir, we were both very much attached to Sir Charles, and his death gave us a shock and made these surroundings very painful to us. I fear that we shall never again be easy in our minds at Baskerville Hall."

"But what do you intend to do?"

"I have no doubt, sir, that we shall succeed in establishing ourselves in some business. Sir Charles's generosity has given us the means to do so. And now, sir, perhaps I had best show you to your rooms."

A square balustraded gallery ran round the top of the old hall, approached by a double stair. From this central point two long corridors extended the whole length of the building, from which all the bedrooms opened. My own was in the same wing as Baskerville's and almost next door to it. These rooms appeared to be much more modern than the central part of the house, and the bright paper and numerous candles did something to remove the sombre impression which our arrival had left upon my mind.

But the dining-room which opened out of the hall was a place of shadow and gloom. It was a long chamber with a step separating the daïs where the family sat from the lower portion reserved for their dependents. At one end a minstrels' gallery overlooked it. Black beams shot across above our heads, with a smoke-darkened ceiling beyond them. With rows of flaring torches to light it up, and the colour and rude hilarity of an old-time banquet, it might have softened; but now, when two black-clothed gentlemen sat in the little circle of light thrown by a shaded lamp, one's voice became hushed and one's spirit subdued. A dim line of ancestors, in every variety of dress, from the Elizabethan knight to the buck of the Regency, stared down upon us and daunted us by their silent company. We talked little, and I for one was glad when the meal was over and we were able to retire into the modern billiard-room and smoke a cigarette.

"My word, it isn't a very cheerful place," said Sir Henry. "I suppose one can tone down to it, but I feel a bit out of the picture at present. I don't wonder that my uncle got a little jumpy if he lived all alone in such a house as this. However, if it suits you, we will retire early to-night, and perhaps things may seem more cheerful in the morning."

I drew aside my curtains before I went to bed and looked out from my window. It opened upon the grassy space which lay in front of the hall door. Beyond, two copses of trees moaned and swung in a rising wind. A half moon broke through the rifts of racing clouds. In its cold light I saw beyond the trees a broken fringe of rocks and the long, low curve of the melancholy moor. I closed the curtain, feeling that my last impression was in keeping with the rest.

And yet it was not quite the last. I found myself weary and yet wakeful, tossing restlessly from side to side, seeking for the sleep which would not come. Far away a chiming clock struck out the quarters of the hours, but otherwise a deathly silence lay upon the old house. And then suddenly, in the very dead of the night, there came a sound to my ears, clear, resonant, and unmistakable. It was the sob of a woman, the muffled, strangling gasp of one who is torn by an uncontrollable sorrow. I sat up in bed and listened intently. The noise could not have been far away, and was certainly in the house. For half an hour I waited with every nerve on the alert, but there came no other sound save the chiming clock and the rustle of the ivy on the wall.

CHAPTER VII.

THE STAPLETONS OF MERRIPIT HOUSE.

 HE fresh beauty of the following morning did something to efface from our minds the grim and grey impression which had been left upon both of us by our first experience of Baskerville Hall. As Sir Henry and I sat at breakfast the sunlight flooded in through the high mullioned windows, throwing watery patches of colour from the coats of arms which covered them. The dark panelling glowed like bronze in the golden rays, and it was hard to realize that this was indeed the chamber which had struck such a gloom into our souls upon the evening before.

"I guess it is ourselves and not the house that we have to blame!" said the baronet. "We were tired with our journey and chilled by our drive, so we took a grey view of the place. Now we are fresh and well, so it is all cheerful once more."

"And yet it was not entirely a question of imagination," I answered. "Did you, for example, happen to hear someone, a woman I think, sobbing in the night?"

"That is curious, for I did when I was half asleep fancy that I heard something of the sort. I waited quite a time, but there was no more of it, so I concluded that it was all a dream."

"I heard it distinctly, and I am sure that it was really the sob of a woman."

"We must ask about this right away." He rang the bell and asked Barrymore whether he could account for our experience. It seemed to me that the pallid features of the butler turned a shade paler still as he listened to his master's question.

"There are only two women in the house, Sir Henry," he answered. "One is the scullery-maid, who sleeps in the other wing. The other is my wife, and I can answer for it that the sound could not have come from her."

And yet he lied as he said it, for it chanced that after breakfast I met Mrs. Barrymore in the long corridor with the sun full upon her face. She was a large, impassive, heavy-featured woman with a stern, set expression of mouth. But her tell-tale eyes were red and glanced at me from between swollen lids. It was she, then, who wept in the night, and if she did so her husband must know it. Yet he had taken the obvious risk of discovery in declaring that it was not so. Why had he done this? And why did she weep so bitterly? Already round this pale-faced, handsome, black-bearded man there was gathering an atmosphere of mystery and of gloom. It was he who had been the first to discover the body of Sir Charles, and we had only his word for all the circumstances which led up to the old man's death. Was it possible that it was Barrymore after all whom we had seen in the cab in Regent Street? The beard might well have been the same. The cabman had described a somewhat shorter man, but such an impression might easily have been erroneous. How could I settle the point forever? Obviously the first thing to do was to see the Grimpen postmaster and find whether the test telegram had really been placed in Barrymore's own hands. Be the answer what it might, I should at least have something to report to Sherlock Holmes.

Sir Henry had numerous papers to examine after breakfast, so that the time was propitious for my excursion. It was a pleasant walk of four miles along the edge of the moor, leading me at last to a small grey hamlet, in which two larger buildings, which proved to be the inn and the house of Dr. Mortimer, stood high above the rest. The postmaster, who was also the village grocer, had a clear recollection of the telegram.

"Certainly, sir," said he, "I had the telegram delivered to Mr. Barrymore exactly as directed."

"Who delivered it?"

"My boy here. James, you delivered that telegram to Mr. Barrymore at the Hall last week, did you not?"

"Yes, father, I delivered it."

"Into his own hands?" I asked.

"Well, he was up in the loft at the time, so that I could not put it into his own hands, but I gave it into Mrs. Barrymore's hands, and she promised to deliver it at once."

"Did you see Mr. Barrymore?"

"No, sir; I tell you he was in the loft."

"If you didn't see him, how do you know he was in the loft?"

"Well, surely his own wife ought to know where he is," said the postmaster, testily. "Didn't he get the telegram? If there is any mistake it is for Mr. Barrymore himself to complain."

It seemed hopeless to pursue the inquiry any farther, but it was clear that in spite of Holmes's ruse we had no proof that Barrymore had not been in London all the time. Suppose that it were so - suppose that the same man had been the last who had seen Sir Charles alive, and the first to dog the new heir when he returned to England. What then? Was he the agent of others, or had he some sinister design of his own? What interest could he have in persecuting the Baskerville family? I thought of the strange warning clipped out of the leading article of the *Times*. Was that his work, or was it possibly the doing of someone who was bent upon counteracting his schemes? The only conceivable motive was that which had been suggested by Sir Henry, that if the family could be scared away a comfortable and permanent home would be secured for the Barrymores. But surely such an explanation as that would be quite inadequate to account for the deep and subtle scheming which seemed to be weaving an invisible net round the young baronet. Holmes himself had said that no more complex case had come to him in all the long series of his sensational investigations. I prayed, as I walked back along the grey, lonely road, that my friend might soon be freed from his preoccupations and able to come down to take this heavy burden of responsibility from my shoulders.

Suddenly my thoughts were interrupted by the sound of running feet behind me and by a voice which called me by name. I turned, expecting to see Dr. Mortimer, but to my surprise it was a stranger who was pursuing me. He was a small, slim, clean-shaven, prim-faced man, flaxen-haired and lean-jawed, between thirty and forty years of age, dressed in a grey suit and wearing a straw hat. A tin box for botanical specimens hung over his shoulder and he carried a green butterfly-net in one of his hands.

"You will, I am sure, excuse my presumption, Dr. Watson," said he, as he came panting up to where I stood. "Here on the moor we are homely folk and do not wait for formal introductions. You may possibly have heard my name from our mutual friend, Mortimer. I am Stapleton, of Merripit House."

"Your net and box would have told me as much," said I, "for I knew that Mr. Stapleton was a naturalist. But how did you know me?"

"I have been calling on Mortimer, and he pointed you out to me from the window of his surgery as you passed. As our road lay the same way I thought that I would overtake you and introduce myself. I trust that Sir Henry is none the worse for his journey?"

"He is very well, thank you."

"We were all rather afraid that after the sad death of Sir Charles the new baronet might refuse to live here. It is asking much of a wealthy man to come down and bury himself in a place of this kind, but I need not tell you that it means a very great deal to the country-side. Sir Henry has, I suppose, no superstitious fears in the matter?"

"I do not think that it is likely."

"Of course you know the legend of the fiend dog which haunts the family?"

"I have heard it."

"It is extraordinary how credulous the peasants are about here! Any number of them are ready to swear that they have seen such a creature upon the moor." He spoke with a smile, but I seemed to read in his eyes that he took the matter more seriously. "The story took a great hold upon the imagination of Sir Charles, and I have no doubt that it led to his tragic end."

"But how?"

"His nerves were so worked up that the appearance of any dog might have had a fatal effect upon his diseased heart. I fancy that he really did see something of the kind upon that last night in the Yew Alley. I feared that some disaster might occur, for I was very fond of the old man, and I knew that his heart was weak."

"How did you know that?"

"My friend Mortimer told me."

"You think, then, that some dog pursued Sir Charles, and that he died of fright in consequence?"

"Have you any better explanation?"

"I have not come to any conclusion."

"Has Mr. Sherlock Holmes?"

The words took away my breath for an instant, but a glance at the placid face and steadfast eyes of my companion showed that no surprise was intended.

"It is useless for us to pretend that we do not know you, Dr. Watson," said he. "The records of your detective have reached us here, and you could not celebrate him without being known yourself. When Mortimer told me your name he could not deny your identity. If you are here, then it follows that Mr. Sherlock Holmes is interesting himself in the matter, and I am naturally curious to know what view he may take."

"I am afraid that I cannot answer that question."

"May I ask if he is going to honour us with a visit himself?"

"He cannot leave town at present. He has other cases which engage his attention."

"What a pity! He might throw some light on that which is so dark to us. But as to your own researches if there is any possible way in which I can be of service to you I trust that you will command me. If I had any indication of the nature of your suspicions, or how you propose to investigate the case, I might perhaps even now give you some aid or advice."

"I assure you that I am simply here upon a visit to my friend Sir Henry, and that I need no help of any kind."

"Excellent!" said Stapleton. "You are perfectly right to be wary and discreet. I am justly reproved for what I feel was an unjustifiable intrusion, and I promise you that I will not mention the matter again."

We had come to a point where a narrow grassy path struck off from the road and wound away across the moor. A steep, boulder-sprinkled hill lay upon the right which had in bygone days been cut into a granite quarry. The face which was turned towards us formed a dark cliff, with ferns and brambles growing in its niches. From over a distant rise there floated a grey plume of smoke.

"A moderate walk along this moor-path brings us to Merripit House," said he. "Perhaps you will spare an hour that I may have the pleasure of introducing you to my sister."

My first thought was that I should be by Sir Henry's side. But then I remembered the pile of papers and bills with which his study table was littered. It was certain that I could not help him with those. And Holmes had expressly said that I should study the neighbours upon the moor. I accepted Stapleton's invitation, and we turned together down the path.

"It is a wonderful place, the moor," said he, looking round over the undulating downs, long green rollers, with crests of jagged granite foaming up into fantastic surges. "You never tire of the moor. You cannot think the wonderful secrets which it contains. It is so vast, and so barren, and so mysterious."

"You know it well, then?"

"I have only been here two years. The residents would call me a new-comer. We came shortly after Sir Charles settled. But my tastes led me to explore every part of the country round, and I should think that there are few men who know it better than I do."

"Is it so hard to know?"

"Very hard. You see, for example, this great plain to the north here, with the queer hills breaking out of it. Do you observe anything remarkable about that?"

"It would be a rare place for a gallop."

"You would naturally think so, and the thought has cost folk their lives before now. You notice those bright green spots scattered thickly over it?"

"Yes, they seem more fertile than the rest."

Stapleton laughed.

"That is the great Grimpen Mire," said he. "A false step yonder means death to man or beast. Only yesterday I saw one of the moor ponies wander into it. He never came out. I saw his head for quite a long time craning out of the bog-hole, but it sucked him down at last. Even in dry seasons it is a danger to cross it, but after these autumn rains it is an awful place. And yet I can find my way to the very heart of it and return alive. By George, there is another of those miserable ponies!"

Something brown was rolling and tossing among the green sedges. Then a long, agonized, writhing neck shot upwards and a dreadful cry echoed over the moor. It turned me cold with horror, but my companion's nerves seemed to be stronger than mine.

"It's gone!" said he. "The Mire has him. Two in two days, and many more, perhaps, for they get in the way of going there in the dry weather, and never know the difference until the Mire has them in its clutch. It's a bad place, the great Grimpen Mire."

"And you say you can penetrate it?"

"Yes, there are one or two paths which a very active man can take. I have found them out."

"But why should you wish to go into so horrible a place?"

"Well, you see the hills beyond? They are really islands cut off on all sides by the impassable Mire, which has crawled round them in the course of years. That is where the rare plants and the butterflies are, if you have the wit to reach them."

"I shall try my luck some day."

He looked at me with a surprised face.

"That is the great Grimpen Mire".
Stapleton and Watson viewing the
'*great Grimpen Mire*' from the South.

"For God's sake put such an idea out of your mind," said he. "Your blood would be upon my head. I assure you that there would not be the least chance of your coming back alive. It is only by remembering certain complex landmarks that I am able to do it."

"Halloa!" I cried. "What is that?"

A long, low moan, indescribably sad, swept over the moor. It filled the whole air, and yet it was impossible to say whence it came. From a dull murmur it swelled into a deep roar, and then sank back into a melancholy, throbbing murmur once again. Stapleton looked at me with a curious expression in his face.

"Queer place, the moor!" said he.

"But what is it?"

"The peasants say it is the Hound of the Baskervilles calling for its prey. I've heard it once or twice before, but never quite so loud."

I looked round, with a chill of fear in my heart, at the huge swelling plain, mottled with the green patches of rushes. Nothing stirred over the vast expanse save a pair of ravens, which croaked loudly from a tor behind us.

"You are an educated man. You don't believe such nonsense as that?" said I. "What do you think is the cause of so strange a sound?"

"Bogs make queer noises sometimes. It's the mud settling, or the water rising, or something."

"No, no, that was a living voice."

"Well, perhaps it was. Did you ever hear a bittern booming?"

"No, I never did."

"It's a very rare bird - practically extinct - in England now, but all things are possible upon the moor. Yes, I should not be surprised to learn that what we have heard is the cry of the last of the bitterns."

"It's the weirdest, strangest thing that ever I heard in my life."

"Yes, it's rather an uncanny place altogether. Look at the hill-side yonder. What do you make of those?"

The whole steep slope was covered with grey circular rings of stone, a score of them at least.

"What are they? Sheep-pens?"

"No, they are the homes of our worthy ancestors. Prehistoric man lived thickly on the moor, and as no one in particular has lived there since, we find all his little arrangements exactly as he left them. These are his wigwams with the roofs off. You can even see his hearth and his couch if you have the curiosity to go inside."

"But it is quite a town. When was it inhabited?"

"Neolithic man - no date."

"What did he do?"

"He grazed his cattle on these slopes, and he learned to dig for tin when the bronze sword began to supersede the stone axe. Look at the great trench in the opposite hill. That is his mark. Yes, you will find some very singular points about the moor, Dr. Watson. Oh, excuse me an instant! It is surely Cyclopides."

A small fly or moth had fluttered across our path, and in an instant Stapleton was rushing with extraordinary energy and speed in pursuit of it. To my dismay the creature flew straight for the great Mire, but my acquaintance never paused for an instant, bounding from tuft to tuft behind it, his green net waving in the air. His grey clothes and jerky, zig-zag, irregular progress made him not unlike some huge moth himself. I was standing watching his pursuit with a mixture of admiration for his extraordinary activity and fear lest he should lose his footing in the treacherous Mire when I heard the sound of steps, and turning round, found a woman near me upon the path. She had come from the direction in which the plume of smoke indicated the position of Merripit House, but the dip of the moor had hid her until she was quite close.

I could not doubt that this was the Miss Stapleton of whom I had been told, since ladies of any sort must be few upon the moor, and I remembered that I had heard someone describe her as being a beauty. The woman who approached me was certainly that, and of a most uncommon type. There could not have been a greater contrast between brother and sister, for Stapleton was neutral tinted, with light hair and grey eyes, while she was darker than any brunette whom I have seen in England - slim, elegant, and tall. She had a proud, finely-cut face, so regular that it might have seemed impassive were it not for the sensitive mouth and the beautiful dark, eager eyes. With her perfect figure and elegant dress she was, indeed, a strange apparition upon a lonely moorland path. Her eyes were on her brother as I turned, and then she quickened her pace towards me. I had raised my hat and was about to make some explanatory remark, when her own words turned all my thoughts into a new channel.

"Go back!" she said. "Go straight back to London, instantly."

I could only stare at her in stupid surprise. Her eyes blazed at me, and she tapped the ground impatiently with her foot.

"Why should I go back?" I asked.

"I cannot explain." She spoke in a low, eager voice, with a curious lisp in her utterance. "But for God's sake do what I ask you. Go back and never set foot upon the moor again."

"But I have only just come."

"Man, man!" she cried. "Can you not tell when a warning is for your own good? Go back to London! Start to-night! Get away from this place at all costs! Hush, my brother is coming! Not a word of what I have said. Would you mind getting that orchid for me among the mare's-tails yonder? We are very rich in orchids on the moor, though, of course, you are rather late to see the beauties of the place."

Stapleton had abandoned the chase and came back to us breathing hard and flushed with his exertions.

"Halloa, Beryl!" said he, and it seemed to me that the tone of his greeting was not altogether a cordial one.

"Well, Jack, you are very hot."

"Yes, I was chasing a Cyclopides. He is very rare, and seldom found in the late autumn. What a pity that I should have missed him!" He spoke unconcernedly, but his small light eyes glanced incessantly from the girl to me.

"You have introduced yourselves, I can see."

"Yes. I was telling Sir Henry that it was rather late for him to see the true beauties of the moor."

"Why, who do you think this is?"

"I imagine that it must be Sir Henry Baskerville."

"No, no," said I. "Only a humble commoner, but his friend. My name is Dr. Watson."

A flush of vexation passed over her expressive face. "We have been talking at cross purposes," said she.

"Why, you had not very much time for talk," her brother remarked, with the same questioning eyes.

"I talked as if Dr. Watson were a resident instead of being merely a visitor," said she. "It cannot much matter to him whether it is early or late for the orchids. But you will come on, will you not, and see Merripit House?"

A short walk brought us to it, a bleak moorland house, once the farm of some grazier in the old prosperous days, but now put into repair and turned into a modern dwelling. An orchard surrounded it, but the trees, as is usual upon the moor, were stunted and nipped, and the effect of the whole place was mean and melancholy. We were admitted by a strange, wizened, rusty-coated old manservant, who seemed in keeping with the house. Inside, however, there were large rooms furnished with an elegance in which I seemed to recognise the taste of the lady. As I looked from their windows at the interminable granite-flecked moor rolling unbroken to the far-thest horizon I could not but marvel at what could have brought this highly educated man and this beautiful woman to live in such a place.

"Queer spot to choose, is it not?" said he, as if in answer to my thought. "And yet we manage to make ourselves fairly happy, do we not, Beryl?"

"Quite happy," said she, but there was no ring of conviction in her words.

"I had a school," said Stapleton. "It was in the north country. The work to a man of my temperament was mechanical and uninteresting, but the privilege of living with youth, of helping to mould those young minds and of impressing them with one's own character and ideals was very dear to me. However, the fates were against us. A serious epidemic broke out in the school and three of the boys died. It never recovered from the blow, and much of my capital was irre-trievably swallowed up. And yet, if it were not for the loss of the charming companionship of the boys, I could rejoice over my own misfortune, for, with my strong tastes for botany and zoology, I find an unlimited field of work here, and my sister is as devoted to Nature as I am. All this, Dr. Watson, has been brought upon your head by your expression as you surveyed the moor out of our window."

"It certainly did cross my mind that it might be a little dull - less for you, perhaps, than for your sister."

"No, no, I am never dull," said she, quickly.

"We have books, we have our studies, and we have interesting neighbours. Dr. Mortimer is a most learned man in his own line. Poor Sir Charles was also an admirable companion. We knew him well, and miss him more than I can tell. Do you think that I should intrude if I were to call this afternoon and make the acquaintance of Sir Henry?"

"I am sure that he would be delighted."

"Then perhaps you would mention that I propose to do so. We may in our humble way do something to make things more easy for him until he becomes accustomed to his new surround-ings. Will you come upstairs, Dr. Watson, and inspect my collection of lepidoptera? I think it is the most complete one in the south-west of England. By the time that you have looked through them lunch will be almost ready."

But I was eager to get back to my charge. The melancholy of the moor, the death of the unfortunate pony, the weird sound which had been associated with the grim legend of the Baskervilles, all these things tinged my thoughts with sadness. Then on the top of these more or less vague impressions there had come the definite and distinct warning of Miss Stapleton, deliv-ered with such intense earnestness that I could not doubt that some grave and deep reason lay behind it. I resisted all pressure to stay for lunch, and I set off at once upon my return journey, taking the grass-grown path by which we had come.

It seems, however, that there must have been some short cut for those who knew it, for before I had reached the road I was astounded to see Miss Stapleton sitting upon a rock by the side of the track. Her face was beautifully flushed with her exertions, and she held her hand to her side.

"I have run all the way in order to cut you off, Dr. Watson," said she. "I had not even time to put on my hat. I must not stop, or my brother may miss me. I wanted to say to you how sorry I am about the stupid mistake I made in thinking that you were Sir Henry. Please forget the words I said, which have no application whatever to you."

"But I can't forget them, Miss Stapleton," said I. "I am Sir Henry's friend, and his welfare is a very close concern of mine. Tell me why it was that you were so eager that Sir Henry should return to London."

"A woman's whim, Dr. Watson. When you know me better you will understand that I cannot always give reasons for what I say or do."

"No, no. I remember the thrill in your voice. I remember the look in your eyes. Please, please, be frank with me, Miss Stapleton, for ever since I have been here I have been conscious of shadows all round me. Life has become like that great Grimpen Mire, with little green patches everywhere into which one may sink and with no guide to point the track. Tell me then what it was that you meant, and I will promise to convey your warning to Sir Henry."

An expression of irresolution passed for an instant over her face, but her eyes had hardened again when she answered me.

"You make too much of it, Dr. Watson," said she. "My brother and I were very much shocked by the death of Sir Charles. We knew him very intimately, for his favourite walk was over the moor to our house. He was deeply impressed with the curse which hung over his family, and when this tragedy came I naturally felt that there must be some grounds for the fears which he had expressed. I was distressed therefore when another member of the family came down to live here, and I felt that he should be warned of the danger which he will run. That was all which I intended to convey."

"But what is the danger?"

"You know the story of the hound?"

"I do not believe in such nonsense."

"But I do. If you have any influence with Sir Henry, take him away from a place which has always been fatal to his family. The world is wide. Why should he wish to live at the place of danger?"

"Because it *is* the place of danger. That is Sir Henry's nature. I fear that unless you can give me some more definite information than this it would be impossible to get him to move."

"I cannot say anything definite, for I do not know anything definite."

"I would ask you one more question, Miss Stapleton. If you meant no more than this when you first spoke to me, why should you not wish your brother to overhear what you said? There is nothing to which he, or anyone else, could object."

"My brother is very anxious to have the Hall inhabited, for he thinks that it is for the good of the poor folk upon the moor. He would be very angry if he knew that I had said anything which might induce Sir Henry to go away. But I have done my duty now and I will say no more. I must get back, or he will miss me and suspect that I have seen you. Good-bye!" She turned, and had disappeared in a few minutes among the scattered boulders, while I, with my soul full of vague fears, pursued my way to Baskerville Hall.

CHAPTER VIII.

FIRST REPORT OF DR. WATSON.

FROM this point onwards I will follow the course of events by transcribing my own letters to Mr. Sherlock Holmes which lie before me on the table. One page is missing, but otherwise they are exactly as written and show my feelings and suspicions of the moment more accurately than my memory, clear as it is upon these tragic events, can possibly do.

BASKERVILLE HALL,
October 13th.

MY DEAR HOLMES, - My previous letters and telegrams have kept you pretty well up-to-date as to all that has occurred in this most God-forsaken corner of the world. The longer one stays here the more does the spirit of the moor sink into one's soul, its vastness, and also its grim charm. When you are once out upon its bosom you have left all traces of modern England behind you, but on the other hand you are conscious everywhere of the homes and the work of the prehistoric people. On all sides of you as you walk are the houses of these forgotten folk, with their graves and the huge monoliths which are supposed to have marked their temples. As you look at their grey stone huts against the scarred hill-sides you leave your own age behind you, and if you were to see a skin-clad, hairy man crawl out from the low door, fitting a flint-tipped arrow on to the string of his bow, you would feel that his presence there was more natural than your own. The strange thing is that they should have lived so thickly on what must always have been most unfruitful soil. I am no antiquarian, but I could imagine that they were some unwarlike and harried race who were forced to accept that which none other would occupy.

All this, however, is foreign to the mission on which you sent me, and will probably be very uninteresting to your severely practical mind. I can still remember your complete indifference as to whether the sun moved round the earth or the earth round the sun. Let me, therefore, return to the facts concerning Sir Henry Baskerville.

If you have not had any report within the last few days it is because up to to-day there was nothing of importance to relate. Then a very surprising circumstance occurred, which I shall tell you in due course. But, first of all, I must keep you in touch with some of the other factors in the situation.

One of these, concerning which I have said little, is the escaped convict upon the moor. There is strong reason now to believe that he has got right away, which is a considerable relief to the lonely householders of this district. A fortnight has passed since his flight, during which he has not been seen and nothing has been heard of him. It is surely inconceivable that he could have held out upon the moor during all that time. Of course, so far as his concealment goes there is no difficulty at all. Any one of these stone huts would give him a hiding-place. But there is nothing to eat unless he were to catch and slaughter one of the moor sheep. We think, therefore, that he has gone, and the outlying farmers sleep the better in consequence.

We are four able-bodied men in this household, so that we could take good care of ourselves, but I confess that I have had uneasy moments when I have thought of the Stapletons. They live miles from any help. There are one maid, an old manservant, the sister, and the brother, the latter not a very strong man. They would be helpless in the hands of a desperate fellow like this Notting Hill criminal, if he could once effect an entrance. Both Sir Henry and I were concerned at their situation, and it was suggested that Perkins the groom should go over to sleep there, but Stapleton would not hear of it.

The fact is that our friend the baronet begins to display a considerable interest in our fair neighbour. It is not to be wondered at, for time hangs heavily in this lonely spot to an active man like him, and she is a very fascinating and beautiful woman. There is something tropical and exotic about her which forms a singular contrast to her cool and unemotional brother. Yet he also gives the idea of hidden fires. He has certainly a very marked influence over her, for I have seen her continually glance at him as she talked as if seeking approbation for what she said. I trust that he is kind to her. There is a dry glitter in his eyes, and a firm set of his thin lips, which go with a positive and possibly a harsh nature. You would find him an interesting study.

He came over to call upon Baskerville on that first day, and the very next morning he took us both to show us the spot where the legend of the wicked Hugo is supposed to have had its origin. It was an excursion of some miles across the moor to a place which is so dismal that it might have suggested the story. We found a short valley between rugged tors which led to an open, grassy space flecked over with the white cotton grass. In the middle of it rose two great stones, worn and sharpened at the upper end, until they looked like the huge, corroding fangs of some monstrous beast. In every way it corresponded with the scene of the old tragedy. Sir Henry was much interested, and asked Stapleton more than once whether he did really believe in the possibility of the interference of the supernatural in the affairs of men. He spoke lightly, but it was evident that he was very much in earnest. Stapleton was guarded in his replies, but it was easy to see that he said less than he might, and that he would not express his whole opinion out of consideration for the feelings of the baronet. He told us of similar cases, where families had suffered from some evil influence, and he left us with the impression that he shared the popular view upon the matter.

On our way back we stayed for lunch at Merripit House, and it was there that Sir Henry made the acquaintance of Miss Stapleton. From the first moment that he saw her he appeared to be strongly attracted by her, and I am much mistaken if the feeling was not mutual. He referred to her again and again on our walk home, and since then hardly a day has passed that we have not seen something of the brother and sister. They dine here to-night, and there is some talk of our going to them next week. One would imagine that such a match would be very welcome to Stapleton, and yet I have more than once caught a look of the strongest disapprobation in his face when Sir Henry has been paying some attention to his sister. He is much attached to her, no doubt, and would lead a lonely life without her, but it would seem the height of selfishness if he were to stand in the way of her making so brilliant a marriage. Yet I am certain that he does not wish their intimacy to ripen into love, and I have several times observed that he has taken pains to prevent them from being *tête-à-tête*. By the way, your instructions to me never to allow Sir Henry to go out alone will become very much more onerous if a love affair were to be added to our other difficulties. My popularity would soon suffer if I were to carry out your orders to the letter.

The other day - Thursday, to be more exact - Dr. Mortimer lunched with us. He has been excavating a barrow at Long Down and has got a prehistoric skull which fills him with great joy. Never was there such a single-minded enthusiast as he! The Stapletons came in afterwards, and the good doctor took us all to the Yew Alley at Sir Henry's request, to show us exactly how everything occurred upon that fatal night. It is a long, dismal walk, the Yew Alley, between two high walls of clipped hedge, with a narrow band of grass upon either side. At the far end is an old, tumble-down summer-house. Half-way down is the moor-gate, where the old gentleman left his cigar-ash. It is a white wooden gate with a latch. Beyond it lies the wide moor. I remembered your theory of the affair and tried to picture all that had occurred. As the old man stood there he saw something coming across the moor, something which terrified him so that he lost his wits, and ran and ran until he died of sheer horror and exhaustion. There was the long, gloomy tunnel down which he fled. And from what? A sheep-dog of the moor? Or a spectral hound, black, silent, and monstrous? Was there a human agency in the matter? Did the pale, watchful Barrymore know more than he cared to say? It was all dim and vague, but always there is the dark shadow of crime behind it.

One other neighbour I have met since I wrote last. This is Mr. Frankland, of Lafter Hall, who lives some four miles to the south of us. He is an elderly man, red faced, white haired, and choleric. His passion is for the British law, and he has spent a large fortune in litigation. He fights for the mere pleasure of fighting, and is equally ready to take up either side of a question, so that it is no wonder that he has found it a costly amusement. Sometimes he will shut up a right of way and defy the parish to make him open it. At others he will with his own hands tear down some other man's gate and declare that a path has existed there from time immemorial, defying the owner to prosecute him for trespass. He is learned in old manorial and communal rights, and he applies his knowledge sometimes in favour of the villagers of Fernworthy and sometimes against them, so that he is periodically either carried in triumph down the village street or else burned in effigy, according to his latest exploit. He is said to have about seven law-suits upon his hands at present, which will probably swallow up the remainder of his fortune and so draw his sting and leave him harmless for the future. Apart from the law he seems a kindly, good-natured person, and I only mention him because you were particular that I should send some description of the people who surround us. He is curiously employed at present, for, being an amateur astronomer, he has an excellent telescope, with which he lies upon the roof of his own house and sweeps the moor all day in the hope of catching a glimpse of the escaped convict. If he would confine his energies to this all would be well, but there are rumours that he intends to prosecute Dr. Mortimer for opening a grave without the consent of the next-of-kin, because he dug up the neolithic skull in the barrow on Long Down. He helps to keep our lives from being monotonous and gives a little comic relief where it is badly needed.

And now, having brought you up to date in the escaped convict, the Stapletons, Dr. Mortimer, and Frankland, of Lafter Hall, let me end on that which is most important and tell you more about the Barrymores, and especially about the surprising development of last night.

First of all about the test telegram, which you sent from London in order to make sure that Barrymore was really here. I have already explained that the testimony of the postmaster shows that the test was worthless and that we have no proof one way or the other. I told Sir Henry how the matter stood, and he at once, in his downright fashion, had Barrymore up and asked him whether he had received the telegram himself. Barrymore said that he had.

"Did the boy deliver it into your own hands?" asked Sir Henry.

Barrymore looked surprised, and considered for a little time.

"No," said he, "I was in the box-room at the time, and my wife brought it up to me."

"Did you answer it yourself?"

"No; I told my wife what to answer and she went down to write it."

In the evening he recurred to the subject of his own accord.

"I could not quite understand the object of your questions this morning, Sir Henry," said he. "I trust that they do not mean that I have done anything to forfeit your confidence?"

Sir Henry had to assure him that it was not so and pacify him by giving him a considerable part of his old wardrobe, the London outfit having now all arrived.

Mrs. Barrymore is of interest to me. She is a heavy, solid person, very limited, intensely respectable, and inclined to be puritanical. You could hardly conceive a less emotional subject. Yet I have told you how, on the first night here, I heard her sobbing bitterly, and since then I have more than once observed traces of tears upon her face. Some deep sorrow gnaws ever at her heart. Sometimes I wonder if she has a guilty memory which haunts her, and sometimes I suspect Barrymore of being a domestic tyrant. I have always felt that there was something singular and questionable in this man's character, but the adventure of last night brings all my suspicions to a head.

And yet it may seem a small matter in itself. You are aware that I am not a very sound sleeper, and since I have been on guard in this house my slumbers have been lighter than ever. Last night, about two in the morning, I was aroused by a stealthy step passing my room. I rose, opened my door, and peeped out. A long black shadow was trailing down the corridor. It was thrown by a man who walked softly down the passage with a candle held in his hand. He was in shirt and trousers, with no covering to his feet. I could merely see the outline, but his height told me that it was Barrymore. He walked very slowly and circumspectly, and there was something indescribably guilty and furtive in his whole appearance.

I have told you that the corridor is broken by the balcony which runs round the hall, but that it is resumed upon the farther side. I waited until he had passed out of sight and then I followed him. When I came round the balcony he had reached the end of the farther corridor, and I could see from the glimmer of light through an open door that he had entered one of the rooms. Now, all these rooms are unfurnished and unoccupied, so that his expedition became more mysterious than ever. The light shone steadily as if he were standing motionless. I crept down the passage as noiselessly as I could and peeped round the corner of the door.

Barrymore was crouching at the window with the candle held against the glass. His profile was half turned towards me, and his face seemed to be rigid with expectation as he stared out into the blackness of the moor. For some minutes he stood watching intently. Then he gave a deep groan and with an impatient gesture he put out the light. Instantly I made my way back to my room, and very shortly came the stealthy steps passing once more upon their return journey. Long afterwards when I had fallen into a light sleep I heard a key turn somewhere in a lock, but I could not tell whence the sound came. What it all means I cannot guess, but there is some secret business going on in this house of gloom which sooner or later we shall get to the bottom of. I do not trouble you with my theories, for you asked me to furnish you only with facts. I have had a long talk with Sir Henry this morning, and we have made a plan of campaign founded upon my observations of last night. I will not speak about it just now, but it should make my next report interesting reading.

CHAPTER IX.

[Second Report of Dr. Watson.]
THE LIGHT UPON THE MOOR.

Baskerville Hall, Oct. 15th.

Y DEAR HOLMES, - If I was compelled to leave you without much news during the early days of my mission you must acknowledge that I am making up for lost time, and that events are now crowding thick and fast upon us. In my last report I ended upon my top note with Barrymore at the window, and now I have quite a budget already which will, unless I am much mistaken, considerably surprise you. Things have taken a turn which I could not have anticipated. In some ways they have within the last forty-eight hours become much clearer and in some ways they have become more complicated. But I will tell you all and you shall judge for yourself.

Before breakfast on the morning following my adventure I went down the corridor and examined the room in which Barrymore had been on the night before. The western window through which he had stared so intently has, I noticed, one peculiarity above all other windows in the house - it commands the nearest outlook on to the moor. There is an opening between two trees which enables one from this point of view to look right down upon it, while from all the other windows it is only a distant glimpse which can be obtained. It follows, therefore, that Barrymore, since only this window would serve his purpose, must have been looking out for something or somebody upon the moor. The night was very dark, so that I can hardly imagine how he could have hoped to see anyone. It had struck me that it was possible that some love intrigue was on foot. That would have accounted for his stealthy movements and also for the uneasiness of his wife. The man is a striking-looking fellow, very well equipped to steal the heart of a country girl, so that this theory seemed to have something to support it. That opening of the door which I had heard after I had returned to my room might mean that he had gone out to keep some clandestine appointment. So I reasoned with myself in the morning, and I tell you the direction of my suspicions, however much the result may have shown that they were unfounded.

But whatever the true explanation of Barrymore's movements might be, I felt that the responsibility of keeping them to myself until I could explain them was more than I could bear. I had an interview with the baronet in his study after breakfast, and I told him all that I had seen. He was less surprised than I had expected.

"I knew that Barrymore walked about nights, and I had a mind to speak to him about it," said he. "Two or three times I have heard his steps in the passage, coming and going, just about the hour you name."

"Perhaps then he pays a visit every night to that particular window," I suggested.

"Perhaps he does. If so, we should be able to shadow him, and see what it is that he is after. I wonder what your friend Holmes would do if he were here?"

"I believe that he would do exactly what you now suggest," said I. "He would follow Barrymore and see what he did."

"Then we shall do it together."

"But surely he would hear us."

"The man is rather deaf, and in any case we must take our chance of that. We'll sit up in my room to-night and wait until he passes." Sir Henry rubbed his hands with pleasure, and it was evident that he hailed the adventure as a relief to his somewhat quiet life upon the moor.

The baronet has been in communication with the architect who prepared the plans for Sir Charles, and with a contractor from London, so that we may expect great changes to begin here soon. There have been decorators and furnishers up from Plymouth, and it is evident that our friend has large ideas, and means to spare no pains or expense to restore the grandeur of his family. When the house is renovated and refurnished, all that he will need will be a wife to make it complete. Between ourselves there are pretty clear signs that this will not be wanting if the lady is willing, for I have seldom seen a man more infatuated with a woman than he is with our beautiful neighbour, Miss Stapleton. And yet the course of true love does not run quite as smoothly as one would under the circumstances expect. To-day, for example, its surface was broken by a very unexpected ripple, which has caused our friend considerable perplexity and annoyance.

After the conversation which I have quoted about Barrymore Sir Henry put on his hat and prepared to go out. As a matter of course I did the same.

"What, are _you_ coming, Watson?" he asked, looking at me in a curious way.

"That depends on whether you are going on the moor," said I.

"Yes, I am."

"Well, you know what my instructions are. I am sorry to intrude, but you heard how earnestly Holmes insisted that I should not leave you, and especially that you should not go alone upon the moor."

Sir Henry put his hand upon my shoulder, with a pleasant smile.

"My dear fellow," said he, "Holmes, with all his wisdom, did not foresee some things which have happened since I have been on the moor. You understand me? I am sure that you are the last man in the world who would wish to be a spoil-sport. I must go out alone."

It put me in a most awkward position. I was at a loss what to say or what to do, and before I had made up my mind he picked up his cane and was gone.

But when I came to think the matter over my conscience reproached me bitterly for having on any pretext allowed him to go out of my sight. I imagined what my feelings would be if I had to return to you and to confess that some misfortune had occurred through my disregard for your instructions. I assure you my cheeks flushed at the very thought. It might not even now be too late to overtake him, so I set off at once in the direction of Merripit House.

I hurried along the road at the top of my speed without seeing anything of Sir Henry, until I came to the point where the moor path branches off. There, fearing that perhaps I had come in the wrong direction after all, I mounted a hill from which I could command a view - the same hill which is cut into the dark quarry. Thence I saw him at once. He was on the moor path, about a quarter of a mile off, and a lady was by his side who could only be Miss Stapleton. It was clear that there was already an understanding between them and that they had met by appointment. They were walking slowly along in deep conversation, and I saw her making quick little movements of her hands as if she were very earnest in what she was saying, while he listened intently, and once or twice shook his head in strong dissent. I stood among the rocks watching them, very much puzzled as to what I should do next. To follow them and break into their intimate conversation seemed to be an outrage, and yet my clear duty was never for an instant to let him out of my sight. To act the spy upon a friend was a hateful task. Still, I could see no better course than to observe him from the hill, and to clear my conscience by confessing to him afterwards what I had done. It is true that if any sudden danger had threatened him I was too far away to be of use, and yet I am sure that you will agree with me that the position was very difficult, and that there was nothing more which I could do.

Our friend, Sir Henry, and the lady had halted on the path and were standing deeply absorbed in their conversation, when I was suddenly aware that I was not the only witness of their interview. A wisp of green floating in the air caught my eye, and another glance showed me that it was carried on a stick by a man who was moving among the broken ground. It was Stapleton with his butterfly-net. He was very much closer to the pair than I was, and he appeared to be moving in their direction. At this instant Sir Henry suddenly drew Miss Stapleton to his side. His arm was round her, but it seemed to me that she was straining away from him with her face averted. He stooped his head to hers, and she raised one hand as if in protest. Next moment I saw them spring apart and turn hurriedly round. Stapleton was the cause of the interruption. He was running wildly towards them, his absurd net dangling behind him. He gesticulated and almost danced with excitement in front of the lovers. What the scene meant I could not imagine, but it seemed to me that Stapleton was abusing Sir Henry, who offered explanations, which became more angry as the other refused to accept them. The lady stood by in haughty silence. Finally Stapleton turned upon his heel and beckoned in a peremptory way to his sister, who, after an irresolute glance at Sir Henry, walked off by the side of her brother. The naturalist's angry gestures showed that the lady was included in his displeasure. The baronet stood for a minute looking after them, and then he walked slowly back the way that he had come, his head hanging, the very picture of dejection.

What all this meant I could not imagine, but I was deeply ashamed to have witnessed so intimate a scene without my friend's knowledge. I ran down the hill therefore and met the baronet at the bottom. His face was flushed with anger and his brows were wrinkled, like one who is at his wits' ends what to do.

"Halloa, Watson! Where have you dropped from?" said he. "You don't mean to say that you came after me in spite of all?"

I explained everything to him: how I had found it impossible to remain behind, how I had followed him, and how I had witnessed all that had occurred. For an instant his eyes blazed at me, but my frankness disarmed his anger, and he broke at last into a rather rueful laugh.

"You would have thought the middle of that prairie a fairly safe place for a man to be private," said he, "but, by thunder, the whole country-side seems to have been out to see me do my wooing - and a mighty poor wooing at that! Where had you engaged a seat?"

"I was on that hill."

"Quite in the back row, eh? But her brother was well up to the front. Did you see him come out on us?"

"Yes, I did."

"Did he ever strike you as being crazy - this brother of hers?"

"I can't say that he ever did."

"I dare say not. I always thought him sane enough until to-day, but you can take it from me that either he or I ought to be in a strait-jacket. What's the matter with me, anyhow? You've lived near me for some weeks, Watson. Tell me straight, now! Is there anything that would prevent me from making a good husband to a woman that I loved?"

"I should say not."

"He can't object to my worldly position, so it must be myself that he has this down on. What has he against me? I never hurt man or woman in my life that I know of. And yet he would not so much as let me touch the tips of her fingers."

"Did he say so?"

"That, and a deal more. I tell you, Watson, I've only known her these few weeks, but from the first I just felt that she was made for me, and she, too - she was happy when she was with me, and that I'll swear. There's a light in a woman's eyes that speaks louder than words. But he has never let us get together, and it was only to-day for the first time that I saw a chance of having a few words with her alone. She was glad to meet me, but when she did it was not love that she would talk about, and she wouldn't have let me talk about it either if she could have stopped it.

She kept coming back to it that this was a place of danger, and that she would never be happy until I had left it. I told her that since I had seen her I was in no hurry to leave it, and that if she really wanted me to go the only way to work it was for her to arrange to go with me. With that I offered in as many words to marry her, but before she could answer, down came this brother of hers, running at us with a face on him like a madman. He was just white with rage, and those light eyes of his were blazing with fury. What was I doing with the lady? How dared I offer her attentions which were distasteful to her? Did I think that because I was a baronet I could do what I liked? If he had not been her brother I should have known better how to answer him. As it was I told him that my feelings towards his sister were such as I was not ashamed of, and that I hoped that she might honour me by becoming my wife. That seemed to make the matter no better, so then I lost my temper too, and I answered him rather more hotly than I should perhaps, considering that she was standing by. So it ended by his going off with her, as you saw, and here am I as badly puzzled a man as any in this county. Just tell me what it all means, Watson, and I'll owe you more than ever I can hope to pay."

I tried one or two explanations, but, indeed, I was completely puzzled myself. Our friend's title, his fortune, his age, his character, and his appearance are all in his favour, and I know nothing against him, unless it be this dark fate which runs in his family. That his advances should be rejected so brusquely without any reference to the lady's own wishes, and that the lady should accept the situation without protest, is very amazing. However, our conjectures were set at rest by a visit from Stapleton himself that very afternoon. He had come to offer apologies for his rudeness of the morning, and after a long private interview with Sir Henry in his study the upshot of their conversation was that the breach is quite healed, and that we are to dine at Merripit House next Friday as a sign of it.

"I don't say now that he isn't a crazy man," said Sir Henry; "I can't forget the look in his eyes when he ran at me this morning, but I must allow that no man could make a more handsome apology than he has done."

"Did he give any explanation of his conduct?"

"His sister is everything in his life, he says. That is natural enough, and I am glad that he should understand her value. They have always been together, and according to his account he has been a very lonely man with only her as a companion, so that the thought of losing her was really terrible to him. He had not understood, he said, that I was becoming attached to her, but when he saw with his own eyes that it was really so, and that she might be taken away from him, it gave him such a shock that for a time he was not responsible for what he said or did. He was very sorry for all that had passed, and he recognised how foolish and how selfish it was that he should imagine that he could hold a beautiful woman like his sister to himself for her whole life. If she had to leave him he had rather it was to a neighbour like myself than to anyone else. But in any case it was a blow to him, and it would take him some time before he could prepare himself to meet it. He would withdraw all opposition upon his part if I would promise for three months to let the matter rest and to be content with cultivating the lady's friendship during that time without claiming her love. This I promised, and so the matter rests."

So there is one of our small mysteries cleared up. It is something to have touched bottom anywhere in this bog in which we are floundering. We know now why Stapleton looked with disfavour upon his sister's suitor - even when that suitor was so eligible a one as Sir Henry. And now I pass on to another thread which I have extricated out of the tangled skein, the mystery of the sobs in the night, of the tear-stained face of Mrs. Barrymore, of the secret journey of the butler to the western lattice window. Congratulate me, my dear Holmes, and tell me that I have not disappointed you as an agent - that you do not regret the confidence which you showed in me when you sent me down. All these things have by one night's work been thoroughly cleared.

I have said "by one night's work," but, in truth, it was by two nights' work, for on the first we drew entirely blank. I sat up with Sir Henry in his room until nearly three o'clock in the morning, but no sound of any sort did we hear except the chiming clock upon the stairs. It was a most melancholy vigil, and ended by each of us falling asleep in our chairs. Fortunately we were not discouraged, and we determined to try again. The next night we lowered the lamp and sat smoking cigarettes without making the least sound. It was incredible how slowly the hours crawled by, and yet we were helped through it by the same sort of patient interest which the hunter must feel as he watches the trap into which he hopes the game may wander. One struck, and two, and we had almost for the second time given it up in despair, when in an instant we both sat bolt upright in our chairs with all our weary senses keenly on the alert once more. We had heard the creak of a step in the passage.

Very stealthily we heard it pass along until it died away in the distance. Then the baronet gently opened his door and we set out in pursuit. Already our man had gone round the gallery, and the corridor was all in darkness. Softly we stole along until we had come into the other wing. We were just in time to catch a glimpse of the tall, black-bearded figure, his shoulders rounded, as he tip-toed down the passage. Then he passed through the same door as before, and the light of the candle framed it in the darkness and shot one single yellow beam across the gloom of the corridor. We shuffled cautiously towards it, trying every plank before we dared to put our whole weight upon it. We had taken the precaution of leaving our boots behind us, but, even so, the old boards snapped and creaked beneath our tread. Sometimes it seemed impossible that he should fail to hear our approach. However, the man is fortunately rather deaf, and he was entirely preoccupied in that which he was doing. When at last we reached the door and peeped through we found him crouching at the window, candle in hand, his white, intent face pressed against the pane, exactly as I had seen him two nights before.

We had arranged no plan of campaign, but the baronet is a man to whom the most direct way is always the most natural. He walked into the room, and as he did so Barrymore sprang up from the window with a sharp hiss of his breath, and stood, livid and trembling, before us. His dark eyes, glaring out of the white mask of his face, were full of horror and astonishment as he gazed from Sir Henry to me.

"What are you doing here, Barrymore?"

"Nothing, sir." His agitation was so great that he could hardly speak, and the shadows sprang up and down from the shaking of his candle. "It was the window, sir. I go round at night to see that they are fastened."

"On the second floor?"

"Yes, sir, all the windows."

"Look here, Barrymore," said Sir Henry, sternly; "we have made up our minds to have the truth out of you, so it will save you trouble to tell it sooner rather than later. Come, now! No lies! What were you doing at that window?'

The fellow looked at us in a helpless way, and he wrung his hands together like one who is in the last extremity of doubt and misery.

"I was doing no harm, sir. I was holding a candle to the window."

"And why were you holding a candle to the window?"

"Don't ask me, Sir Henry - don't ask me! I give you my word, sir, that it is not my secret, and that I cannot tell it. If it concerned no one but myself I would not try to keep it from you."

A sudden idea occurred to me, and I took the candle from the window-sill where the butler had placed it.

"He must have been holding it as a signal," said I. "Let us see if there is any answer." I held it as he had done, and stared out into the darkness of the night. Vaguely I could discern the black bank of the trees and the lighter expanse of the moor, for the moon was behind the clouds. And then I gave a cry of exultation, for a tiny pin-point of yellow light had suddenly transfixed the dark veil, and glowed steadily in the centre of the black square framed by the window.

"There it is!" I cried.

"No, no, sir, it is nothing - nothing at all!" the butler broke in; "I assure you, sir - "

"Move your light across the window, Watson!" cried the baronet. "See, the other moves also! Now, you rascal, do you deny that it is a signal? Come, speak up! Who is your confederate out yonder, and what is this conspiracy that is going on?"

The man's face became openly defiant.

"It is my business, and not yours. I will not tell."

"Then you leave my employment right away."

"Very good, sir. If I must I must."

"And you go in disgrace. By thunder, you may well be ashamed of yourself. Your family has lived with mine for over a hundred years under this roof, and here I find you deep in some dark plot against me."

"No, no, sir; no, not against you!" It was a woman's voice, and Mrs. Barrymore, paler and more horror-struck than her husband, was standing at the door. Her bulky figure in a shawl and skirt might have been comic were it not for the intensity of feeling upon her face.

"We have to go, Eliza. This is the end of it. You can pack our things," said the butler.

"Oh, John, John, have I brought you to this? It is my doing, Sir Henry - all mine. He has done nothing except for my sake, and because I asked him."

"Speak out, then! What does it mean?"

"My unhappy brother is starving on the moor. We cannot let him perish at our very gates. The light is a signal to him that food is ready for him, and his light out yonder is to show the spot to which to bring it."

"Then your brother is - "

"The escaped convict, sir - Selden, the criminal."

"That's the truth, sir," said Barrymore. "I said that it was not my secret and that I could not tell it to you. But now you have heard it, and you will see that if there was a plot it was not against you."

This, then, was the explanation of the stealthy expeditions at night and the light at the window. Sir Henry and I both stared at the woman in amazement. Was it possible that this stolidly respectable person was of the same blood as one of the most notorious criminals in the country?

"Yes, sir, my name was Selden, and he is my younger brother. We humoured him too much when he was a lad, and gave him his own way in everything until he came to think that the world was made for his pleasure, and that he could do what he liked in it. Then, as he grew older, he met wicked companions, and the devil entered into him until he broke my mother's heart and dragged our name in the dirt. From crime to crime he sank lower and lower, until it is only the mercy of God which has snatched him from the scaffold; but to me, sir, he was always the little curly-headed boy that I had nursed and played with, as an elder sister would. That was why he broke prison, sir. He knew that I was here and that we could not refuse to help him. When he dragged himself here one night, weary and starving, with the warders hard at his heels, what could we do? We took him in and fed him and cared for him. Then you returned, sir, and my brother thought he would be safer on the moor than anywhere else until the hue and cry was over, so he lay in hiding there. But every second night we made sure if he was still there by putting a light in the window, and if there was an answer my husband took out some bread and meat to him. Every day we hoped that he was gone, but as long as he was there we could not desert him.

That is the whole truth, as I am an honest Christian woman, and you will see that if there is blame in the matter it does not lie with my husband, but with me, for whose sake he has done all that he has."

The woman's words came with an intense earnestness which carried conviction with them.

"Is this true, Barrymore?"

"Yes, Sir Henry. Every word of it."

"Well, I cannot blame you for standing by your own wife. Forget what I have said. Go to your room, you two, and we shall talk further about this matter in the morning."

When they were gone we looked out of the window again. Sir Henry had flung it open, and the cold night wind beat in upon our faces. Far away in the black distance there still glowed that one tiny point of yellow light.

"I wonder he dares," said Sir Henry.

"It may be so placed as to be only visible from here."

"Very likely. How far do you think it is?"

"Out by the Cleft Tor, I think."

"Not more than a mile or two off."

"Hardly that."

"Well, it cannot be far if Barrymore had to carry out the food to it. And he is waiting, this villain, beside that candle. By thunder, Watson, I am going out to take that man!"

The same thought had crossed my own mind. It was not as if the Barrymores had taken us into their confidence. Their secret had been forced from them. The man was a danger to the community, an unmitigated scoundrel for whom there was neither pity nor excuse. We were only doing our duty in taking this chance of putting him back where he could do no harm. With his brutal and violent nature, others would have to pay the price if we held our hands. Any night, for example, our neighbours the Stapletons might be attacked by him, and it may have been the thought of this which made Sir Henry so keen upon the adventure.

"I will come," said I.

"Then get your revolver and put on your boots. The sooner we start the better, as the fellow may put out his light and be off."

In five minutes we were outside the door, starting upon our expedition. We hurried through the dark shrubbery, amid the dull moaning of the autumn wind and the rustle of the falling leaves. The night air was heavy with the smell of damp and decay. Now and again the moon peeped out for an instant, but clouds were driving over the face of the sky, and just as we came out on the moor a thin rain began to fall. The light still burned steadily in front.

"Are you armed?" I asked.

"I have a hunting-crop."

"We must close in on him rapidly, for he is said to be a desperate fellow. We shall take him by surprise and have him at our mercy before he can resist."

"I say, Watson," said the baronet, "what would Holmes say to this? How about that hour of darkness in which the power of evil is exalted?"

As if in answer to his words there rose suddenly out of the vast gloom of the moor that strange cry which I had already heard upon the borders of the great Grimpen Mire. It came with the wind through the silence of the night, a long, deep mutter, then a rising howl, and then the sad moan in which it died away. Again and again it sounded, the whole air throbbing with it, strident, wild, and menacing. The baronet caught my sleeve and his face glimmered white through the darkness.

"Good heavens, what's that, Watson?"

"I don't know. It's a sound they have on the moor. I heard it once before."

It died away, and an absolute silence closed in upon us. We stood straining our ears, but nothing came.

"Watson," said the baronet, "it was the cry of a hound."

My blood ran cold in my veins, for there was a break in his voice which told of the sudden horror which had seized him.

"What do they call this sound?" he asked.

"Who?"

"The folk on the country-side."

"Oh, they are ignorant people. Why should you mind what they call it?"

"Tell me, Watson. What do they say of it?"

I hesitated, but could not escape the question.

"They say it is the cry of the Hound of the Baskervilles."

He groaned, and was silent for a few moments.

"A hound it was," he said, at last, "but it seemed to come from miles away, over yonder, I think."

"It was hard to say whence it came."

"It rose and fell with the wind. Isn't that the direction of the great Grimpen Mire?"

"Yes, it is."

"Well, it was up there. Come now, Watson, didn't you think yourself that it was the cry of a hound? I am not a child. You need not fear to speak the truth."

"Stapleton was with me when I heard it last. He said that it might be the calling of a strange bird."

"No, no, it was a hound. My God, can there be some truth in all these stories? Is it possible that I am really in danger from so dark a cause? You don't believe it, do you, Watson?"

"No, no."

"And yet it was one thing to laugh about it in London, and it is another to stand out here in the darkness of the moor and to hear such a cry as that. And my uncle! There was the footprint of the hound beside him as he lay. It all fits together. I don't think that I am a coward, Watson, but that sound seemed to freeze my very blood. Feel my hand!"

It was as cold as a block of marble.

"You'll be all right to-morrow."

"I don't think I'll get that cry out of my head. What do you advise that we do now?"

"Shall we turn back?"

"No, by thunder; we have come out to get our man, and we will do it. We are after the convict, and a hell-hound, as likely as not, after us. Come on! We'll see it through if all the fiends of the pit were loose upon the moor."

We stumbled slowly along in the darkness, with the black loom of the craggy hills around us, and the yellow speck of light burning steadily in front. There is nothing so deceptive as the distance of a light upon a pitch-dark night, and sometimes the glimmer seemed to be far away upon the horizon and sometimes it might have been within a few yards of us. But at last we could see whence it came, and then we knew that we were indeed very close. A guttering candle was stuck in a crevice of the rocks which flanked it on each side so as to keep the wind from it, and also to prevent it from being visible, save in the direction of Baskerville Hall. A boulder of granite concealed our approach, and crouching behind it we gazed over it at the signal light. It was strange to see this single candle burning there in the middle of the moor, with no sign of life near it - just the one straight yellow flame and the gleam of the rock on each side of it.

"What shall we do now?" whispered Sir Henry.

"Wait here. He must be near his light. Let us see if we can get a glimpse of him."

The words were hardly out of my mouth when we both saw him. Over the rocks, in the crevice of which the candle burned, there was thrust out an evil yellow face, a terrible animal face, all seamed and scored with vile passions. Foul with mire, with a bristling beard, and hung with matted hair, it might well have belonged to one of those old savages who dwelt in the burrows on the hill-sides. The light beneath him was reflected in his small, cunning eyes, which peered fiercely to right and left through the darkness, like a crafty and savage animal who has heard the steps of the hunters.

Something had evidently aroused his suspicions. It may have been that Barrymore had some private signal which we had neglected to give, or the fellow may have had some other reason for thinking that all was not well, but I could read his fears upon his wicked face. Any instant he might dash out the light and vanish in the darkness. I sprang forward therefore, and Sir Henry did the same. At the same moment the convict screamed out a curse at us and hurled a rock which splintered up against the boulder which had sheltered us. I caught one glimpse of his short, squat, strongly-built figure as he sprang to his feet and turned to run. At the same moment by a lucky chance the moon broke through the clouds. We rushed over the brow of the hill, and there was our man running with great speed down the other side, springing over the stones in his way with the activity of a mountain goat. A lucky long shot of my revolver might have crippled him, but I had brought it only to defend myself if attacked, and not to shoot an unarmed man who was running away.

We were both fair runners and in good condition, but we soon found that we had no chance of overtaking him. We saw him for a long time in the moonlight until he was only a small speck moving swiftly among the boulders upon the side of a distant hill. We ran and ran until we were completely blown, but the space between us grew ever wider. Finally we stopped and sat panting on two rocks, while we watched him disappearing in the distance.

And it was at this moment that there occurred a most strange and unexpected thing. We had risen from our rocks and were turning to go home, having abandoned the hopeless chase. The moon was low upon the right, and the jagged pinnacle of a granite tor stood up against the lower curve of its silver disc. There, outlined as black as an ebony statue on that shining background, I saw the figure of a man upon the tor. Do not think that it was a delusion, Holmes. I assure you that I have never in my life seen anything more clearly. As far as I could judge, the figure was that of a tall, thin man. He stood with his legs a little separated, his arms folded, his head bowed, as if he were brooding over that enormous wilderness of peat and granite which lay before him. He might have been the very spirit of that terrible place. It was not the convict. This man was far from the place where the latter had disappeared. Besides, he was a much taller man. With a cry of surprise I pointed him out to the baronet, but in the instant during which I had turned to grasp his arm the man was gone. There was the sharp pinnacle of granite still cutting the lower edge of the moon, but its peak bore no trace of that silent and motionless figure.

I wished to go in that direction and to search the tor, but it was some distance away. The baronet's nerves were still quivering from that cry, which recalled the dark story of his family, and he was not in the mood for fresh adventures. He had not seen this lonely man upon the tor and could not feel the thrill which his strange presence and his commanding attitude had given to me. "A warder, no doubt," said he. "The moor has been thick with them since this fellow escaped." Well, perhaps his explanation may be the right one, but I should like to have some further proof of it. To-day we mean to communicate to the Princetown people where they should look for their missing man, but it is hard lines that we have not actually had the triumph of bringing him back as our own prisoner. Such are the adventures of last night, and you must acknowledge, my dear Holmes, that I have done you very well in the matter of a report. Much of what I tell you is no doubt quite irrelevant, but still I feel that it is best that I should let you have all the facts and leave you to select for yourself those which will be of most service to you in helping you to your conclusions. We are certainly making some progress. So far as the Barrymores go we have found the motive of their actions, and that has cleared up the situation very much. But the moor with its mysteries and its strange inhabitants remains as inscrutable as ever. Perhaps in my next I may be able to throw some light upon this also. Best of all would it be if if you could come down to us.

"I saw the figure of a man upon the tor".
As Watson and Sir Henry are returning Eastwards
to 'Baskerville Hall' the low Moon suggests that the
mysterious Man on the Tor is to the South of
Watson and Sir Henry.

The shadow of Sherlock Holmes
Paget's very substantial *'stone hut'* reveals his lack of Dartmoor knowledge. Being at the start of
the relevant chapter, the caption gave the identity of the mysterious inhabitant away!

CHAPTER X.

EXTRACT FROM THE DIARY OF DR. WATSON.

O far I have been able to quote from the reports which I have forwarded during these early days to Sherlock Holmes. Now, however, I have arrived at a point in my narrative where I am compelled to abandon this method and to trust once more to my recollections, aided by the diary which I kept at the time. A few extracts from the latter will carry me on to those scenes which are indelibly fixed in every detail upon my memory. I proceed, then, from the morning which followed our abortive chase of the convict and our other strange experiences upon the moor.

October 16th. - A dull and foggy day, with a drizzle of rain. The house is banked in with rolling clouds, which rise now and then to show the dreary curves of the moor, with thin, silver veins upon the sides of the hills, and the distant boulders gleaming where the light strikes upon their wet faces. It is melancholy outside and in. The baronet is in a black reaction after the excitements of the night. I am conscious myself of a weight at my heart and a feeling of impending danger - ever-present danger, which is the more terrible because I am unable to define it.

And have I not cause for such a feeling? Consider the long sequence of incidents which have all pointed to some sinister influence which is at work around us. There is the death of the last occupant of the Hall, fulfilling so exactly the conditions of the family legend, and there is the repeated reports from peasants of the appearance of a strange creature upon the moor. Twice I have with my own ears heard the sound which resembled the distant baying of a hound. It is incredible, impossible, that it should really be outside the ordinary laws of Nature. A spectral hound which leaves material footmarks and fills the air with its howling is surely not to be thought of. Stapleton may fall in with such a superstition, and Mortimer also; but if I have one quality upon earth it is common sense, and nothing will persuade me to believe in such a thing. To do so would be to descend to the level of these poor peasants who are not content with a mere fiend dog, but must needs describe him with hell-fire shooting from his mouth and eyes. Holmes would not listen to such fancies, and I am his agent. But facts are facts, and I have twice heard this crying upon the moor. Suppose that there were really some huge hound loose upon it; that would go far to explain everything. But where could such a hound lie concealed, where did it get its food, where did it come from, how was it that no one saw it by day? It must be confessed that the natural explanation offers almost as many difficulties as the other. And always, apart from the hound, there was the fact of the human agency in London, the man in the cab, and the letter which warned Sir Henry against the moor. This at least was real, but it might have been the work of a protecting friend as easily as an enemy. Where was that friend or enemy now? Had he remained in London, or had he followed us down here? Could he - could he be the stranger whom I had seen upon the Tor?

It is true that I have had only the one glance at him, and yet there are some things to which I am ready to swear. He is no one whom I have seen down here, and I have now met all the neighbours. The figure was far taller than that of Stapleton, far thinner than that of Frankland. Barrymore it might possibly have been, but we had left him behind us, and I am certain that he could not have followed us. A stranger then is still dogging us, just as a stranger had dogged us in London. We have never shaken him off. If I could lay my hands upon that man, then at last we might find ourselves at the end of all our difficulties. To this one purpose I must now devote all my energies.

My first impulse was to tell Sir Henry all my plans. My second and wisest one is to play my own game and speak as little as possible to anyone. He is silent and distrait. His nerves have been strangely shaken by that sound upon the moor. I will say nothing to add to his anxieties, but I will take my own steps to attain my own end.

We had a small scene this morning after breakfast. Barrymore asked leave to speak with Sir Henry, and they were closeted in his study some little time. Sitting in the billiard-room I more than once heard the sound of voices raised, and I had a pretty good idea what the point was which was under discussion. After a time the baronet opened his door and called for me.

"Barrymore considers that he has a grievance," he said. "He thinks that it was unfair on our part to hunt his brother-in-law down when he, of his own free will, had told us the secret."

The butler was standing, very pale but very collected, before us.

"I may have spoken too warmly, sir," said he, "and if I have I am sure that I beg your pardon. At the same time, I was very much surprised when I heard you two gentlemen come back this morning and learned that you had been chasing Selden. The poor fellow has enough to fight against without my putting more upon his track."

"If you had told us of your own free will it would have been a different thing," said the baronet. "You only told us, or rather your wife only told us, when it was forced from you and you could not help yourself."

"I didn't think you would have taken advantage of it, Sir Henry - indeed I didn't."

"The man is a public danger. There are lonely houses scattered over the moor, and he is a fellow who would stick at nothing. You only want to get a glimpse of his face to see that. Look at Mr. Stapleton's house, for example, with no one but himself to defend it. There's no safety for anyone until he is under lock and key."

"He'll break into no house, sir. I give you my solemn word upon that. But he will never trouble anyone in this country again. I assure you, Sir Henry, that in a very few days the necessary arrangements will have been made and he will be on his way to South America. For God's sake, sir, I beg of you not to let the police know that he is still on the moor. They have given up the chase there, and he can lie quiet until the ship is ready for him. You can't tell on him without getting my wife and me into trouble. I beg you, sir, to say nothing to the police."

"What do you say, Watson?"

I shrugged my shoulders. "If he were safely out of the country it would relieve the taxpayer of a burden."

"But how about the chance of his holding someone up before he goes?"

"He would not do anything so mad, sir. We have provided him with all that he can want. To commit a crime would be to show where he was hiding."

"That is true," said Sir Henry. "Well, Barrymore - "

"God bless you, sir, and thank you from my heart! It would have killed my poor wife had he been taken again."

"I guess we are aiding and abetting a felony, Watson? But, after what we have heard, I don't feel as if I could give the man up, so there is an end of it. All right, Barrymore, you can go."

With a few broken words of gratitude the man turned, but he hesitated and then came back.

"You've been so kind to us, sir, that I should like to do the best I can for you in return. I know something, Sir Henry, and perhaps I should have said it before, but it was long after the inquest that I found it out. I've never breathed a word about it yet to mortal man. It's about poor Sir Charles's death."

The baronet and I were both upon our feet. "Do you know how he died?"

"No, sir, I don't know that."

"What, then?"

"I know why he was at the gate at that hour. It was to meet a woman."

"To meet a woman! He?"

"Yes, sir."

"And the woman's name?"

"I can't give you the name, sir, but I can give you the initials. Her initials were L. L."

"How do you know this, Barrymore?"

"Well, Sir Henry, your uncle had a letter that morning. He had usually a great many letters, for he was a public man and well known for his kind heart, so that everyone who was in trouble was glad to turn to him. But that morning, as it chanced, there was only this one letter, so I took the more notice of it. It was from Coombe Tracey, and it was addressed in a woman's hand."

"Well?"

"Well, sir, I thought no more of the matter, and never would have done had it not been for my wife. Only a few weeks ago she was cleaning out Sir Charles's study - it had never been touched since his death - and she found the ashes of a burned letter in the back of the grate. The greater part of it was charred to pieces, but one little slip, the end of a page, hung together, and the writing could still be read, though it was grey on a black ground. It seemed to us to be a post-script at the end of the letter, and it said: 'Please, please, as you are a gentleman, burn this letter, and be at the gate by ten o'clock.' Beneath it were signed the initials L. L."

"Have you got that slip?"

"No, sir, it crumbled all to bits after we moved it."

"Had Sir Charles received any other letters in the same writing?"

"Well, sir, I took no particular notice of his letters. I should not have noticed this one only it happened to come alone."

"And you have no idea who L. L. is?"

"No, sir. No more than you have. But I expect if we could lay our hands upon that lady we should know more about Sir Charles's death."

"I cannot understand, Barrymore, how you came to conceal this important information."

"Well, sir, it was immediately after that our own trouble came to us. And then again, sir, we were both of us very fond of Sir Charles, as we well might be considering all that he has done for us. To rake this up couldn't help our poor master, and it's well to go carefully when there's a lady in the case. Even the best of us - "

"You thought it might injure his reputation?"

"Well, sir, I thought no good could come of it. But now you have been kind to us, and I feel as if it would be treating you unfairly not to tell you all that I know about the matter."

"Very good, Barrymore; you can go." When the butler had left us Sir Henry turned to me. "Well, Watson, what do you think of this new light?"

"It seems to leave the darkness rather blacker than before."

"So I think. But if we can only trace L. L. it should clear up the whole business. We have gained that much. We know that there is someone who has the facts if we can only find her. What do you think we should do?"

"Let Holmes know all about it at once. It will give him the clue for which he has been seeking. I am much mistaken if it does not bring him down."

I went at once to my room and drew up my report of the morning's conversation for Holmes. It was evident to me that he had been very busy of late, for the notes which I had from Baker Street were few and short, with no comments upon the information which I had supplied, and hardly any reference to my mission. No doubt his blackmailing case is absorbing all his faculties. And yet this new factor must surely arrest his attention and renew his interest. I wish that he were here.

October 17th. - All day to-day the rain poured down, rustling on the ivy and dripping from the eaves. I thought of the convict out upon the bleak, cold, shelterless moor. Poor fellow!

*"From its craggy summit I looked out myself across
the melancholy downs"*
Watson on his *'black Tor'* in the wet and windy conditions which
are known well by all Moormen. The river below might be the
River Aune or the River Meavy.

Whatever his crimes, he has suffered something to atone for them. And then I thought of that other one - the face in the cab, the figure against the moon. Was he also out in that deluge - the unseen watcher, the man of darkness? In the evening I put on my waterproof and I walked far upon the sodden moor, full of dark imaginings, the rain beating upon my face and the wind whistling about my ears. God help those who wander into the Great Mire now, for even the firm uplands are becoming a morass. I found the black Tor upon which I had seen the solitary watcher, and from its craggy summit I looked out myself across the melancholy downs. Rain squalls drifted across their russet face, and the heavy, slate-coloured clouds hung low over the landscape, trailing in grey wreaths down the sides of the fantastic hills. In the distant hollow on the left, half hidden by the mist, the two thin towers of Baskerville Hall rose above the trees. They were the only signs of human life which I could see, save only those prehistoric huts which lay thickly upon the slopes of the hills. Nowhere was there any trace of that lonely man whom I had seen on the same spot two nights before.

As I walked back I was overtaken by Dr. Mortimer driving in his dog-cart, over a rough moorland track, which led from the out-lying farmhouse of Foulmire. He has been very attentive to us, and hardly a day has passed that he has not called at the Hall to see how we were getting on. He insisted upon my climbing into his dog-cart, and he gave me a lift homewards. I found him much troubled over the disappear-ance of his little spaniel. It had wandered on to the moor and had never come back. I gave him such consolation as I might, but I thought of the pony on the Grimpen Mire, and I do not fancy that he will see his little dog again.

"By the way, Mortimer," said I, as we jolted along the rough road, "I suppose there are few people living within driving distance of this whom you do not know?"

"Hardly any, I think."

"Can you, then, tell me the name of any woman whose initials are L. L.?"

He thought for a few minutes.

"No," said he. "There are a few gipsies and labouring folk for whom I can't answer, but among the farmers or gentry there is no one whose initials are those. Wait a bit, though," he added, after a pause. "There is Laura Lyons - her initials are L. L. - but she lives in Coombe Tracey."

"Who is she?" I asked.

"She is Frankland's daughter."

"What? Old Frankland the crank?"

"Exactly. She married an artist named Lyons, who came sketching on the moor. He proved to be a blackguard and deserted her. The fault from what I hear may not have been entirely on one side. Her father refused to have anything to do with her, because she had married without his consent, and perhaps for one or two other reasons as well. So, between the old sinner and the young one the girl has had a pretty bad time."

"How does she live?"

"I fancy old Frankland allows her a pittance, but it cannot be more, for his own affairs are considerably involved. Whatever she may have deserved one could not allow her to go hopelessly to the bad. Her story got about, and several of the people here did something to enable her to earn an honest living. Stapleton did for one, and Sir Charles for another. I gave a trifle myself. It was to set her up in a typewriting business."

He wanted to know the object of my inquiries, but I managed to satisfy his curiosity without telling him too much, for there is no reason why we should take anyone into our confidence. To-morrow morning I shall find my way to Coombe Tracey, and if I can see this Mrs. Laura Lyons, of equivocal reputation, a long step will have been made towards clearing one incident in this chain of mysteries. I am certainly developing the wisdom of the serpent, for when Mortimer pressed his questions to an inconvenient extent I asked him casually to what type Frankland's skull belonged, and so heard nothing but craniology for the rest of our drive. I have not lived for years with Sherlock Holmes for nothing.

I have only one other incident to record upon this tempestuous and melancholy day. This was my conversation with Barrymore just now, which gives me one more strong card which I can play in due time.

Mortimer had stayed to dinner, and he and the baronet played écarté afterwards. The butler brought me my coffee into the library, and I took the chance to ask him a few questions.

"Well," said I, "has this precious relation of yours departed, or is he still lurking out yonder?"

"I don't know, sir. I hope to Heaven that he has gone, for he has brought nothing but trouble here! I've not heard of him since I left out food for him last, and that was three days ago."

"Did you see him then?"

"No, sir, but the food was gone when next I went that way."

"Then he was certainly there?"

"So you would think, sir, unless it was the other man who took it."

I sat with my coffee-cup half-way to my lips and stared at Barrymore.

"You know that there is another man, then?"

"Yes, sir; there is another man upon the moor."

"Have you seen him?"

"No, sir."

"How do you know of him, then?"

"Selden told me of him, sir, a week ago or more. He's in hiding, too, but he's not a convict so far as I can make out. I don't like it, Dr. Watson - I tell you straight, sir, that I don't like it." He spoke with a sudden passion of earnestness.

"Now, listen to me, Barrymore! I have no interest in this matter but that of your master. I have come here with no object except to help him. Tell me, frankly, what it is that you don't like."

Barrymore hesitated for a moment, as if he regretted his outburst, or found it difficult to express his own feelings in words.

"It's all these goings-on, sir," he cried, at last, waving his hand towards the rain-lashed window which faced the moor. "There's foul play somewhere, and there's black villainy brewing, to that I'll swear! Very glad I should be, sir, to see Sir Henry on his way back to London again!"

"But what is it that alarms you?"

"Look at Sir Charles's death! That was bad enough, for all that the coroner said. Look at the noises on the moor at night. There's not a man would cross it after sundown if he was paid for it. Look at this stranger hiding out yonder, and watching and waiting! What's he waiting for? What does it mean? It means no good to anyone of the name of Baskerville, and very glad I shall be to be quit of it all on the day that Sir Henry's new servants are ready to take over the Hall."

"But about this stranger," said I. "Can you tell me anything about him? What did Selden say? Did he find out where he hid, or what he was doing?"

"He saw him once or twice, but he is a deep one, and gives nothing away. At first he thought that he was the police, but soon he found that he had some lay of his own. A kind of gentleman he was, as far as he could see, but what he was doing he could not make out."

"And where did he say that he lived?"

"Among the old houses on the hillside - the stone huts where the old folk used to live."

"But how about his food?"

"Selden found out that he has got a lad who works for him and brings him all he needs. I daresay he goes to Coombe Tracey for what he wants."

"Very good, Barrymore. We may talk further of this some other time." When the butler had gone I walked over to the black window, and I looked through a blurred pane at the driving clouds and at the tossing outline of the wind-swept trees. It is a wild night indoors, and what must it be in a stone hut upon the moor? What passion of hatred can it be which leads a man to lurk in such a place at such a time? And what deep and earnest purpose can he have which calls for such a trial? There, in that hut upon the moor, seems to lie the very centre of that problem which has vexed me so sorely. I swear that another day shall not have passed before I have done all that man can do to reach the heart of the mystery.

CHAPTER XI.

THE MAN ON THE TOR.

THE extract from my private diary which forms the last chapter has brought my narrative up to the 18th of October, a time when these strange events began to move swiftly towards their terrible conclusion. The incidents of the next few days are indelibly graven upon my recollection, and I can tell them without reference to the notes made at the time. I start, then, from the day which succeeded that upon which I had established two facts of great importance, the one that Mrs. Laura Lyons of Coombe Tracey had written to Sir Charles Baskerville and made an appointment with him at the very place and hour that he met his death, the other that the lurking man upon the moor was to be found among the stone huts upon the hill-side. With these two facts in my possession I felt that either my intelligence or my courage must be deficient if I could not throw some further light upon these dark places.

I had no opportunity to tell the baronet what I had learned about Mrs. Lyons upon the evening before, for Dr. Mortimer remained with him at cards until it was very late. At breakfast, however, I informed him about my discovery, and asked him whether he would care to accompany me to Coombe Tracey. At first he was very eager to come, but on second thoughts it seemed to both of us that if I went alone the results might be better. The more formal we made the visit the less information we might obtain. I left Sir Henry behind, therefore, not without some prickings of conscience, and drove off upon my new quest.

When I reached Coombe Tracey I told Perkins to put up the horses, and I made inquiries for the lady whom I had come to interrogate. I had no difficulty in finding her rooms, which were central and well appointed. A maid showed me in without ceremony, and as I entered the sitting-room a lady, who was sitting before a Remington typewriter, sprang up with a pleasant smile of welcome. Her face fell, however, when she saw that I was a stranger, and she sat down again and asked me the object of my visit.

The first impression left by Mrs. Lyons was one of extreme beauty. Her eyes and hair were of the same rich hazel colour, and her cheeks, though considerably freckled, were flushed with the exquisite bloom of the brunette, the dainty pink which lurks at the heart of the sulphur rose. Admiration was, I repeat, the first impression. But the second was criticism. There was something subtly wrong with the face, some coarseness of expression, some hardness, perhaps, of eye, some looseness of lip which marred its perfect beauty. But these, of course, are after-thoughts. At the moment I was simply conscious that I was in the presence of a very handsome woman, and that she was asking me the reasons for my visit. I had not quite understood until that instant how delicate my mission was.

"I have the pleasure," said I, "of knowing your father."

It was a clumsy introduction, and the lady made me feel it.

"There is nothing in common between my father and me," she said. "I owe him nothing, and his friends are not mine. If it were not for the late Sir Charles Baskerville and some other kind hearts I might have starved for all that my father cared."

"It was about the late Sir Charles Baskerville that I have come here to see you."

The freckles started out on the lady's face.

"What can I tell you about him?" she asked, and her fingers played nervously over the stops of her typewriter.

"You knew him, did you not?"

"I have already said that I owe a great deal to his kindness. If I am able to support myself it is largely due to the interest which he took in my unhappy situation."

"Did you correspond with him?"

The lady looked quickly up, with an angry gleam in her hazel eyes.

"What is the object of these questions?" she asked, sharply.

"The object is to avoid a public scandal. It is better that I should ask them here than that the matter should pass outside our control."

She was silent and her face was very pale. At last she looked up with something reckless and defiant in her manner.

"Well, I'll answer," she said. "What are your questions?"

"Did you correspond with Sir Charles?"

"I certainly wrote to him once or twice to acknowledge his delicacy and his generosity."

"Have you the dates of those letters?"

"No."

"Have you ever met him?"

"Yes, once or twice, when he came into Coombe Tracey. He was a very retiring man, and he preferred to do good by stealth."

"But if you saw him so seldom and wrote so seldom, how did he know enough about your affairs to be able to help you, as you say that he has done?"

She met my difficulty with the utmost readiness.

"There were several gentlemen who knew my sad history and united to help me. One was Mr. Stapleton, a neighbour and intimate friend of Sir Charles. He was exceedingly kind, and it was through him that Sir Charles learned about my affairs."

I knew already that Sir Charles Baskerville had made Stapleton his almoner upon several occasions, so the lady's statement bore the impress of truth upon it.

"Did you ever write to Sir Charles asking him to meet you?" I continued.

Mrs. Lyons flushed with anger again.

"Really, sir, this is a very extraordinary question."

"I am sorry, madam, but I must repeat it."

"Then I answer - certainly not."

"Not on the very day of Sir Charles's death?"

The flush had faded in an instant, and a deathly face was before me. Her dry lips could not speak the "No" which I saw rather than heard.

"Surely your memory deceives you," said I. "I could even quote a passage of your letter. It ran, 'Please, please, as you are a gentleman, burn this letter, and be at the gate by ten o'clock.' "

I thought that she had fainted, but she recovered herself by a supreme effort.

"Is there no such thing as a gentleman?" she gasped.

"You do Sir Charles an injustice. He *did* burn the letter. But sometimes a letter may be legible even when burned. You acknowledge now that you wrote it?"

"Yes, I did write it," she cried, pouring out her soul in a torrent of words. "I did write it. Why should I deny it? I have no reason to be ashamed of it. I wished him to help me. I believed that if I had an interview I could gain his help, so I asked him to meet me."

"But why at such an hour?"

"Because I had only just learned that he was going to London next day and might be away for months. There were reasons why I could not get there earlier."

"But why a rendezvous in the garden instead of a visit to the house?"

"Do you think a woman could go alone at that hour to a bachelor's house?"

"Well, what happened when you did get there?"

"I never went."

"Mrs. Lyons!"

"No, I swear it to you on all I hold sacred. I never went. Something intervened to prevent my going."

"What was that?"

"That is a private matter. I cannot tell it."

"You acknowledge, then, that you made an appointment with Sir Charles at the very hour and place at which he met his death, but you deny that you kept the appointment?"

"That is the truth."

Again and again I cross-questioned her, but I could never get past that point.

"Mrs. Lyons," said I, as I rose from this long and inconclusive interview, "you are taking a very great responsibility and putting yourself in a very false position by not making an absolutely clean breast of all that you know. If I have to call in the aid of the police you will find how seriously you are compromised. If your position is innocent, why did you in the first instance deny having written to Sir Charles upon that date?"

"Because I feared that some false conclusion might be drawn from it, and that I might find myself involved in a scandal."

"And why were you so pressing that Sir Charles should destroy your letter?"

"If you have read the letter you will know."

"I did not say that I had read all the letter."

"You quoted some of it."

"I quoted the postscript. The letter had, as I said, been burned, and it was not all legible. I ask you once again why it was that you were so pressing that Sir Charles should destroy this letter which he received on the day of his death."

"The matter is a very private one."

"The more reason why you should avoid a public investigation."

"I will tell you, then. If you have heard anything of my unhappy history you will know that I made a rash marriage and had reason to regret it."

"I have heard so much."

"My life has been one incessant persecution from a husband whom I abhor. The law is upon his side, and every day I am faced by the possibility that he may force me to live with him. At the time that I wrote this letter to Sir Charles I had learned that there was a prospect of my regaining my freedom if certain expenses could be met. It meant everything to me - peace of mind, happiness, self-respect - everything. I knew Sir Charles's generosity, and I thought that if he heard the story from my own lips he would help me."

"Then how is it that you did not go?"

"Because I received help in the interval from another source."

"Why, then, did you not write to Sir Charles and explain this?"

"So I should have done had I not seen his death in the paper next morning."

The woman's story hung coherently together, and all my questions were unable to shake it. I could only check it by finding if she had, indeed, instituted divorce proceedings against her husband at or about the time of the tragedy.

It was unlikely that she would dare to say that she had not been to Baskerville Hall if she really had been, for a trap would be necessary to take her there, and could not have returned to Coombe Tracey until the early hours of the morning. Such an excursion could not be kept secret. The probability was, therefore, that she was telling the truth, or, at least, a part of the truth. I came away baffled and disheartened. Once again I had reached that dead wall which seemed to be built across every path by which I tried to get at the object of my mission. And yet the more I thought of the lady's face and of her manner the more I felt that something was being held back from me. Why should she turn so pale? Why should she fight against every admission until it was forced from her? Why should she have been so reticent at the time of the tragedy? Surely the explanation of all this could not be as innocent as she would have me believe. For the moment I could proceed no farther in that direction, but must turn back to that other clue which was to be sought for among the stone huts upon the moor.

And that was a most vague direction. I realized it as I drove back and noted how hill after hill showed traces of the ancient people. Barrymore's only indication had been that the stranger lived in one of these abandoned huts, and many hundreds of them are scattered throughout the length and breadth of the moor. But I had my own experience for a guide, since it had shown me the man himself standing upon the summit of the Black Tor. That, then, should be the centre of my search. From there I should explore every hut upon the moor until I lighted upon the right one. If this man were inside it I should find out from his own lips, at the point of my revolver if necessary, who he was and why he had dogged us so long. He might slip away from us in the crowd of Regent Street, but it would puzzle him to do so upon the lonely moor. On the other hand, if I should find the hut and its tenant should not be within it I must remain there, however long the vigil, until he returned. Holmes had missed him in London. It would indeed be a triumph for me if I could run him to earth where my master had failed.

Luck had been against us again and again in this inquiry, but now at last it came to my aid. And the messenger of good fortune was none other than Mr. Frankland, who was standing, grey-whiskered and red-faced, outside the gate of his garden, which opened on to the high road along which I travelled.

"Good-day, Dr. Watson," cried he, with unwonted good humour, "you must really give your horses a rest, and come in to have a glass of wine and to congratulate me."

My feelings towards him were very far from being friendly after what I had heard of his treatment of his daughter, but I was anxious to send Perkins and the wagonette home, and the opportunity was a good one. I alighted and sent a message to Sir Henry that I should walk over in time for dinner. Then I followed Frankland into his dining-room.

"It is a great day for me, sir - one of the red-letter days of my life," he cried, with many chuckles. "I have brought off a double event. I mean to teach them in these parts that law is law, and that there is a man here who does not fear to invoke it. I have established a right of way through the centre of old Middleton's park, slap across it, sir, within a hundred yards of his own front door. What do you think of that? We'll teach these magnates that they cannot ride rough-shod over the rights of the commoners, confound them! And I've closed the wood where the Fernworthy folk used to picnic. These infernal people seem to think that there are no rights of property, and that they can swarm where they like with their papers and their bottles. Both cases decided, Dr. Watson, and both in my favour. I haven't had such a day since I had Sir John Morland for trespass, because he shot in his own warren."

"How on earth did you do that?"

"Look it up in the books, sir. It will repay reading - Frankland v. Morland, Court of Queen's Bench. It cost me £200, but I got my verdict."

"Did it do you any good?"

"None, sir, none. I am proud to say that I had no interest in the matter. I act entirely from a sense of public duty. I have no doubt, for example, that the Fernworthy people will burn me in effigy to-night. I told the police last time they did it that they should stop these disgraceful exhibitions. The county constabulary is in a scandalous state, sir, and it has not afforded me the protection to which I am entitled. The case of Frankland v. Regina will bring the matter before the attention of the public. I told them that they would have occasion to regret their treatment of me, and already my words have come true."

"How so?" I asked.

The old man put on a very knowing expression.

"Because I could tell them what they are dying to know; but nothing would induce me to help the rascals in any way."

I had been casting round for some excuse by which I could get away from his gossip, but now I began to wish to hear more of it. I had seen enough of the contrary nature of the old sinner to understand that any strong sign of interest would be the surest way to stop his confidences.

"Some poaching case, no doubt?" said I, with an indifferent manner."

"Ha, ha, my boy, a very much more important matter than that! What about the convict on the moor?"

I started. "You don't mean that you know where he is?" said I.

"I may not know exactly where he is, but I am quite sure that I could help the police to lay their hands on him. Has it never struck you that the way to catch that man was to find out where he got his food, and so trace it to him?"

He certainly seemed to be getting uncomfortably near the truth. "No doubt," said I; "but how do you know that he is anywhere upon the moor?"

"I know it because I have seen with my own eyes the messenger who takes him his food."

My heart sank for Barrymore. It was a serious thing to be in the power of this spiteful old busybody. But his next remark took a weight from my mind.

"You'll be surprised to hear that his food is taken to him by a child. I see him every day through my telescope upon the roof. He passes along the same path at the same hour, and to whom should he be going except to the convict?"

Here was luck indeed! And yet I suppressed all appearance of interest. A child! Barrymore had said that our unknown was supplied by a boy. It was on his track, and not upon the convict's, that Frankland had stumbled. If I could get his knowledge it might save me a long and weary hunt. But incredulity and indifference were evidently my strongest cards.

"I should say that it was much more likely that it was the son of one of the moorland shepherds taking out his father's dinner."

The least appearance of opposition struck fire out of the old autocrat. His eyes looked malignantly at me, and his grey whiskers bristled like those of an angry cat.

"Indeed, sir!" said he, pointing out over the wide-stretching moor. "Do you see that Black Tor over yonder? Well, do you see the low hill beyond with the thorn-bush upon it? It is the stoniest part of the whole moor. Is that a place where a shepherd would be likely to take his station? Your suggestion, sir, is a most absurd one."

I meekly answered that I had spoken without knowing all the facts. My submission pleased him and led him to further confidences.

"You may be sure, sir, that I have very good grounds before I come to an opinion. I have seen the boy again and again with his bundle. Every day, and sometimes twice a day, I have been able - but wait a moment, Dr. Watson. Do my eyes deceive me, or is there at the present moment something moving upon that hillside?"

It was several miles off, but I could distinctly see a small dark dot against the dull green and grey.

"Come, sir, come!" cried Frankland, rushing upstairs. "You will see with your own eyes and judge for yourself."

The telescope, a formidable instrument mounted upon a tripod, stood upon the flat leads of the house. Frankland clapped his eye to it and gave a cry of satisfaction.

"Quick, Dr. Watson, quick, before he passes over the hill!"

There he was, sure enough, a small urchin with a little bundle upon his shoulder, toiling slowly up the hill. When he reached the crest I saw the ragged, uncouth figure outlined for an instant against the cold blue sky. He looked round him, with a furtive and stealthy air, as one who dreads pursuit. Then he vanished over the hill.

"Well! Am I right?"

"Certainly, there is a boy who seems to have some secret errand."

"And what the errand is even a county constable could guess. But not one word shall they have from me, and I bind you to secrecy also, Dr. Watson. Not a word! You understand?"

"Just as you wish."

"They have treated me shamefully - shamefully. When the facts come out in Frankland v. Regina I venture to think that a thrill of indignation will run through the country. Nothing would induce me to help the police in any way. For all they cared it might have been me, instead of my effigy, which these rascals burned at the stake. Surely you are not going! You will help me to empty the decanter in honour of this great occasion!"

But I resisted all his solicitations and succeeded in dissuading him from his announced intention of walking home with me. I kept the road as long as his eye was on me, and then I struck off across the moor and made for the stony hill over which the boy had disappeared. Everything was working in my favour, and I swore that it should not be through lack of energy or perseverance that I should miss the chance which Fortune had thrown in my way.

The sun was already sinking when I reached the summit of the hill, and the long slopes beneath me were all golden-green on one side and grey shadow on the other. A haze lay low upon the farthest sky-line, out of which jutted the fantastic shapes of Belliver and Vixen Tor. Over the wide expanse there was no sound and no movement. One great grey bird, a gull or curlew, soared aloft in the blue heaven. He and I seemed to be the only living things between the huge arch of the sky and the desert beneath it. The barren scene, the sense of loneliness, and the mystery and urgency of my task all struck a chill into my heart. The boy was nowhere to be seen. But down beneath me in a cleft of the hills there was a circle of the old stone huts, and in the middle of them there was one which retained sufficient roof to act as a screen against the weather. My heart leaped within me as I saw it. This must be the burrow where the stranger lurked. At last my foot was on the threshold of his hiding-place - his secret was within my grasp.

As I approached the hut, walking as warily as Stapleton would do when with poised net he drew near the settled butterfly, I satisfied myself that the place had indeed been used as a habitation. A vague pathway among the boulders led to the dilapidated opening which served as a door. All was silent within. The unknown might be lurking there, or he might be prowling on the moor. My nerves tingled with the sense of adventure. Throwing aside my cigarette I closed my hand upon the butt of my revolver and, walking swiftly up to the door, I looked in. The place was empty.

But there were ample signs that I had not come upon a false scent. This was certainly where the man lived. Some blankets rolled in a waterproof lay upon that very stone slab upon which neolithic man had once slumbered. The ashes of a fire were heaped in a rude grate. Beside it lay some cooking utensils and a bucket half-full of water. A litter of empty tins showed that the place had been occupied for some time, and I saw, as my eyes became accustomed to the chequered light, a pannikin and a half-full bottle of spirits standing in the corner. In the middle of the hut a flat stone served the purpose of a table, and upon this stood a small cloth bundle - the same, no doubt, which I had seen through the telescope upon the shoulder of the boy. It contained a loaf of bread, a tinned tongue, and two tins of preserved peaches. As I set it down again, after having examined it, my heart leaped to see that beneath it there lay a sheet of paper with writing upon it. I raised it, and this was what I read, roughly scrawled in pencil:-

"Dr. Watson has gone to Coombe Tracey."

For a minute I stood there with the paper in my hands thinking out the meaning of this curt message. It was I, then, and not Sir Henry, who was being dogged by this secret man. He had not followed me himself, but he had set an agent - the boy, perhaps - upon my track, and this was his report. Possibly I had taken no step since I had been upon the moor which had not been observed and repeated. Always there was this feeling of an unseen force, a fine net drawn round us with infinite skill and delicacy, holding us so lightly that it was only at some supreme moment that one realized that one was indeed entangled in its meshes.

If there was one report there might be others, so I looked round the hut in search of them. There was no trace, however, of anything of the kind, nor could I discover any sign which might indicate the character or intentions of the man who lived in this singular place, save that he must be of Spartan habits, and cared little for the comforts of life. When I thought of the heavy rains and looked at the gaping roof I understood how strong and immutable must be the purpose which had kept him in that inhospitable abode. Was he our malignant enemy, or was he by chance our guardian angel? I swore that I would not leave the hut until I knew.

Outside the sun was sinking low and the west was blazing with scarlet and gold. Its reflection was shot back in ruddy patches by the distant pools which lay amid the Great Grimpen Mire. There were the two towers of Baskerville Hall, and there a distant blur of smoke which marked the village of Grimpen. Between the two, behind the hill, was the house of the Stapletons. All was sweet and mellow and peaceful in the golden evening light, and yet as I looked at them my soul shared none of the peace of Nature, but quivered at the vagueness and the terror of that interview which every instant was bringing nearer. With tingling nerves, but a fixed purpose, I sat in the dark recess of the hut and waited with sombre patience for the coming of its tenant.

And then at last I heard him. Far away came the sharp clink of a boot striking upon a stone. Then another and yet another, coming nearer and nearer. I shrank back into the darkest corner, and cocked the pistol in my pocket, determined not to discover myself until I had an opportunity of seeing something of the stranger. There was a long pause which showed that he had stopped. Then once more the footsteps approached and a shadow fell across the opening of the hut.

"It is a lovely evening, my dear Watson," said a well-known voice. "I really think that you will be more comfortable outside than in."

CHAPTER XII.

DEATH ON THE MOOR.

OR a moment or two I sat breathless, hardly able to believe my ears. Then my senses and my voice came back to me, while a crushing weight of responsibility seemed in an instant to be lifted from my soul. That cold, incisive, ironical voice could belong to but one man in all the world.

"Holmes!" I cried - "Holmes!"

"Come out," said he, "and please be careful with the revolver."

I stooped under the rude lintel, and there he sat upon a stone outside, his grey eyes dancing with amusement as they fell upon my astonished features. He was thin and worn, but clear and alert, his keen face bronzed by the sun and roughened by the wind. In his tweed suit and cloth cap he looked like any other tourist upon the moor, and he had contrived, with that cat-like love of personal cleanliness which was one of his characteristics, that his chin should be as smooth and his linen as perfect as if he were in Baker Street.

"I never was more glad to see anyone in my life," said I, as I wrung him by the hand.

"Or more astonished, eh?"

"Well, I must confess to it."

"The surprise was not all on one side, I assure you. I had no idea that you had found my occasional retreat, still less that you were inside it, until I was within twenty paces of the door."

"My footprint, I presume?"

"No, Watson; I fear that I could not undertake to recognise your footprint amid all the foot-prints of the world. If you seriously desire to deceive me you must change your tobacconist; for when I see the stub of a cigarette marked Bradley, Oxford Street, I know that my friend Watson is in the neighbourhood. You will see it there beside the path. You threw it down, no doubt, at that supreme moment when you charged into the empty hut."

"Exactly."

"I thought as much - and knowing your admirable tenacity I was convinced that you were sitting in ambush, a weapon within reach, waiting for the tenant to return. So you actually thought that I was the criminal?"

"I did not know who you were, but I was determined to find out."

"Excellent, Watson! And how did you localize me? You saw me, perhaps, on the night of the convict hunt, when I was so imprudent as to allow the moon to rise behind me?"

"Yes, I saw you then."

"And have, no doubt, searched all the huts until you came to this one?"

"No, your boy had been observed, and that gave me a guide where to look."

"The old gentleman with the telescope, no doubt. I could not make it out when first I saw the light flashing upon the lens." He rose and peeped into the hut. "Ha, I see that Cartwright has brought up some supplies. What's this paper? So you have been to Coombe Tracey, have you?"

"Yes."

"To see Mrs. Laura Lyons?"

"Exactly."

"Well done! Our researches have evidently been running on parallel lines, and when we unite our results I expect we shall have a fairly full knowledge of the case."

"Well, I am glad from my heart that you are here, for indeed the responsibility and the mystery were both becoming too much for my nerves. But how in the name of wonder did you come here, and what have you been doing? I thought that you were in Baker Street working out that case of blackmailing."

"That was what I wished you to think."

"Then you use me, and yet do not trust me!" I cried, with some bitterness. "I think that I have deserved better at your hands, Holmes."

"My dear fellow, you have been invaluable to me in this as in many other cases, and I beg that you will forgive me if I have seemed to play a trick upon you. In truth, it was partly for your own sake that I did it, and it was my appreciation of the danger which you ran which led me to come down and examine the matter for myself. Had I been with Sir Henry and you it is evident that my point of view would have been the same as yours, and my presence would have warned our very formidable opponents to be on their guard. As it is, I have been able to get about as I could not possibly have done had I been living at the Hall, and I remain an unknown factor in the business, ready to throw in all my weight at a critical moment."

"But why keep me in the dark?"

"For you to know could not have helped us, and might possibly have led to my discovery. You would have wished to tell me something, or in your kindness you would have brought me out some comfort or other, and so an unnecessary risk would be run. I brought Cartwright down with me - you remember the little chap at the Express office - and he has seen after my simple wants: a loaf of bread and a clean collar. What does man want more? He has given me an extra pair of eyes upon a very active pair of feet, and both have been invaluable."

"Then my reports have all been wasted!" My voice trembled as I recalled the pains and the pride with which I had composed them.

Holmes took a bundle of papers from his pocket.

"Here are your reports, my dear fellow, and very well thumbed, I assure you. I made excellent arrangements, and they are only delayed one day upon their way. I must compliment you exceedingly upon the zeal and the intelligence which you have shown over an extraordinarily difficult case."

I was still rather raw over the deception which had been practised upon me, but the warmth of Holmes's praise drove my anger from my mind. I felt also in my heart that he was right in what he said, and that it was really best for our purpose that I should not have known that he was upon the moor.

"That's better," said he, seeing the shadow rise from my face.

"And now tell me the result of your visit to Mrs. Laura Lyons - it was not difficult for me to guess that it was to see her that you had gone, for I am already aware that she is the one person in Coombe Tracey who might be of service to us in the matter. In fact, if you had not gone to-day it is exceedingly probable that I should have gone to-morrow."

The sun had set and dusk was settling over the moor. The air had turned chill, and we withdrew into the hut for warmth. There, sitting together in the twilight, I told Holmes of my conversation with the lady. So interested was he that I had to repeat some of it twice before he was satisfied.

"This is most important," said he, when I had concluded. "It fills up a gap which I had been unable to bridge, in this most complex affair. You are aware, perhaps, that a close intimacy exists between this lady and the man Stapleton?"

"I did not know of a close intimacy."

"There can be no doubt about the matter. They meet, they write, there is a complete understanding between them. Now, this puts a very powerful weapon into our hands. If I could only use it to detach his wife -"

"His wife?"

"I am giving you some information now, in return for all that you have given me. The lady who has passed here as Miss Stapleton is in reality his wife."

"Good heavens, Holmes! Are you sure of what you say? How could he have permitted Sir Henry to fall in love with her?"

"Sir Henry's falling in love could do no harm to anyone except Sir Henry. He took particular care that Sir Henry did not *make* love to her, as you have yourself observed. I repeat that the lady is his wife and not his sister."

"But why this elaborate deception?"

"Because he foresaw that she would be very much more useful to him in the character of a free woman."

All my unspoken instincts, my vague suspicions, suddenly took shape and centred upon the naturalist. In that impassive, colourless man, with his straw hat and his butterfly-net, I seemed to see something terrible - a creature of infinite patience and craft, with a smiling face and a murderous heart.

"It is he, then, who is our enemy - it is he who dogged us in London?"

"So I read the riddle."

"And the warning - it must have come from her!"

"Exactly."

The shape of some monstrous villainy, half seen, half guessed, loomed through the darkness which had girt me so long.

"But are you sure of this, Holmes? How do you know that the woman is his wife?"

"Because he so far forgot himself as to tell you a true piece of autobiography upon the occasion when he first met you, and I dare say he has many a time regretted it since. He *was* once a schoolmaster in the North of England. Now, there is no one more easy to trace than a schoolmaster. There are scholastic agencies by which one may identify any man who has been in the profession. A little investigation showed me that a school had come to grief under atrocious circumstances, and that the man who had owned it - the name was different - had disappeared with his wife. The descriptions agreed. When I learned that the missing man was devoted to entomology the identification was complete."

The darkness was rising, but much was still hidden by the shadows.

"If this woman is in truth his wife, where does Mrs. Laura Lyons come in?" I asked.

"That is one of the points upon which your own researches have shed a light. Your interview with the lady has cleared the situation very much. I did not know about a projected divorce between herself and her husband. In that case, regarding Stapleton as an unmarried man, she counted no doubt upon becoming his wife."

"And when she is undeceived?"

"Why, then we may find the lady of service. It must be our first duty to see her - both of us - to-morrow. Don't you think, Watson, that you are away from your charge rather long? Your place should be at Baskerville Hall."

The last red streaks had faded away in the west and night had settled upon the moor. A few faint stars were gleaming in a violet sky.

"One last question, Holmes," I said, as I rose. "Surely there is no need of secrecy between you and me. What is the meaning of it all? What is he after?"

Holmes's voice sank as he answered:-

"It is murder, Watson - refined, cold-blooded, deliberate murder. Do not ask me for particulars. My nets are closing upon him, even as his are upon Sir Henry, and with your help he is already almost at my mercy. There is but one danger which can threaten us. It is that he should strike before we are ready to do so. Another day - two at the most - and I have my case complete, but until then guard your charge as closely as ever a fond mother watched her ailing child. Your mission to-day has justified itself, and yet I could almost wish that you had not left his side - Hark!”

A terrible scream - a prolonged yell of horror and anguish burst out of the silence of the moor. That frightful cry turned the blood to ice in my veins.

“Oh, my God!” I gasped. “What is it? What does it mean?”

Holmes had sprung to his feet, and I saw his dark, athletic outline at the door of the hut, his shoulders stooping, his head thrust forward, his face peering into the darkness.

“Hush!” he whispered. “Hush!”

The cry had been loud on account of its vehemence, but it had pealed out from somewhere far off on the shadowy plain. Now it burst upon our ears, nearer, louder, more urgent than before.

“Where is it?” Holmes whispered; and I knew from the thrill of his voice that he, the man of iron, was shaken to the soul. “Where is it, Watson?”

“There, I think.” I pointed into the darkness.

“No, there!”

Again the agonized cry swept through the silent night, louder and much nearer than ever. And a new sound mingled with it, a deep, muttered rumble, musical and yet menacing, rising and falling like the low, constant murmur of the sea.

“The hound!” cried Holmes. “Come, Watson, come! Great heavens, if we are too late!”

He had started running swiftly over the moor, and I had followed at his heels. But now from somewhere among the broken ground immediately in front of us there came one last despairing yell, and then a dull, heavy thud. We halted and listened. Not another sound broke the heavy silence of the windless night.

I saw Holmes put his hand to his forehead like a man distracted. He stamped his feet upon the ground.

“He has beaten us, Watson. We are too late.”

“No, no, surely not!”

“Fool that I was to hold my hand. And you, Watson, see what comes of abandoning your charge! But, by Heaven, if the worst has happened, we’ll avenge him!”

Blindly we ran through the gloom, blundering against boulders, forcing our way through gorse bushes, panting up hills and rushing down slopes, heading always in the direction whence those dreadful sounds had come. At every rise Holmes looked eagerly round him, but the shadows were thick upon the moor and nothing moved upon its dreary face.

“Can you see anything?”

“Nothing.”

“But, hark, what is that?”

A low moan had fallen upon our ears. There it was again upon our left! On that side a ridge of rocks ended in a sheer cliff which overlooked a stone-strewn slope. On its jagged face was spread-eagled some dark, irregular object. As we ran towards it the vague outline hardened into a definite shape. It was a prostrate man face downwards upon the ground, the head doubled under him at a horrible angle, the shoulders rounded and the body hunched together as if in the act of throwing a somersault. So grotesque was the attitude that I could not for the instant realize that that moan had been the passing of his soul. Not a whisper, not a rustle, rose now from the dark figure over which we stooped. Holmes laid his hand upon him, and held it up again, with an exclamation of horror. The gleam of the match which he struck shone upon his clotted fingers and upon the ghastly pool which widened slowly from the crushed skull of the victim. And it shone upon something else which turned our hearts sick and faint within us - the body of Sir Henry Baskerville!

There was no chance of either of us forgetting that peculiar ruddy tweed suit - the very one which he had worn on the first morning that we had seen him in Baker Street. We caught the one clear glimpse of it, and then the match flickered and went out, even as the hope had gone out of our souls. Holmes groaned, and his face glimmered white through the darkness.

"The brute! the brute!" I cried, with clenched hands. "Oh, Holmes, I shall never forgive myself for having left him to his fate."

"I am more to blame than you, Watson. In order to have my case well rounded and complete, I have thrown away the life of my client. It is the greatest blow which has befallen me in my career. But how could I know - how *could* I know - that he would risk his life alone upon the moor in the face of all my warnings?"

"That we should have heard his screams - my God, those screams! - and yet have been unable to save him! Where is this brute of a hound which drove him to his death? It may be lurking among these rocks at this instant. And Stapleton, where is he? He shall answer for this deed."

"He shall. I will see to that. Uncle and nephew have been murdered - the one frightened to death by the very sight of a beast which he thought to be supernatural, the other driven to his end in his wild flight to escape from it. But now we have to prove the connection between the man and the beast. Save from what we heard, we cannot even swear to the existence of the latter, since Sir Henry has evidently died from the fall. But, by heavens, cunning as he is, the fellow shall be in my power before another day is past!"

We stood with bitter hearts on either side of the mangled body, overwhelmed by this sudden and irrevocable disaster which had brought all our long and weary labours to so piteous an end. Then, as the moon rose we climbed to the top of the rocks over which our poor friend had fallen, and from the summit we gazed out over the shadowy moor, half silver and half gloom. Far away, miles off, in the direction of Grimpen, a single steady yellow light was shining. It could only come from the lonely abode of the Stapletons. With a bitter curse I shook my fist at it as I gazed.

"Why should we not seize him at once?"

"Our case is not complete. The fellow is wary and cunning to the last degree. It is not what we know, but what we can prove. If we make one false move the villain may escape us yet."

"What can we do?"

"There will be plenty for us to do to-morrow. To-night we can only perform the last offices to our poor friend."

Together we made our way down the precipitous slope and approached the body, black and clear against the silvered stones. The agony of those contorted limbs struck me with a spasm of pain and blurred my eyes with tears.

"We must send for help, Holmes! We cannot carry him all the way to the Hall. Good heavens, are you mad?"

He had uttered a cry and bent over the body. Now he was dancing and laughing and wringing my hand. Could this be my stern, self-contained friend? These were hidden fires, indeed!

"A beard! A beard! The man has a beard!"

"A beard?"

"It is not the Baronet - it is - why, it is my neighbour, the convict!"

With feverish haste we had turned the body over, and that dripping beard was pointing up to the cold, clear moon. There could be no doubt about the beetling forehead, the sunken animal eyes. It was, indeed, the same face which had glared upon me in the light of the candle from over the rock - the face of Selden, the criminal.

Then in an instant it was all clear to me. I remembered how the Baronet had told me that he had handed his old wardrobe to Barrymore. Barrymore had passed it on in order to help Selden in his escape. Boots, shirt, cap - it was all Sir Henry's. The tragedy was still black enough, but this man had at least deserved death by the laws of his country. I told Holmes how the matter stood, my heart bubbling over with thankfulness and joy.

"Then the clothes have been the poor fellow's death," said he. "It is clear enough that the hound has been laid on from some article of Sir Henry's - the boot which was abstracted in the hotel, in all probability - and so ran this man down. There is one very singular thing, however: How came Selden, in the darkness, to know that the hound was on his trail?"

"He heard him."

"To hear a hound upon the moor would not work a hard man like this convict into such a paroxysm of terror that he would risk recapture by screaming wildly for help. By his cries he must have run a long way after he knew the animal was on his track. How did he know?"

"A greater mystery to me is why this hound, presuming that all our conjectures are correct - "

"I presume nothing."

"Well, then, why this hound should be loose to-night. I suppose that it does not always run loose upon the moor. Stapleton would not let it go unless he had reason to think that Sir Henry would be there."

"My difficulty is the more formidable of the two, for I think that we shall very shortly get an explanation of yours, while mine may remain for ever a mystery. The question now is, what shall we do with this poor wretch's body? We cannot leave it here to the foxes and the ravens."

"I suggest that we put it in one of the huts until we can communicate with the police."

"Exactly. I have no doubt that you and I could carry it so far. Halloa, Watson, what's this? It's the man himself, by all that's wonderful and audacious! Not a word to show your suspicions - not a word, or my plans crumble to the ground."

A figure was approaching us over the moor, and I saw the dull red glow of a cigar. The moon shone upon him, and I could distinguish the dapper shape and jaunty walk of the naturalist. He stopped when he saw us, and then came on again.

"Why, Dr. Watson, that's not you, is it? You are the last man that I should have expected to see out on the moor at this time of night. But, dear me, what's this? Somebody hurt? Not - don't tell me that it is our friend Sir Henry!" He hurried past me and stooped over the dead man. I heard a sharp intake of his breath and the cigar fell from his fingers.

"Who - who's this?" he stammered.

"It is Selden, the man who escaped from Princetown."

Stapleton turned a ghastly face upon us, but by a supreme effort he had overcome his amazement and his disappointment. He looked sharply from Holmes to me.

"Dear me! What a very shocking affair! How did he die?"

"He appears to have broken his neck by falling over these rocks. My friend and I were strolling on the moor when we heard a cry."

"I heard a cry also. That was what brought me out. I was uneasy about Sir Henry."

"Why about Sir Henry in particular?" I could not help asking.

"Because I had suggested that he should come over. When he did not come I was surprised, and I naturally became alarmed for his safety when I heard cries upon the moor. By the way" - his eyes darted again from my face to Holmes's - "did you hear anything else besides a cry?"

"No," said Holmes; "did you?"

"No."

"What do you mean, then?"

"Oh, you know the stories that the peasants tell about a phantom hound, and so on. It is said to be heard at night upon the moor. I was wondering if there were any evidence of such a sound to-night."

"We heard nothing of the kind," said I.

"And what is your theory of this poor fellow's death?"

"I have no doubt that anxiety and exposure have driven him off his head. He has rushed about the moor in a crazy state and eventually fallen over here and broken his neck."

"That seems the most reasonable theory," said Stapleton, and he gave a sigh which I took to indicate his relief. "What do you think about it, Mr. Sherlock Holmes?"

My friend bowed his compliments.

"You are quick at identification," said he.

"We have been expecting you in these parts since Dr. Watson came down. You are in time to see a tragedy."

"Yes, indeed. I have no doubt that my friend's explanation will cover the facts. I will take an unpleasant remembrance back to London with me to-morrow."

"Oh, you return to-morrow?"

"That is my intention."

"I hope your visit has cast some light upon those occurrences which have puzzled us?"

Holmes shrugged his shoulders.

"One cannot always have the success for which one hopes. An investigator needs facts, and not legends or rumours. It has not been a satisfactory case."

My friend spoke in his frankest and most unconcerned manner. Stapleton still looked hard at him. Then he turned to me.

"I would suggest carrying this poor fellow to my house, but it would give my sister such a fright that I do not feel justified in doing it. I think that if we put something over his face he will be safe until morning."

And so it was arranged. Resisting Stapleton's offer of hospitality, Holmes and I set off to Baskerville Hall, leaving the naturalist to return alone. Looking back we saw the figure moving slowly away over the broad moor, and behind him that one black smudge on the silvered slope which showed where the man was lying who had come so horribly to his end.

"We're at close grips at last," said Holmes, as we walked together across the moor. "What a nerve the fellow has! How he pulled himself together in the face of what must have been a paralyzing shock when he found that the wrong man had fallen a victim to his plot. I told you in London, Watson, and I tell you now again, that we have never had a foeman more worthy of our steel."

"I am sorry that he has seen you."

"And so was I at first. But there was no getting out of it."

"What effect do you think it will have upon his plans, now that he knows you are here?"

"It may cause him to be more cautious, or it may drive him to desperate measures at once. Like most clever criminals, he may be too confident in his own cleverness and imagine that he has completely deceived us."

"Why should we not arrest him at once?"

"My dear Watson, you were born to be a man of action. Your instinct is always to do something energetic. But supposing, for argument's sake, that we had him arrested to-night, what on earth the better off should we be for that? We could prove nothing against him. There's the devilish cunning of it! If he were acting through a human agent we could get some evidence, but if we were to drag this great dog to the light of day it would not help us in putting a rope round the neck of its master."

"Surely we have a case."

"Not a shadow of one - only surmise and conjecture. We should be laughed out of court if we came with such a story and such evidence."

"There is Sir Charles's death."

"Found dead without a mark upon him. You and I know that he died of sheer fright, and we know also what frightened him; but how are we to get twelve stolid jurymen to know it? What signs are there of a hound? Where are the marks of its fangs? Of course, we know that a hound does not bite a dead body, and that Sir Charles was dead before ever the brute overtook him. But we have to *prove* all this, and we are not in a position to do it."

"Well, then, to-night?"

"We are not much better off to-night. Again, there was no direct connection between the hound and the man's death. We never saw the hound. We heard it; but we could not prove that it was running upon this man's trail. There is a complete absence of motive. No, my dear fellow; we must reconcile ourselves to the fact that we have no case at present, and that it is worth our while to run any risk in order to establish one."

"And how do you propose to do so?"

"I have great hopes of what Mrs. Laura Lyons may do for us when the position of affairs is made clear to her. And I have my own plan as well. Sufficient for to-morrow is the evil thereof; but I hope before the day is past to have the upper hand at last."

I could draw nothing farther from him, and he walked, lost in thought, as far as the Baskerville gates.

"Are you coming up?"

"Yes; I see no reason for further concealment. But one last word, Watson. Say nothing of the hound to Sir Henry. Let him think that Selden's death was as Stapleton would have us believe. He will have a better nerve for the ordeal which he will have to undergo to-morrow, when he is engaged, if I remember your report aright, to dine with these people."

"And so am I."

"Then you must excuse yourself and he must go alone. That will be easily arranged. And now, if we are too late for dinner, I think that we are both ready for our suppers."

CHAPTER XIII.

FIXING THE NETS.

IR HENRY was more pleased than surprised to see Sherlock Holmes, for he had for some days been expecting that recent events would bring him down from London. He did raise his eyebrows, however, when he found that my friend had neither any luggage nor any explanations for its absence. Between us we soon supplied his wants, and then over a belated supper we explained to the Baronet as much of our experience as it seemed desirable that he should know. But first I had the unpleasant duty of breaking the news of Selden's death to Barrymore and his wife. To him it may have been an unmitigated relief, but she wept bitterly in her apron. To all the world he was the man of violence, half animal and half demon; but to her he always remained the little wilful boy of her own girlhood, the child who had clung to her hand. Evil indeed is the man who has not one woman to mourn him.

"I've been moping in the house all day since Watson went off in the morning," said the Baronet. "I guess I should have some credit, for I have kept my promise. If I hadn't sworn not to go about alone I might have had a more lively evening, for I had a message from Stapleton asking me over there."

"I have no doubt that you would have had a more lively evening," said Holmes, drily. "By the way, I don't suppose you appreciate that we have been mourning over you as having broken your neck?"

Sir Henry opened his eyes. "How was that?"

"This poor wretch was dressed in your clothes. I fear your servant who gave them to him may get into trouble with the police."

"That is unlikely. There was no mark on any of them, so far as I know."

"That's lucky for him - in fact, it's lucky for all of you, since you are all on the wrong side of the law in this matter. I am not sure that as a conscientious detective my first duty is not to arrest the whole household. Watson's reports are most incriminating documents."

"But how about the case?" asked the Baronet. "Have you made anything out of the tangle? I don't know that Watson and I are much the wiser since we came down."

"I think that I shall be in a position to make the situation rather more clear to you before long. It has been an exceedingly difficult and most complicated business. There are several points upon which we still want light - but it is coming, all the same."

"We've had one experience, as Watson has no doubt told you. We heard the hound on the moor, so I can swear that it is not all empty superstition. I had something to do with dogs when I was out West, and I know one when I hear one. If you can muzzle that one and put him on a chain I'll be ready to swear you are the greatest detective of all time."

"I think I will muzzle him and chain him all right if you will give me your help."

"Whatever you tell me to do I will do."

"Very good; and I will ask you also to do it blindly, without always asking the reason."

"Just as you like."

"If you will do this I think the chances are that our little problem will soon be solved. I have no doubt -"

He stopped suddenly and stared fixedly up over my head into the air. The lamp beat upon his face, and so intent was it and so still that it might have been that of a clear-cut classical statue, a personification of alertness and expectation.

"What is it?" we both cried.

I could see as he looked down that he was repressing some internal emotion. His features were still composed, but his eyes shone with amused exultation.

"Excuse the admiration of a connoisseur," said he, as he waved his hand towards the line of portraits which covered the opposite wall. "Watson won't allow that I know anything of art, but that is mere jealousy, because our views upon the subject differ. Now, these are a really very fine series of portraits."

"Well, I'm glad to hear you say so," said Sir Henry, glancing with some surprise at my friend. "I don't pretend to know much about these things, and I'd be a better judge of a horse or a steer than of a picture. I didn't know that you found time for such things. "

"I know what is good when I see it, and I see it now. That's a Kneller, I'll swear, that lady in the blue silk over yonder, and the stout gentleman with the wig ought to be a Reynolds. They are all family portraits, I presume?"

"Every one."

"Do you know the names?"

"Barrymore has been coaching me in them, and I think I can say my lessons fairly well."

"Who is the gentleman with the telescope?"

"That is Rear-Admiral Baskerville, who served under Rodney in the West Indies. The man with the blue coat and the roll of paper is Sir William Baskerville, who was Chairman of Committees of the House of Commons under Pitt."

"And this Cavalier opposite to me - the one with the black velvet and the lace?"

"Ah, you have a right to know about him. That is the cause of all the mischief, the wicked Hugo, who started the Hound of the Baskervilles. We're not likely to forget him."

I gazed with interest and some surprise upon the portrait.

"Dear me!" said Holmes, "he seems a quiet, meek-mannered man enough, but I dare say that there was a lurking devil in his eyes. I had pictured him as a more robust and ruffianly person."

"There's no doubt about the authenticity, for the name and the date, 1647, are on the back of the canvas."

Holmes said little more, but the picture of the old roysterer seemed to have a fascination for him, and his eyes were continually fixed upon it during supper. It was not until later, when Sir Henry had gone to his room, that I was able to follow the trend of his thoughts. He led me back into the banqueting-hall, his bedroom candle in his hand, and he held it up against the time-stained portrait on the wall.

"Do you see anything there?"

I looked at the broad plumed hat, the curling love-locks, the white lace collar, and the straight, severe face which was framed between them. It was not a brutal countenance, but it was prim, hard, and stern, with a firm-set, thin-lipped mouth, and a coldly intolerant eye.

"Is it like anyone you know?"

"There is something of Sir Henry about the jaw."

"Just a suggestion, perhaps. But wait an instant!" He stood upon a chair, and holding up the light in his left hand he curved his right arm over the broad hat and round the long ringlets.

"Good heavens!" I cried in amazement.

The face of Stapleton had sprung out of the canvas.

"Ha, you see it now. My eyes have been trained to examine faces and not their trimmings. It is the first quality of a criminal investigator that he should see through a disguise."

"But this is marvellous. It might be his portrait."

"Yes, it is an interesting instance of a throw-back, which appears to be both physical and spiritual. A study of family portraits is enough to convert a man to the doctrine of reincarnation. The fellow is a Baskerville - that is evident."

"With designs upon the succession."

"Exactly. This chance of the picture has supplied us with one of our most obvious missing links. We have him, Watson, we have him, and I dare swear that before to-morrow night he will be fluttering in our net as helpless as one of his own butterflies. A pin, a cork, and a card, and we add him to the Baker Street collection!" He burst into one of his rare fits of laughter as he turned away from the picture. I have not heard him laugh often, and it has always boded ill to somebody.

I was up betimes in the morning, but Holmes was afoot earlier still, for I saw him as I dressed coming up the drive.

"Yes, we should have a full day to-day," he remarked, and he rubbed his hands with the joy of action. "The nets are all in place, and the drag is about to begin. We'll know before the day is out whether we have caught our big, lean-jawed pike, or whether he has got through the meshes."

"Have you been on the moor already?"

"I have sent a report from Grimpen to Princetown as to the death of Selden. I think I can promise that none of you will be troubled in the matter. And I have also communicated with my faithful Cartwright, who would certainly have pined away at the door of my hut as a dog does at his master's grave if I had not set his mind at rest about my safety."

"What is the next move?"

"To see Sir Henry. Ah, here he is!"

"Good morning, Holmes," said the Baronet. "You look like a general who is planning a battle with his chief of the staff."

"That is the exact situation. Watson was asking for orders."

"And so do I."

"Very good. You are engaged, as I understand, to dine with our friends the Stapletons to-night."

"I hope that you will come also. They are very hospitable people, and I am sure that they would be very glad to see you."

"I fear that Watson and I must go to London."

"To London?"

"Yes, I think that we should be more useful there at the present juncture."

The Baronet's face perceptibly lengthened.

"I hoped that you were going to see me through this business. The Hall and the moor are not very pleasant places when one is alone."

"My dear fellow, you must trust me implicitly and do exactly what I tell you. You can tell your friends that we should have been happy to have come with you, but that urgent business required us to be in town. We hope very soon to return to Devonshire. Will you remember to give them that message?"

"If you insist upon it."

"There is no alternative, I assure you."

I saw by the Baronet's clouded brow that he was deeply hurt by what he regarded as our desertion.

"When do you desire to go?" he asked, coldly.

"Immediately after breakfast. We will drive in to Coombe Tracey, but Watson will leave his things as a pledge that he will come back to you. Watson, you will send a note to Stapleton to tell him that you regret that you cannot come."

"I have a good mind to go to London with you," said the Baronet. "Why should I stay here alone?"

"Because it is your post of duty. Because you gave me your word that you would do as you were told, and I tell you to stay."

"All right, then, I'll stay."

"One more direction! I wish you to drive to Merripit House. Send back your trap, however, and let them know that you intend to walk home."

"To walk across the moor?"

"Yes."

"But that is the very thing which you have so often cautioned me not to do."

"This time you may do it with safety. If I had not every confidence in your nerve and courage I would not suggest it, but it is essential that you should do it."

"Then I will do it."

"And as you value your life do not go across the moor in any direction save along the straight path which leads from Merripit House to the Grimpen Road, and is your natural way home."

"I will do just what you say."

"Very good. I should be glad to get away as soon after breakfast as possible, so as to reach London in the afternoon."

I was much astounded by this programme, though I remembered that Holmes had said to Stapleton on the night before that his visit would terminate next day. It had not crossed my mind, however, that he would wish me to go with him, nor could I understand how we could both be absent at a moment which he himself declared to be critical. There was nothing for it, however, but implicit obedience; so we bade good-bye to our rueful friend, and a couple of hours afterwards we were at the station of Coombe Tracey and had dispatched the trap upon its return journey. A small boy was waiting upon the platform.

"Any orders, sir?"

"You will take this train to town, Cartwright. The moment you arrive you will send a wire to Sir Henry Baskerville, in my name, to say that if he finds the pocket-book which I have dropped he is to send it by registered post to Baker Street."

"Yes, sir."

"And ask at the station office if there is a message for me."

The boy returned with a telegram, which Holmes handed to me. It ran: "Wire received. Coming down with unsigned warrant. Arrive five-forty.—LESTRADE. "

"That is in answer to mine of this morning. He is the best of the professionals, I think, and we may need his assistance. Now, Watson, I think that we cannot employ our time better than by calling upon your acquaintance, Mrs. Laura Lyons."

His plan of campaign was beginning to be evident. He would use the Baronet in order to convince the Stapletons that we were really gone, while we should actually return at the instant when we were likely to be needed. That telegram from London, if mentioned by Sir Henry to the Stapletons, must remove the last suspicions from their minds. Already I seemed to see our nets drawing closer round that lean-jawed pike.

Mrs. Laura Lyons was in her office, and Sherlock Holmes opened his interview with a frankness and directness which considerably amazed her.

"I am investigating the circumstances which attended the death of the late Sir Charles Baskerville," said he. "My friend here, Dr. Watson, has informed me of what you have communicated, and also of what you have withheld in connection with that matter."

"What have I withheld?" she asked, defiantly.

"You have confessed that you asked Sir Charles to be at the gate at ten o'clock. We know that that was the place and hour of his death. You have withheld what the connection is between these events."

"There is no connection."

"In that case the coincidence must indeed be an extraordinary one. But I think that we shall succeed in establishing a connection after all. I wish to be perfectly frank with you, Mrs. Lyons. We regard this case as one of murder, and the evidence may implicate not only your friend Mr. Stapleton, but his wife as well."

The lady sprang from her chair.

"His wife!" she cried.

"The fact is no longer a secret. The person who has passed for his sister is really his wife."

Mrs. Lyons had resumed her seat. Her hands were grasping the arms of her chair, and I saw that the pink nails had turned white with the pressure of her grip.

"His wife!" she said, again. "His wife! He was not a married man."

Sherlock Holmes shrugged his shoulders.

"Prove it to me! Prove it to me! And if you can do so -!" The fierce flash of her eyes said more than any words.

"I have come prepared to do so," said Holmes, drawing several papers from his pocket. "Here is a photograph of the couple taken in York four years ago. It is indorsed 'Mr. and Mrs. Vandeleur,' but you will have no difficulty in recognising him, and her also, if you know her by sight. Here are three written descriptions by trustworthy witnesses of Mr. and Mrs. Vandeleur, who at that time kept St. Oliver's private school. Read them, and see if you can doubt the identity of these people."

She glanced at them, and then looked up at us with the set, rigid face of a desperate woman.

"Mr. Holmes," she said, "this man had offered me marriage on condition that I could get a divorce from my husband. He has lied to me, the villain, in every conceivable way. Not one word of truth has he ever told me. And why - why? I imagined that all was for my own sake. But now I see that I was never anything but a tool in his hands. Why should I preserve faith with him who never kept any with me? Why should I try to shield him from the consequences of his own wicked acts? Ask me what you like, and there is nothing which I shall hold back. One thing I swear to you, and that is, that when I wrote the letter I never dreamed of any harm to the old gentleman, who had been my kindest friend."

"I entirely believe you, madam," said Sherlock Holmes. "The recital of these events must be very painful to you, and perhaps it will make it easier if I tell you what occurred, and you can check me if I make any material mistake. The sending of this letter was suggested to you by Stapleton?"

"He dictated it."

"I presume that the reason he gave was that you would receive help from Sir Charles for the legal expenses connected with your divorce?"

"Exactly."

"And then after you had sent the letter he dissuaded you from keeping the appointment?"

"He told me that it would hurt his self-respect that any other man should find the money for such an object, and that though he was a poor man himself he would devote his last penny to removing the obstacles which divided us."

"He appears to be a very consistent character. And then you heard nothing until you read the reports of the death in the paper?"

"No."

"And he made you swear to say nothing about your appointment with Sir Charles?"

"He did. He said that the death was a very mysterious one, and that I should certainly be suspected if the facts came out. He frightened me into remaining silent."

"Quite so. But you had your suspicions?"

She hesitated and looked down.

"I knew him," she said. "But if he had kept faith with me I should always have done so with him."

"I think that on the whole you have had a fortunate escape," said Sherlock Holmes. "You have had him in your power and he knew it, and yet you are alive. You have been walking for some months very near to the edge of a precipice. We must wish you good morning now, Mrs. Lyons, and it is probable that you will very shortly hear from us again."

"Our case becomes rounded off, and difficulty after difficulty thins away in front of us," said Holmes, as we stood waiting for the arrival of the express from town. "I shall soon be in the position of being able to put into a single connected narrative one of the most singular and sensational crimes of modern times. Students of criminology will remember the analogous incidents in Grodno, in Little Russia, in the year '66, and of course there are the Anderson murders in North Carolina, but this case possesses some features which are entirely its own. Even now we have no clear case against this very wily man. But I shall be very much surprised if it is not clear enough before we go to bed this night."

The London express came roaring into the station, and a small, wiry bulldog of a man had sprung from a first-class carriage. We all three shook hands, and I saw at once from the reverential way in which Lestrade gazed at my companion that he had learned a good deal since the days when they had first worked together. I could well remember the scorn which the theories of the reasoner used then to excite in the practical man.

"Anything good?" he asked.

"The biggest thing for years," said Holmes. "We have two hours before we need think of starting. I think we might employ it in getting some dinner, and then, Lestrade, we will take the London fog out of your throat by giving you a breath of the pure night air of Dartmoor. Never been there? Ah, well, I don't suppose you will forget your first visit."

CHAPTER XIV.

THE HOUND OF THE BASKERVILLES.

ONE of Sherlock Holmes's defects - if, indeed, one may call it a defect - was that he was exceedingly loth to communicate his full plans to any other person until the instant of their fulfilment. Partly it came no doubt from his own masterful nature, which loved to dominate and surprise those who were around him. Partly also from his professional caution, which urged him never to take any chances. The result, however, was very trying for those who were acting as his agents and assistants. I had often suffered under it, but never more so than during that long drive in the darkness. The great ordeal was in front of us; at last we were about to make our final effort, and yet Holmes had said nothing, and I could only surmise what his course of action would be. My nerves thrilled with anticipation when at last the cold wind upon our faces and the dark, void spaces on either side of the narrow road told me that we were back upon the moor once again. Every stride of the horses and every turn of the wheels was taking us nearer to our supreme adventure.

Our conversation was hampered by the presence of the driver of the hired wagonette, so that we were forced to talk of trivial matters when our nerves were tense with emotion and anticipation. It was a relief to me, after that unnatural restraint, when we at last passed Frankland's house and knew that we were drawing near to the Hall and to the scene of action. We did not drive up to the door, but got down near the gate of the avenue. The wagonette was paid off and ordered to return to Temple Coombe forthwith, while we started to walk to Merripit House.

"Are you armed, Lestrade?"

The little detective smiled.

"As long as I have my trousers I have a hip-pocket, and as long as I have my hip-pocket I have something in it."

"Good! My friend and I are also ready for emergencies."

"You're mighty close about this affair, Mr. Holmes. What's the game now?"

"A waiting game."

"My word, it does not seem a very cheerful place," said the detective, with a shiver, glancing round him at the gloomy slopes of the hill and at the huge lake of fog which lay over the Grimpen Mire. "I see the lights of a house ahead of us."

"That is Merripit House and the end of our journey. I must request you to walk on tiptoe and not to talk above a whisper."

We moved cautiously along the track as if we were bound for the house, but Holmes halted us when we were about two hundred yards from it.

"This will do," said he. "These rocks upon the right make an admirable screen."

"We are to wait here?"

"Yes, we shall make our little ambush here. Get into this hollow, Lestrade. You have been inside the house, have you not, Watson? Can you tell the position of the rooms? What are those latticed windows at this end?"

"I think they are the kitchen windows."

"And the one beyond, which shines so brightly?"

"That is certainly the dining-room."

"The blinds are up. You know the lie of the land best. Creep forward quietly and see what they are doing - but for Heaven's sake don't let them know that they are watched!"

I tip-toed down the path and stooped behind the low wall which surrounded the stunted orchard. Creeping in its shadow I reached a point whence I could look straight through the uncurtained window.

There were only two men in the room, Sir Henry and Stapleton. They sat with their profiles towards me on either side of the round table. Both of them were smoking cigars, and coffee and wine were in front of them. Stapleton was talking with animation, but the Baronet looked pale and distrait. Perhaps the thought of that lonely walk across the ill-omened moor was weighing heavily upon his mind.

As I watched them Stapleton rose and left the room, while Sir Henry filled his glass again and leaned back in his chair, puffing at his cigar. I heard the creak of a door and the crisp sound of boots upon gravel. The steps passed along the path on the other side of the wall under which I crouched. Looking over, I saw the naturalist pause at the door of an out-house in the corner of the orchard. A key turned in a lock, and as he passed in there was a curious scuffling noise from within. He was only a minute or so inside, and then I heard the key turn once more and he passed me and re-entered the house. I saw him rejoin his guest, and I crept quietly back to where my companions were waiting to tell them what I had seen.

"You say, Watson, that the lady is not there?" Holmes asked, when I had finished my report.

"No."

"Where can she be, then, since there is no light in any other room except the kitchen?"

"I cannot think where she is."

I have said that over the great Grimpen Mire there hung a dense, white fog. It was drifting slowly in our direction and banked itself up like a wall on that side of us, low, but thick and well defined. The moon shone on it, and it looked like a great shimmering icefield, with the heads of the distant tors as rocks borne upon its surface. Holmes's face was turned towards it, and he muttered impatiently as he watched its sluggish drift.

"It's moving towards us, Watson."

"Is that serious?"

"Very serious, indeed - the one thing upon earth which could have disarranged my plans. He can't be very long, now. It is already ten o'clock. Our success and even his life may depend upon his coming out before the fog is over the path."

The night was clear and fine above us. The stars shone cold and bright, while a half-moon bathed the whole scene in a soft, uncertain light. Before us lay the dark bulk of the house, its serrated roof and bristling chimneys hard outlined against the silver-spangled sky. Broad bars of golden light from the lower windows stretched across the orchard and the moor. One of them was suddenly shut off. The servants had left the kitchen. There only remained the lamp in the dining-room where the two men, the murderous host and the unconscious guest, still chatted over their cigars.

Every minute that white woolly plain which covered one half of the moor was drifting closer and closer to the house. Already the first thin wisps of it were curling across the golden square of the lighted window. The farther wall of the orchard was already invisible, and the trees were standing out of a swirl of white vapour. As we watched it the fog-wreaths came crawling round both corners of the house and rolled slowly into one dense bank, on which the upper floor and the roof floated like a strange ship upon a shadowy sea. Holmes struck his hand passionately upon the rock in front of us, and stamped his feet in his impatience.

"If he isn't out in a quarter of an hour the path will be covered. In half an hour we won't be able to see our hands in front of us."

"Shall we move farther back upon higher ground?"

"Yes, I think it would be as well."

So as the fog-bank flowed onwards we fell back before it until we were half a mile from the house, and still that dense white sea, with the moon silvering its upper edge, swept slowly and inexorably on.

"We are going too far," said Holmes. "We dare not take the chance of his being overtaken before he can reach us. At all costs we must hold our ground where we are." He dropped on his knees and clapped his ear to the ground. "Thank Heaven, I think that I hear him coming."

A sound of quick steps broke the silence of the moor. Crouching among the stones we stared intently at the silver-tipped bank in front of us. The steps grew louder, and through the fog, as through a curtain, there stepped the man whom we were awaiting. He looked round him in surprise as he emerged into the clear, star-lit night. Then he came swiftly along the path, passed close to where we lay, and went on up the long slope behind us. As he walked he glanced continually over either shoulder, like a man who is ill at ease.

"Hist!" cried Holmes, and I heard the sharp click of a cocking pistol. "Look out! It's coming!"

There was a thin, crisp, continuous patter from somewhere in the heart of that crawling bank. The cloud was within fifty yards of where we lay, and we glared at it, all three, uncertain what horror was about to break from the heart of it. I was at Holmes's elbow, and I glanced for an instant at his face. It was pale and exultant, his eyes shining brightly in the moonlight. But suddenly they started forward in a rigid, fixed stare, and his lips parted in amazement. At the same instant Lestrade gave a yell of terror and threw himself face downwards upon the ground. I sprang to my feet, my inert hand grasping my pistol, my mind paralyzed by the dreadful shape which had sprung out upon us from the shadows of the fog. A hound it was, an enormous coal-black hound, but not such a hound as mortal eyes have ever seen. Fire burst from its open mouth, its eyes glowed with a smouldering glare, its muzzle and hackles and dewlap were outlined in flickering flame. Never in the delirious dream of a disordered brain could anything more savage, more appalling, more hellish be conceived than that dark form and savage face which broke upon us out of the wall of fog.

ith long bounds the huge black creature was leaping down the track, following hard upon the footsteps of our friend. So paralyzed were we by the apparition that we allowed him to pass before we had recovered our nerve. Then Holmes and I both fired together, and the creature gave a hideous howl, which showed that one at least had hit him. He did not pause, however, but bounded onwards. Far away on the path we saw Sir Henry looking back, his face white in the moonlight, his hands raised in horror, glaring help-lessly at the frightful thing which was hunting him down.

But that cry of pain from the hound had blown all our fears to the winds. If he was vulner-able he was mortal, and if we could wound him we could kill him. Never have I seen a man run as Holmes ran that night. I am reckoned fleet of foot, but he outpaced me as much as I outpaced the little professional. In front of us as we flew up the track we heard scream after scream from Sir Henry and the deep roar of the hound. I was in time to see the beast spring upon its victim, hurl him to the ground, and worry at his throat. But the next instant Holmes had emptied five barrels of his revolver into the creature's flank. With a last howl of agony and a vicious snap in the air it rolled upon its back, four feet pawing furiously, and then fell limp upon its side. I stooped, panting, and pressed my pistol to the dreadful, shimmering head, but it was useless to pull the trigger. The giant hound was dead.

Sir Henry lay insensible where he had fallen. We tore away his collar, and Holmes breathed a prayer of gratitude when we saw that there was no sign of a wound and that the rescue had been in time. Already our friend's eyelids shivered and he made a feeble effort to move. Lestrade thrust his brandy-flask between the Baronet's teeth, and two frightened eyes were looking up at us.

"My God!" he whispered. "What was it? What, in Heaven's name, was it?"

"It's dead, whatever it is," said Holmes. "We've laid the family ghost once and forever."

In mere size and strength it was a terrible creature which was lying stretched before us. It was not a pure bloodhound and it was not a pure mastiff; but it appeared to be a combination of the two - gaunt, savage, and as large as a small lioness. Even now, in the stillness of death, the huge jaws seemed to be dripping with a bluish flame and the small, deep-set, cruel eyes were ringed with fire. I placed my hand upon the glowing muzzle, and as I held them up my own fingers smouldered and gleamed in the darkness.

"Phosphorus," I said.

"A cunning preparation of it," said Holmes, sniffing at the dead animal. "There is no smell which might have interfered with his power of scent. We owe you a deep apology, Sir Henry, for having exposed you to this fright. I was prepared for a hound, but not for such a creature as this. And the fog gave us little time to receive him."

"You have saved my life."

"Having first endangered it. Are you strong enough to stand?"

"Give me another mouthful of that brandy and I shall be ready for anything. So! Now, if you will help me up. What do you propose to do?"

"To leave you here. You are not fit for further adventures to-night. If you will wait, one or other of us will go back with you to the Hall."

He tried to stagger to his feet; but he was still ghastly pale and trembling in every limb. We helped him to a rock, where he sat shivering with his face buried in his hands.

"We must leave you now," said Holmes. "The rest of our work must be done, and every moment is of importance. We have our case, and now we only want our man.

Holmes emptied five barrels of his revolver into the creature's flank
Once again, coming at the start of the relevant chapter, this drawing reveals the fate of The
Hound. Paget's Hound seems to be influenced more by the Great Dane than by the Bloodhound
and Mastiff elements described by Watson.

"It's a thousand to one against our finding him at the house," he continued, as we retraced our steps swiftly down the path. "Those shots must have told him that the game was up."

"We were some distance off, and this fog may have deadened them."

"He followed the hound to call him off - of that you may be certain. No, no, he's gone by this time! But we'll search the house and make sure."

The front door was open, so we rushed in and hurried from room to room, to the amazement of a doddering old manservant, who met us in the passage. There was no light save in the dining-room, but Holmes caught up the lamp and left no corner of the house unexplored. No sign could we see of the man whom we were chasing. On the upper floor, however, one of the bedroom doors was locked.

"There's someone in here," cried Lestrade. "I can hear a movement. Open this door!"

A faint moaning and rustling came from within. Holmes struck the door just over the lock with the flat of his foot and it flew open. Pistol in hand, we all three rushed into the room.

But there was no sign within it of that desperate and defiant villain whom we expected to see. Instead we were faced by an object so strange and so unexpected that we stood for a moment staring at it in amazement.

The room had been fashioned into a small museum, and the walls were lined by a number of glass-topped cases full of that collection of butterflies and moths the formation of which had been the relaxation of this complex and dangerous man. In the centre of this room there was an upright beam, which had been placed at some period as a support for the old, worm-eaten balk of timber which spanned the roof. To this post a figure was tied, so swathed and muffled in the sheets which had been used to secure it that one could not for the moment tell whether it was that of a man or a woman. One towel passed round the throat and was secured at the back of the pillar. Another covered the lower part of the face, and over it two dark eyes - eyes full of grief and shame and a dreadful questioning - stared back at us. In a minute we had torn off the gag, unswathed the bonds, and Mrs. Stapleton sank upon the floor in front of us. As her beautiful head fell upon her chest I saw the clear red weal of a whiplash across her neck.

"The brute!" cried Holmes. "Here, Lestrade, your brandy-bottle! Put her in the chair! She has fainted from ill-usage and exhaustion."

She opened her eyes again.

"Is he safe?" she asked. "Has he escaped?"

"He cannot escape us, madam."

"No, no, I did not mean my husband. Sir Henry? Is he safe?"

"Yes."

"And the hound?"

"It is dead."

She gave a long sigh of satisfaction.

"Thank God! Thank God! Oh, this villain! See how he has treated me!" She shot her arms out from her sleeves, and we saw with horror that they were all mottled with bruises. "But this is nothing - nothing! It is my mind and soul that he has tortured and defiled. I could endure it all, ill-usage, solitude, a life of deception, everything, as long as I could still cling to the hope that I had his love, but now I know that in this also I have been his dupe and his tool." She broke into passionate sobbing as she spoke.

"You bear him no good will, madam," said Holmes. "Tell us then where we shall find him. If you have ever aided him in evil, help us now and so atone."

"There is but one place where he can have fled," she answered. "There is an old tin mine on an island in the heart of the Mire. It was there that he kept his hound and there also he had made preparations so that he might have a refuge. That is where he would fly."

The fog-bank lay like white wool against the window. Holmes held the lamp towards it.
"See," said he. "No one could find his way into the Grimpen Mire to-night."

She laughed and clapped her hands. Her eyes and teeth gleamed with fierce merriment.

"He may find his way in, but never out," she cried. "How can he see the guiding wands to-night? We planted them together, he and I, to mark the pathway through the Mire. Oh, if I could only have plucked them out to-day. Then indeed you would have had him at your mercy!"

It was evident to us that all pursuit was in vain until the fog had lifted. Meanwhile we left Lestrade in possession of the house while Holmes and I went back with the Baronet to Baskerville Hall. The story of the Stapletons could no longer be withheld from him, but he took the blow bravely when he learned the truth about the woman whom he had loved. But the shock of the night's adventures had shattered his nerves, and before morning he lay delirious in a high fever, under the care of Dr. Mortimer. The two of them were destined to travel together round the world before Sir Henry had become once more the hale, hearty man that he had been before he became master of that ill-omened estate.

And now I come rapidly to the conclusion of this singular narrative, in which I have tried to make the reader share those dark fears and vague surmises which clouded our lives so long, and ended in so tragic a manner. On the morning after the death of the hound the fog had lifted and we were guided by Mrs. Stapleton to the point where they had found a pathway through the bog. It helped us to realize the horror of this woman's life when we saw the eagerness and joy with which she laid us on her husband's track. We left her standing upon the thin peninsula of firm, peaty soil which tapered out into the widespread bog. From the end of it a small wand planted here and there showed where the path zig-zagged from tuft to tuft of rushes among those green scummed pits and foul quagmires which barred the way to the stranger. Rank reeds and lush, slimy water-plants sent an odour of decay and a heavy miasmatic vapour into our faces, while a false step plunged us more than once thigh-deep into the dark, quivering mire, which shook for yards in soft undulations around our feet. Its tenacious grip plucked at our heels as we walked, and when we sank into it it was as if some malignant hand were tugging us down into those obscene depths, so grim and purposeful was the clutch in which it held us. Once only we saw a trace that someone had passed that perilous way before us. From amid a tuft of cotton-grass which bore it up out of the slime some dark thing was projecting. Holmes sank to his waist as he stepped from the path to seize it, and had we not been there to drag him out he could never have set his foot upon firm land again. He held an old black boot in the air. "Meyers, Toronto," was printed on the leather inside.

"It is worth a mud bath," said he. "It is our friend Sir Henry's missing boot."

"Thrown there by Stapleton in his flight."

"Exactly. He retained it in his hand after using it to set the hound upon his track. He fled when he knew the game was up, still clutching it. And he hurled it away at this point of his flight. We know at least that he came so far in safety."

But more than that we were never destined to know, though there was much which we might surmise. There was no chance of finding footsteps in the mire, for the rising mud oozed swiftly in upon them, but as we at last reached firmer ground beyond the morass we all looked eagerly for them. But no slightest sign of them ever met our eyes. If the earth told a true story, then Stapleton never reached that island of refuge towards which he struggled through the fog upon that last night. Somewhere in the heart of the great Grimpen Mire, down in the foul slime of the huge morass which had sucked him in, this cold and cruel-hearted man is forever buried.

Many traces we found of him in the bog-girt island where he had hid his savage ally. A huge driving-wheel and a shaft half-filled with rubbish showed the position of an abandoned mine.

He held an old black boot in the air
Holmes looks remarkably clean for someone who had
just sunk 'waist-deep' in the mire.

Beside it were the crumbling remains of the cottages of the miners, driven away no doubt by the foul reek of the surrounding swamp. In one of these a staple and chain with a quantity of gnawed bones showed where the animal had been confined. A skeleton with a tangle of brown hair adhering to it lay among the *débris*.

"A dog!" said Holmes. "By Jove, a curly-haired spaniel. Poor Mortimer will never see his pet again. Well, I do not know that this place contains any secret which we have not already fathomed. He could hide his hound, but he could not hush its voice, and hence came those cries which even in daylight were not pleasant to hear. On an emergency he could keep the hound in the out-house at Merripit, but it was always a risk, and it was only on the supreme day, which he regarded as the end of all his efforts, that he dared to do it. This paste in the tin is no doubt the luminous mixture with which the creature was daubed. It was suggested, of course, by the story of the family hell-hound, and by the desire to frighten old Sir Charles to death. No wonder the poor wretch of a convict ran and screamed, even as our friend did, and as we ourselves might have done, when he saw such a creature bounding through the darkness of the moor upon his track. It was a cunning device, for, apart from the chance of driving your victim to his death, what peasant would venture to inquire too closely into such a creature should he get sight of it, as many have done, upon the moor? I said it in London, Watson, and I say it again now, that never yet have we helped to hunt down a more dangerous man than he who is lying yonder" - he swept his long arm towards the huge mottled expanse of green-splotched bog which stretched away until it merged into the russet slopes of the moor.

CHAPTER XV.

A RETROSPECTION.

IT was the end of November, and Holmes and I sat, upon a raw and foggy night, on either side of a blazing fire in our sitting-room in Baker Street. My friend was in excellent spirits over the success which had attended a succession of difficult and important cases, so that I was able to induce him to discuss the details of the Baskerville mystery. I had waited patiently for the opportunity, for I was aware that he would never permit cases to overlap, and that his clear and logical mind would not be drawn from its present work to dwell upon memories of the past. Sir Henry and Dr. Mortimer were, however, in London, on their way to that long voyage which had been recommended for the restoration of his shattered nerves. They had called upon us that very afternoon, so that it was natural that the subject should come up for discussion.

"The whole course of events," said Holmes, "from the point of view of the man who called himself Stapleton was simple and direct, although to us, who had no means in the beginning of knowing the motives of his actions and could only learn part of the facts, it all appeared exceedingly complex. I have had the advantage of two conversations with Mrs. Stapleton, and the case has now been so entirely cleared up that I am not aware that there is anything which has remained a secret to us. You will find a few notes upon the matter under the heading B in my indexed list of cases."

"Perhaps you would kindly give me a sketch of the course of events from memory."

"Certainly, though I cannot guarantee that I carry all the facts in my mind. Intense mental concentration has a curious way of blotting out what has passed. So far as the case of the Hound goes, however, I will give you the course of events as nearly as I can, and you will suggest anything which I may have forgotten.

"My inquiries show beyond all question that the family portrait did not lie, and that this fellow was indeed a Baskerville. He was a son of that Rodger Baskerville, the younger brother of Sir Charles, who fled with a sinister reputation to South America, where he was said to have died unmarried. He did, as a matter of fact, marry, and had one child, this fellow, whose real name is the same as his father. He married Beryl Garçia, one of the beauties of Costa Rica, and, having purloined a considerable sum of public money, he changed his name to Vandeleur and fled to England, where he established a school in the east of Yorkshire. His reason for attempting this special line of business was that he had struck up an acquaintance with a consumptive tutor upon the voyage home, and that he had used this man's ability to make the undertaking a success. Fraser, the tutor, died, however, and the school which had begun well sank from disrepute into infamy. The Vandeleurs found it convenient to change their name to Stapleton, and he brought the remains of his fortune, his schemes for the future, and his taste for entomology to the south of England. I learned at the British Museum that he was a recognised authority upon the subject, and that the name of Vandeleur has been permanently attached to a certain moth which he had, in his Yorkshire days, been the first to describe.

"We now come to that portion of his life which has proved to be of such intense interest to us. The fellow had evidently made inquiry, and found that only two lives intervened between him and a valuable estate. When he went to Devonshire his plans were, I believe, exceedingly hazy, but that he meant mischief from the first is evident from the way in which he took his wife with him in the character of his sister. The idea of using her as a decoy was clearly already in his mind, though he may not have been certain how the details of his plot were to be arranged. He meant in the end to have the estate, and he was ready to use any tool or run any risk for that end.

His first act was to establish himself as near to his ancestral home as he could, and his second was to cultivate a friendship with Sir Charles Baskerville and with the neighbours.

"The Baronet himself told him about the family hound, and so prepared the way for his own death. Stapleton, as I will continue to call him, knew that the old man's heart was weak and that a shock would kill him. So much he had learned from Dr. Mortimer. He had heard also that Sir Charles was superstitious and had taken this grim legend very seriously. His ingenious mind instantly suggested a way by which the Baronet could be done to death, and yet it would be hardly possible to bring home the guilt to the real murderer.

"Having conceived the idea he proceeded to carry it out with considerable finesse. An ordinary schemer would have been content to work with a savage hound. The use of artificial means to make the creature diabolical was a flash of genius upon his part. The dog he bought in London from Ross and Mangles, the dealers in Fulham Road. It was the strongest and most savage in their possession. He brought it down by the North Devon line and walked a great distance over the moor so as to get it home without exciting any remarks. He had already on his insect hunts learned to penetrate the Grimpen Mire, and so had found a safe hiding-place for the creature. Here he kennelled it and waited his chance.

"But it was some time coming. The old gentleman could not be decoyed outside of his grounds at night. Several times Stapleton lurked about with his hound, but without avail. It was during these fruitless quests that he, or rather his ally, was seen by peasants, and that the legend of the demon dog received a new confirmation. He had hoped that his wife might lure Sir Charles to his ruin, but here she proved unexpectedly independent. She would not endeavour to entangle the old gentleman in a sentimental attachment which might deliver him over to his enemy. Threats and even, I am sorry to say, blows refused to move her. She would have nothing to do with it, and for a time Stapleton was at a deadlock.

"He found a way out of his difficulties through the chance that Sir Charles, who had conceived a friendship for him, made him the minister of his charity in the case of this unfortunate woman, Mrs. Laura Lyons. By representing himself as a single man he acquired complete influence over her, and he gave her to understand that in the event of her obtaining a divorce from her husband he would marry her. His plans were suddenly brought to a head by his knowledge that Sir Charles was about to leave the Hall on the advice of Dr. Mortimer, with whose opinion he himself pretended to coincide. He must act at once, or his victim might get beyond his power. He therefore put pressure upon Mrs. Lyons to write this letter, imploring the old man to give her an interview on the evening before his departure for London. He then, by a specious argument, prevented her from going, and so had the chance for which he had waited.

"Driving back in the evening from Coombe Tracey he was in time to get his hound, to treat it with his infernal paint, and to bring the beast round to the gate at which he had reason to expect that he would find the old gentleman waiting. The dog, incited by its master, sprang over the wicket-gate and pursued the unfortunate Baronet, who fled screaming down the Yew Alley. In that gloomy tunnel it must indeed have been a dreadful sight to see that huge black creature, with its flaming jaws and blazing eyes, bounding after its victim. He fell dead at the end of the alley from heart disease and terror. The hound had kept upon the grassy border while the Baronet had run down the path, so that no track but the man's was visible. On seeing him lying still the creature had probably approached to sniff at him, but finding him dead had turned away again. It was then that it left the print which was actually observed by Dr. Mortimer. The hound was called off and hurried away to its lair in the Grimpen Mire, and a mystery was left which puzzled the authorities, alarmed the countryside, and finally brought the case within the scope of our observation.

"So much for the death of Sir Charles Baskerville. You perceive the devilish cunning of it, for really it would be almost impossible to make a case against the real murderer. His only accomplice was one who could never give him away, and the grotesque, inconceivable nature of the device only served to make it more effective. Both of the women concerned in the case, Mrs. Stapleton and Mrs. Laura Lyons, were left with a strong suspicion against Stapleton. Mrs. Stapleton knew that he had designs upon the old man, and also of the existence of the hound. Mrs. Lyons knew neither of these things, but had been impressed by the death occurring at the time of an uncancelled appointment which was only known to him. However, both of them were under his influence, and he had nothing to fear from them. The first half of his task was successfully accomplished, but the more difficult still remained.

"It is possible that Stapleton did not know of the existence of an heir in Canada. In any case he would very soon learn it from his friend Dr. Mortimer, and he was told by the latter all details about the arrival of Henry Baskerville. Stapleton's first idea was that this young stranger from Canada might possibly be done to death in London without coming down to Devonshire at all. He distrusted his wife ever since she had refused to help him in laying a trap for the old man, and he dared not leave her long out of his sight for fear he should lose his influence over her. It was for this reason that he took her to London with him. They lodged, I find, at the Mexborough Private Hotel, in Craven Street, which was actually one of those called upon by my agent in search of evidence. Here he kept his wife imprisoned in her room while he, disguised in a beard, followed Dr. Mortimer to Baker Street and afterwards to the station and to the Northumberland Hotel. His wife had some inkling of his plans; but she had such a fear of her husband - a fear founded upon brutal ill-treatment - that she dare not write to warn the man whom she knew to be in danger. If the letter should fall into Stapleton's hands her own life would not be safe. Eventually, as we know, she adopted the expedient of cutting out the words which would form the message, and addressing the letter in a disguised hand. It reached the Baronet, and gave him the first warning of his danger.

"It was very essential for Stapleton to get some article of Sir Henry's attire so that, in case he was driven to use the dog, he might always have the means of setting him upon his track. With characteristic promptness and audacity he set about this at once, and we cannot doubt that the boots or chamber-maid of the hotel was well bribed to help him in his design. By chance, however, the first boot which was procured for him was a new one and, therefore, useless for his purpose. He then had it returned and obtained another - a most instructive incident, since it proved conclusively to my mind that we were dealing with a real hound, as no other supposition could explain this anxiety to obtain an old boot and this indifference to a new one. The more *outré* and grotesque an incident is the more carefully it deserves to be examined, and the very point which appears to complicate a case is, when duly considered and scientifically handled, the one which is most likely to elucidate it.

"Then we had the visit from our friends next morning, shadowed always by Stapleton in the cab. From his knowledge of our rooms and of my appearance, as well as from his general conduct, I am inclined to think that Stapleton's career of crime has been by no means limited to this single Baskerville affair. It is suggestive that during the last three years there have been four considerable burglaries in the West Country, for none of which was any criminal ever arrested. The last of these, at Folkestone Court, in May, was remarkable for the cold-blooded pistolling of the page, who surprised the masked and solitary burglar. I cannot doubt that Stapleton recruited his waning resources in this fashion, and that for years he has been a desperate and dangerous man.

"We had an example of his readiness of resource that morning when he got away from us so successfully, and also of his audacity in sending back my own name to me through the cabman. From that moment he understood that I had taken over the case in London, and that therefore there was no chance for him there. He returned to Dartmoor and awaited the arrival of the Baronet."

"One moment!" said I. "You have, no doubt, described the sequence of events correctly, but there is one point which you have left unexplained. What became of the hound when its master was in London?"

"I have given some attention to this matter and it is undoubtedly of importance. There can be no question that Stapleton had a confidant, though it is unlikely that he ever placed himself in his power by sharing all his plans with him. There was an old manservant at Merripit House, whose name was Anthony. His connection with the Stapletons can be traced for several years, as far back as the schoolmastering days, so that he must have been aware that his master and mistress were really husband and wife. This man has disappeared and has escaped from the country. It is suggestive that Anthony is not a common name in England, while Antonio is so in all Spanish or Spanish-American countries. The man, like Mrs. Stapleton herself, spoke good English, but with a curious lisping accent. I have myself seen this old man cross the Grimpen Mire by the path which Stapleton had marked out. It is very probable, therefore, that in the absence of his master it was he who cared for the hound, though he may never have known the purpose for which the beast was used.

"The Stapletons then went down to Devonshire, whither they were soon followed by Sir Henry and you. One word now as to how I stood myself at that time. It may possibly recur to your memory that when I examined the paper upon which the printed words were fastened I made a close inspection for the water-mark. In doing so I held it within a few inches of my eyes, and was conscious of a faint smell of the scent known as white jessamine. There are seventy-five perfumes, which it is very necessary that a criminal expert should be able to distinguish from each other, and cases have more than once within my own experience depended upon their prompt recognition. The scent suggested the presence of a lady, and already my thoughts began to turn towards the Stapletons. Thus I had made certain of the hound, and had guessed at the criminal before ever we went to the West Country.

"It was my game to watch Stapleton. It was evident, however, that I could not do this if I were with you, since he would be keenly on his guard. I deceived everybody, therefore, yourself included, and I came down secretly when I was supposed to be in London. My hardships were not so great as you imagined, though such trifling details must never interfere with the investigation of a case. I stayed for the most part at Coombe Tracey, and only used the hut upon the moor when it was necessary to be near the scene of action. Cartwright had come down with me, and in his disguise as a country boy he was of great assistance to me. I was dependent upon him for food and clean linen. When I was watching Stapleton Cartwright was frequently watching you, so that I was able to keep my hand upon all the strings.

"I have already told you that your reports reached me rapidly, being forwarded instantly from Baker Street to Coombe Tracey. They were of great service to me, and especially that one incidentally truthful piece of biography of Stapleton's. I was able to establish the identity of the man and the woman, and knew at last exactly how I stood. The case had been considerably complicated through the incident of the escaped convict and the relations between him and the Barrymores. This also you cleared up in a very effective way, though I had already come to the same conclusions from my own observations.

"By the time that you discovered me upon the moor I had a complete knowledge of the whole business, but I had not a case which could go to a jury. Even Stapleton's attempt upon Sir Henry that night which ended in the death of the unfortunate convict did not help us much in proving murder against our man. There seemed to be no alternative but to catch him red-handed, and to do so we had to use Sir Henry, alone and apparently unprotected, as a bait. We did so, and at the cost of a severe shock to our client we succeeded in completing our case and driving Stapleton to his destruction. That Sir Henry should have been exposed to this is, I must confess, a reproach to my management of the case, but we had no means of foreseeing the terrible and paralyzing spectacle which the beast presented, nor could we predict the fog which enabled him to burst upon us at such short notice. We succeeded in our object at a cost which both the specialist and Dr. Mortimer assure me will be a temporary one. A long journey may enable our friend to recover not only from his shattered nerves, but also from his wounded feelings. His love for the lady was deep and sincere, and to him the saddest part of all this black business was that he should have been deceived by her.

"It only remains to indicate the part which she had played throughout. There can be no doubt that Stapleton exercised an influence over her which may have been love or may have been fear, or very possibly both, since they are by no means incompatible emotions. It was, at least, absolutely effective. At his command she consented to pass as his sister, though he found the limits of his power over her when he endeavoured to make her the direct accessory to murder. She was ready to warn Sir Henry so far as she could without implicating her husband, and again and again she tried to do so. Stapleton himself seems to have been capable of jealousy, and when he saw the Baronet paying court to the lady, even though it was part of his own plan, still he could not help interrupting with a passionate outburst that revealed the fiery soul which his self-contained manner so cleverly concealed. By encouraging the intimacy he made it certain that Sir Henry would frequently come to Merripit House and that he would sooner or later get the opportunity which he desired. On the day of the crisis, however, his wife turned suddenly against him. She had learned something of the death of the convict, and she knew that the hound was being kept in the out-house on the evening that Sir Henry was coming to dinner. She taxed her husband with his intended crime, and a furious scene followed, in which he showed her for the first time that she had a rival in his love. Her fidelity turned in an instant to bitter hatred and he saw that she would betray him. He tied her up, therefore, that she might have no chance of warning Sir Henry, and he hoped, no doubt, that when the whole countryside put down the Baronet's death to the curse of his family, as they certainly would do, he could win his wife back to accept an accomplished fact and to keep silent upon what she knew. In this I fancy that in any case he made a miscalculation, and that, if we had not been there, his doom would none the less have been sealed. A woman of Spanish blood does not condone such an injury so lightly. And now, my dear Watson, without referring to my notes, I cannot give you a more detailed account of this curious case. I do not know that anything essential has been left unexplained."

"He could not hope to frighten Sir Henry to death as he had done the old uncle with his bogie hound."

"The beast was savage and half-starved. If its appearance did not frighten its victim to death, at least it would paralyze the resistance which might be offered."

"No doubt. There only remains one difficulty. If Stapleton came into the succession, how could he explain the fact that he, the heir, had been living unannounced under another name so close to the property? How could he claim it without causing suspicion and inquiry?"

"It is a formidable difficulty, and I fear that you ask too much when you expect me to solve it. The past and the present are within the field of my inquiry, but what a man may do in the future is a hard question to answer. Mrs. Stapleton has heard her husband discuss the problem on several occasions. There were three possible courses. He might claim the property from South America, establish his identity before the British authorities there, and so obtain the fortune without ever coming to England at all; or he might adopt an elaborate disguise during the short time that he need be in London; or, again, he might furnish an accomplice with the proofs and papers, putting him in as heir, and retaining a claim upon some proportion of his income. We cannot doubt from what we know of him that he would have found some way out of the difficulty. And now, my dear Watson, we have had some weeks of severe work, and for one evening,

I think, we may turn our thoughts into more pleasant channels. I have a box for 'Les Huguenots.' Have you heard the De Reszkes? Might I trouble you then to be ready in half an hour, and we can stop at Marcini's for a little dinner on the way?"

THE END.

Annotations

The index number before each annotation comprises two parts. The first element indicates the page within the main text of *The Hound* upon which the annotated item can be located, and the second element, after the decimal point, indicates the line number on that page upon which the item commences. Chapter headings are included in the line count. Quotation marks and ellipses are omitted from the referenced quotations. Items covered in *The Men on the Tor* are not repeated in detail here, unless some specific individual point needs to be raised directly within the main text. Notes are made about major changes which were made to the one manuscript chapter which still exists (Chapter XI). There will, inevitably, be disagreements with the pronouncements of earlier annotated editions of *The Hound*, for the game remains afoot, but once the basis for any protracted errors in these has been established, the argument is not continued *ad nauseam*. It should be recalled that although the scholarship and research involved is carried out on a serious level, with the highest possible standards, the whole game is meant to be fun. Comments are included at the end of the Annotations on some of the drawings of Sidney Paget.

THE TEXTUAL ANNOTATIONS

119.09 ~ the stick which our visitor had left behind him the night before. It can be calculated from the internal temporal evidence of the case that Mortimer first visited *'221B Baker Street'* on Monday 30 September 1889.

119.11 ~ Penang lawyer. A bulbous-headed walking stick made from the wood of a Malacca cane tree, with the implication of the nickname being that disputes were settled in Penang using such a stick. Gentlemen in late-Victorian England frequently carried a walking stick as a means of defence, and the man who may earlier have introduced Sherlock Holmes to the Japanese art of 'Baritsu', E W Barton-Wright, published an illustrated article in *Pearson's Magazine* in January and February

1901 on the use of a walking stick for self-defence, wherein he mentioned that one could, with an ordinary Malacca cane, sever the throat of an assailant through the collar of his overcoat!

119.12 ~ M.R.C.S. Member of the Royal College of Surgeons, more-correctly the Royal College of Surgeons of England, established in 1800. One did not have to be a Doctor of Medicine to be an MRCS, and in that case one was only entitled to be referred to as 'Mister', as Mortimer correctly points out later. That title has become an elevated distinction for surgeons, now that they all are fully qualified doctors first. ACD graduated as a physician without being an MD, but he obtained his MD four years after initial graduation. Such surgeons would obviously have been useful for those who had been engaged in legal disputes involving Penang lawyers!

119.13 ~ 1884. It is primarily this date which gives us the year in which the case takes place, since Holmes subsequently remarks that the stick was presented *"... five years ago ..."*, making the year of the case 1889. Many minor objections have been raised against this dating, but none of them are convincing. Careful counting back from dates given in Watson's account establishes that the case begins, for Holmes, on Tuesday 1 October 1889.

119.37 ~ in all the accounts. In 1889 Watson had only had one case published, *A Study in Scarlet*, but that case is described as being a reprint from the reminiscences of John H Watson, which indicates that there were earlier accounts, even if they were not published. In addition, Watson would have recorded accounts of all of the cases which he subsequently published which had occurred prior to 1889, as well as accounts of cases which he never published.

120.26 ~ Charing Cross Hospital. The Hospital was established in 1818, with its main building, just North of the West end of The Strand, being completed in 1829. The building is now a police station.

120.39 ~ he could not have been on the *staff*. He was not a member of the formally appointed establishment, merely holding a temporary post.

120.42 ~ a house-surgeon or a house-physician. A junior surgeon or physician, almost certainly living in hospital-arranged quarters attached to or near the hospital.

120.44 ~ a young fellow under thirty. W S Baring-Gould suggested that this statement, the date on the stick, and the date in the Medical Directory, all indicated that the case took place within a few years of 1884, but there is no logical necessity about this.

121.01 ~ it is not difficult to find out a few particulars about the man's age and career. Watson suggests that he could find these details in the *Medical Directory*, but his copy did not include details of the man's age, and neither does any other copy.

121.03 ~ Medical Directory. More-correctly, *The Medical Directory and General Medical Register* (1870-), founded originally as *The London Medical Directory* in 1845.

121.05 ~ Grimpen. There is, in fact, no such hamlet or village on Dartmoor.

121.06 ~ Jackson prize for Comparative Pathology. A fictional prize for the study of the symptoms of physical disease, although the Royal College of Surgeons of England did, from the year of its foundation, offer the annual Jacksonian Prize (presented by Mr Samuel Jackson MRCS) for a thesis on some practical aspect of surgery.

121.07 ~ Reversion. Part of the theory of Atavism, indicating a return to ancestral characteristics.

121.07 ~ Corresponding member of the Swedish Pathological Society. A member of this (fictional) society, whose participation in its activities was primarily by correspondence. There is now a Holmesian 'Swedish Pathological Society' which is a Branch Office of The Franco-Midland Hardware Company, with members living in Sweden, but with corresponding members (including the present commentator) in England.

121.08 ~ Atavism. The theory that physical attributes are ancestral, and that these can be inherited with gaps in the line of descent. A very popular subject at the end of the Nineteenth Century, expounded by SBG amongst many others.

121.08 ~ Lancet. More correctly, *The Lancet*, a weekly medical journal first published in 1823 and still flourishing.

121.08 ~ Journal of Psychology. A fictional journal in Britain in 1889, although an American journal with that name (more-correctly, *The Journal of Psychology: Interdisciplinary and Applied*) began publication in 1887.

121.09 ~ Medical Officer. As such Mortimer would have needed to be qualified in medicine and surgery, and would certainly have been involved in midwifery. Chris Wills-Wood has suggested that Mortimer's basic salary would have been between £120 and £250 per year, as compared with a house surgeon's salary of between £50 and £80 per

year, and he would have earned more for duties such as that of public vaccinator, plus fees for treating his patients. ACD earned around £300 a year at this time.

121.09 ~ Thorsley. A fictional hamlet or village in the Dartmoor area. The name may be based upon that of Thursley, a village located a few miles along the London Road from ACD's house in Hindhead. It was doubly infamous: firstly as a wet and muddy village at the bottom of a steep hill leading up to Hindhead, where coaches used to get stuck in the mire, and secondly as the village from which a sailor, heading for Portsmouth in 1786, was followed, killed and robbed, with his assailants later being hanged near the spot of the crime, with the bodies being tarred and left hanging from a 30 foot gibbet beside the road, less than a mile from the future site of ACD's house. SBG wrote a novel developed from these events, located in the Thursley-Hindhead area, *The Broom Squires* (1896), which would obviously have been of interest to the many literary figures who lived in that area at the time of publication, including ACD. In 1899, ACD wrote the lyrics for a fox-hunting song, *The Old Gray Fox*, which mentions Thursley.

121.09 ~ High Barrow. A fictional hamlet or village in the Dartmoor area. The name may be derived from the many barrows on Dartmoor which were often located on high ridges or saddles, with several existing on Hamel Down above Grimspound.

121.35 ~ frock-coat. A knee length jacket for formal wear during the daytime. This is what Watson would have worn when on medical duty, and what Holmes would usually have worn in town (not an Inverness cape and deerstalker!).

121.39 ~ left it here or in the Shipping Office. W S Baring-Gould suggests that this indicates that the case cannot have begun on a Monday, since Mortimer could not have left his stick in a shipping office on a Sunday, but shipping offices did regularly open on Sundays in late-Victorian London, and it was on a Monday that he left his stick at *'221B'* anyway!

122.07 ~ a picker up of shells on the great unknown ocean. The Oxford edition interestingly suggests that this might have been inspired by Sir Isaac Newton's "... diverting myself in now and then finding a smoother pebble or a prettier shell than ordinary, while the great ocean of truth lay all undiscovered before me."

122.10 ~ I have heard your name mentioned. Although the first book edition corrected some of the typographical errors which existed in the *Strand* edition, that book edition did occasionally introduce new errors, and in the referenced phrase the word *"... you ..."* was substituted for the word *"... your ..."*.

122.11 ~ dolichocephalic. An anthropological term for someone who is relatively long-headed.

122.12 ~ supra-orbital development. Another anthropological term, for someone with relatively large bone ridges above the eyes; something which is common in early hominids and which might thus be thought to suggest a lack of intelligence in a modern man!

122.13 ~ parietal fissure. More-correctly the inter-parietal fissure, which is a gap between some of the bones of the top and side of the skull.

122.31 ~ Monsieur Bertillon. Alphonse Bertillon (1853-1914), the creator of the anthropometric system of physical measurement and identification used by the French police after 1884. He seems to have been quicker than Holmes in incorporating fingerprints into his identification system.

123.10 ~ my little monograph. Holmes indicates that he wrote several monographs, including ones on tobacco ashes, the polyphonic motets of Lassus, ciphers, and the influence of trades upon the form of the hand. Walter Klinefelter suggested that as Holmes thought that Mortimer might have seen Holmes's monograph on the dating of documents, it must have appeared in a medical journal which Mortimer might be expected to have read, but Holmes refers to a monograph, and not an article in a journal. This seems to be a piece of simple conceit on Holmes's part - a not uncommon occurrence.

123.18 ~ the alternative use of the long s and the short. It was considered that the long and the short forms of the letter s (f & s), were used alternatively, but Arthur Godfrey has shown that this is incorrect.

123.20 ~ At the head was written: "Baskerville Hall," and below, in large, scrawling figures: "1742." Leslie Klinger has perceptively commented that if this was written on the 'inch or two' of manuscript which had been protruding from Mortimer's pocket when he met Holmes, then it goes a long way towards explaining how Holmes was so easily able to date the document 'within a decade or so'.

123.40 ~ Lord Clarendon. Edward Hyde (1609-1674), the author of *History of the Great Rebellion* (1702-1704), concerning the English Civil War, a war which had serious consequences for property rights in the Dartmoor area (and elsewhere), including those of the Cabell family.

123.42 ~ Hugo. Far too many Holmesians and Sherlockians (and films) incorrectly refer to this man as 'Sir Hugo Baskerville', to the extent that the present com-

mentator assumed this usage to be correct when he first began writing on the subject. There was, at one time, even a publisher using the name of 'Sir Hugo Books'! In order to distinguish this first-mentioned Hugo Baskerville from the author of the manuscript which described the Baskerville curse, who is also called Hugo Baskerville, the title of 'the wicked Hugo' has been adopted for the earlier Hugo by serious Houndian scholars.

124.02 ~ Michaelmas. St Michael's Day, 29 September. This is a superbly subtle point to make in connection with property rights and with the wicked Hugo collecting the daughter of a yeoman farmer, in that Michaelmas was one of the key quarter days of the farming year, when landlords collected the rents from their tenants. It suggests that the wicked Hugo considered that he maintained the *droit de seigneur*, the right of a feudal lord to copulate with a vassal's bride prior to her marriage.

124.11 ~ three leagues. Approximately nine miles. Neither miles nor leagues were standardised throughout England at that time.

124.16 ~ flagons and trenchers. Large vessels containing wine or beer, and flat boards from which food is eaten.

124.21 ~ unkennel the pack. Releasing the pack of hounds from its kennels in preparation for hunting.

124.22 ~ swung them to the line. A foxhunting term, whereby the hounds are set out across the likely line of travel of the quarry to increase the chance of one of the hounds picking up the scent.

124.36 ~ a galloping. This reads *"... a sound of galloping ..."* in other editions, when it might better have been amended to '... the sound of galloping ...'

124.41 ~ goyal. A Dartmoor word for a dip in the land, or a shallow gully.

125.15 ~ that third or fourth generation which is threatened in Holy Writ. From *The Bible*, Exodus 20-5: "... visiting the iniquity of the fathers upon the children unto the third and fourth generation ...". The Oxford edition interestingly notes that ACD's short story, 'The Third Generation' (1894), concerns the effect of syphilis inherited by a young man from a debauched ancestor which causes him to kill himself.

125.27 ~ Devon County Chronicle. A fictitious newspaper, although a *Devon County Chronicle* has since been published, as the newsletter of a Sherlockian society.

125.28 ~ May 14th. This date was changed to June 14th in the first book edition, which seems to be more-appropriate to the period which exists between the murder of Sir Charles and the arrival of Sir Henry.

125.33 ~ Liberal candidate for Mid-Devon. The Parliamentary candidate for the area, representing the Liberal Party. BFR's father was a close friend of the Liberal candidate for Mid-Devon at the time when the book was written. Since this constituency was not created until August 1888, it is impossible for Sir Charles to have been the candidate for it much before that date, and his death must therefore have occurred on 14 June 1889 at the earliest, which means that the case cannot have occurred prior to the Summer and Autumn of 1889.

125.36 ~ *nouveau riches*. Those having recently acquired wealth. Usually used in a derogatory manner, in suggesting that they do not have the style which supposedly accompanies old wealth.

125.39 ~ South African speculation. Primarily speculations in gold and diamond mining in South Africa, with Sir Charles's fortune later being associated with South African gold, and with ACD himself also having invested in South African gold.

125.40 ~ the wheel. The wheel of fortune, either mythologically or in the form of gambling wheels.

125.40 ~ he realized his gains. He converted his assets to cash.

126.13 ~ 4th of May. This date was changed to 4th of June in the first book edition, to match the change made above.

126.23 ~ One Murphy. The Oxford edition noted that Murphy was the name of the Jesuit at Stonyhurst who caused ACD's loss of his Catholic faith, and suggested that Murphy was an odd name for a 'Dartmoor gipsy'. It should be noted that ACD recorded that he lost his Christian faith, and not just his Catholic faith. Most of the gypsies on Dartmoor at that time were itinerants, and many of them travelled annually from Ireland, often via Wales, to buy Dartmoor ponies.

126.29 ~ dyspnœa. A medical condition resulting in difficult or laboured breathing.

126.31 ~ the coroner's jury. A jury of lay persons appointed to examine any unexpected or unusual deaths under the guidance of a legally-qualified Coroner.

126.36 ~ a tenant for Baskerville Hall. Sir Henry was not, in fact, a tenant, in that he owned *'Baskerville Hall'*.

126.46 ~ the Pope. This would have been Pope Leo XIII (1810-1903) in 1889.

127.17 ~ the Bushman and the Hottentot. Two easily differentiated sub-racial types in South Africa.

127.29 ~ gig. Not a specific type of vehicle, but a general description of any lightweight, two-wheeled carriage for two people, facing forwards, usually drawn by one horse. Essentially a simple frame with a seat.

127.41 ~ chimerical. Fantastically assembled, in being like the *Chimera*, a mythological beast with the head of a lion, the body of a goat and the tail of a serpent.

128.15 ~ Mr. Holmes, they were the footprints of a gigantic hound! Although these might be the most dramatic words in the whole story, it has rightly been objected that it is impossible to distinguish the footprints of a hound from those of other types of dog. Mortimer's speculative identification, in the presence of what must have been gigantic footprints, would, however, have been conditioned by his awareness of the Baskerville legend about a giant hound.

129.30 ~ wicket-gate. Usually a small door or gate set within a larger door, enabling access without opening the larger door, but in this case it is used for a gate constructed from laths with gaps between, similar to the construction of a wicket in cricket.

131.33 ~ farrier. A blacksmith who shoes horses, but also sometimes used for a horse-doctor.

132.01 ~ Waterloo Station. The largest railway station in Britain, located on the South side of the Thames in central London, originally providing access mainly to the central South and South-West, under the London and South-Western Railway Company. This was the London terminus for Portsmouth (where ACD lived and where Holmes was born), and for Sir Henry's journey from Southampton. It would also have provided a direct line for Stapleton to reach the North Devon Line with The Hound, via Salisbury and Exeter.

132.12 ~ and was the very image. Holmes is thus told that Rodger Baskerville senior was the very image of the portrait of the wicked Hugo Baskerville from the start, and this makes his later recognition of the villain in that painting less remarkable!

132.14 ~ yellow fever. A viral disease causing a yellowing of the complexion and high fever, prevalent in Central America, as indicated.

132.15 ~ a wire. A colloquial expression for a telegram. It has been suggested that this is an Americanism which Mortimer would not have used in 1889, but the *Oxford English Dictionary* records it as having been used in precisely that year, by a certain Arthur Conan Doyle, in *The Sign of Four*. Although that story first appeared in print in 1890, the writing was completed in October 1889. The earliest recorded English use of 'wire' for a telegram is in 1859.

132.15 ~ Southampton. A maritime town in Hampshire, only a few miles from the great Netley Hospital where Dr

Watson was trained as an Army surgeon. In 1889 a rapidly developing port for passenger liners, providing a fast means of getting to London from the Atlantic routes without sailing around to the Thames, via a direct railway line on the London and South-Western Railway. Boat trains travelled from lines on the actual quays, although passengers often disembarked and awaited the loading of the boat trains in the London and South Western Railway's splendid hotel, South-Western House, located just outside the dock area, which had its own railway passenger platform.

132.31 ~ parish vestry. A meeting of parishioners in a vestry, an ecclesiastical building usually attached to or close to a church, to conduct parish business.

133.10 ~ Bradley's. A fictitious tobacconist in Oxford Street, near Baker Street.

133.11 ~ shag tobacco. A coarsely cut, shaggy-textured, strong-flavoured, strong-smelling and usually dark-coloured pipe tobacco.

133.47 ~ Stamford's. Clearly based on the map shop of Edward Stanford which was located at No 26 Cockspur Street, just off Trafalgar Square in London in 1889, and which still provides an excellent service in nearby Long Acre, although there is still a sub-branch in Cockspur Street. The name was changed to Stanford's in the first book edition.

133.47 ~ Ordnance map. A map produced by the Ordnance Survey, a governmental organisation producing maps originally for military purposes, and still producing the best maps in the world.

134.01 ~ A large scale map, I presume? // Very large. The only Ordnance Survey map of Dartmoor which would readily have been available to Holmes in London in 1889 would have been that with a scale of one-inch-to-the-mile (1:63,360), which would not nowadays be considered to be a large scale map, let alone a very large scale map. He could possibly have obtained the six-inches-to-the-mile maps of Dartmoor (1:10,560), but he would have required dozens of these maps to cover the whole of Dartmoor, and as Holmes refers to only one map and points out two places which are 14 miles apart on it, it can only have been the one-inch map which he obtained. W S Baring-Gould inappropriately uses a road map of the Dartmoor area to exemplify this map, which incorporates the road letter and number identification system introduced long after the case took place, as well as roads which did not exist in 1889.

134.07 ~ Grimpen. W S Baring-Gould suggests that this is Widecombe-in-the-Moor, although he gives no good

reason for it to be so. Perhaps it was to provide him with an excuse for his reproduction of one version of the chorus of the old song, *Widecombe Fair*, recorded by his grandfather, although he does not mention this last fact. A better candidate would be Hexworthy.

134.08 ~ Lafter Hall, which is mentioned in the narrative. There is no Lafter Hall on Dartmoor, although Laughter Hole Farm may once have had this name. Lafter Hall is not, in fact, mentioned in the narrative!

134.11 ~ High Tor. W S Baring-Gould says that there is no High Tor on his map. There is a High Tor on most good maps of Dartmoor, but it is located beside the River Tavy, between Peter Tavy and Mary Tavy, and it is thus just off the Western side of the Moor and unsuitable as a Houndian location. It is, in addition, a Tor, not a farmhouse. A better candidate would be somewhere like Greendown or Tor Royal.

134.11 ~ Foulmire. W S Baring-Gould suggests that Fox Tor Mire [sic] is Foulmire, in spite of the fact that Fox Tor Mires is a system of mires and not a farmhouse. A better candidate would be somewhere like Forder or Peat Cot.

136.05 ~ Baronet. An hereditary knight, unlike ACD, who became a Knight Bachelor, with no titular inheritance.

136.44 ~ Times. *The Times*, founded in 1785 as the *Daily Universal Register*, once the most important newspaper in the world, now a sad shadow of its former self.

137.01 ~ Free Trade. It has been suggested that Free Trade would not have been discussed as early as 1889, but it had been discussed in British newspapers for more than a century by then, and there had been increased interest in trade tariffs in the 1880s. Leslie Klinger has most pertinently pointed out that the 1888 edition of the *Encyclopædia Britannica* devotes 11 pages to the subject. ACD spoke on trade tariffs in 1900, and BFR wrote the words to a trade tariff song, called 'John Bull's Store', in 1899.

137.16 ~ the one is extracted from the other. Cinematic representations of the note usually show large words pasted onto the note, clearly readable at a distance, but the text of a *Times* leader would have been similar in size to this present text.

137.31 ~ maxillary. Associated with the upper jaw.

137.33 ~ leaded bourgeois type. The word 'bourgeois' is here a specialist printing term which is pronounced 'burr-joyce', not as with the French word. Leaded type had the words separated by strips of lead in the printing frame.

137.36 ~ I confused the *Leeds Mercury* with the *Western Morning News*. It would have been a gross error to have confused the type of these two real newspapers, since they were completely different even to a novice. ACD may well have been familiar with both, since the *Leeds Mercury* had attacked him during his political campaigning, and the *Western Morning News* was his local newspaper when he lived in Plymouth.

138.15 ~ any letter posted up to early morning. As Sir Henry must have left his hotel by about 9.30 am to reach '*221B*' by 10.00 am, it might be thought impossible that he could have received a letter posted early that morning. There were up to six deliveries a day in London at that time, and as the letter was postmarked at the Charing Cross office it would have been set aside as 'local' at that sorting office and delivered on the next round.

138.36 ~ watermark. A trade mark impressed within the paper. This would only have been visible by holding the paper up to a light, and such watermarks were usually used only in expensive paper.

138.40 ~ a dime novel. Cheap (dime = 10 cents) American novels of a sensational nature, copied largely from the style of earlier French *feuilleton* stories, often, initially, with Wild West elements.

139.11 ~ varnished. New leather boots often had to be varnished, to provide a sealed surface, upon which a shine could be developed.

139.29 ~ the pet story of the family. Is this an example of a running canine joke by ACD? If so, there are worse examples to come!

141.32 ~ the district messenger offices. The District Messenger Boys, a fast messenger service within London, using uniformed boys to make deliveries. Some houses had electric bells connected to the nearest District Messenger office to summon a messenger.

142.17 ~ Let me have a report by wire. It is rather undiplomatic for Holmes to suggest that Cartwright send a message by wire, rather than by District Messenger!

142.19 ~ Bond Street. A thoroughfare in central London having several private art galleries in 1889. It was named after Sir Thomas Bond, a relative of SBG.

143.13 ~ Newcastle. A large, heavily industrialised city on the River Tyne in Durham in the North of England, famous as a centre for coal distribution, largely by sea, with the river being known locally for many decades as 'the coaly Tyne' as a result. Coal from Newcastle may well have been unloaded in London by those coal-heavers who frequented The Northumberland Arms in 1889.

143.13 ~ High Lodge, Alton. Alton is a small, quiet, market town in Hampshire, and there was no High Lodge

in 1889, although there was an Alton Lodge in a very prominent position in the High Street in Alton at that time.

143.17 ~ coal-owner. An unusual-seeming expression, in that almost everyone owned coal at that time, but clearly meant to mean the owner of a coal mine or a coal distributor. ACD was not alone in using this expression in this way.

143.23 ~ Gloucester. The county city of Gloucestershire. Mr Oldmore was never the Mayor of Gloucester, and neither he nor his wife were resident in Alton in 1889.

145.18 ~ five hundred cases. Holmes must have been very busy in the 18 months after the Baskerville case, for Watson mentions one thousand cases by the Spring of 1891.

145.29 ~ you are being dogged in London. The running canine joke again?

146.02 ~ They have looked after the Hall for four generations now. The Oxford edition suggests that this indicates that the Hall had been in the hands of caretakers since 1815. This is incorrect, in that the phrase means that the Barrymores had looked after the Hall with Baskerville residents in it for four generations (albeit with the short absence of Sir Charles), for Sir Henry later says that the Barrymore family had been *with* the Baskerville family for generations.

146.28 ~ Westmorland. A mountainous county in the North-West of England, which is now part of Cumbria.

147.24 ~ the 10.30 train from Paddington. Paddington was the London terminus of the Great Western Railway in 1889, located close to Baker Street. It provided one of the two major routes to the South-West of England, via Reading, Bristol and Exeter. The line still used the more comfortable 'broad gauge' in 1889, with a gap of 7ft 0¼in between the lines, as opposed to the 'standard gauge' of 4ft 8½in used on most other UK railways. There was no Saturday 10.30 am train from Paddington to Devonshire in any of the candidate years for *The Hound*.

148.09 ~ 2,704. An inconsistency in the *Strand* edition, in that it is '2704' on the two previous occasions.

148.12 ~ half a sovereign. A small gold coin worth ten shillings (£0.50 in modern currency, but almost equal to a labourer's wage for a day in 1889).

148.16 ~ Turpey Street. A real street in the Borough.

148.16 ~ the Borough. A district of London, to the South of Southwark and to the East of Waterloo.

148.36 ~ a touch, Watson. Holmes uses several metaphors from fencing here. Holmes participated in fencing at college, and Watson describes him on more than one occasion as being an excellent swordsman.

148.41 ~ guineas. A guinea was a gold coin, worth 21 shillings (£1.05 in modern currency, but almost equal to two days' wages for a labourer in 1889).

149.13 ~ shorter than you, sir. As Holmes was well over six feet in height, most people were shorter than him.

149.13 ~ a toff. A slang expression for one who is extremely well-dressed, possibly derived from the word 'tuft', which was a word for a titled undergraduate, who was identifiable through having a gold tassel on his university cap.

149.27 ~ a foeman who is worthy of our steel. Another fencing image. The Oxford edition identifies this as being derived from Scott's *The Lady of the Lake* (1810): "In foemen worthy of their steel!".

150.03 ~ the appointed day. Saturday 5 October 1889.

150.23 ~ there is his wife, of whom we know nothing. At the end of the story we still know nothing of Mortimer's wife, although this has not prevented some wild speculations about her.

150.40 ~ Museum of the College of Surgeons. Located in Lincoln's Inn Fields in central London, and more-correctly called the Hunterian Museum of the Royal College of Surgeons of England. The original collection of 14,000 specimens, made by John Hunter (1728-93), was used by Hunter to demonstrate his theories of comparative anatomy, physiology and morbid anatomy, and would thus have been of great interest to Mortimer. It was willed to the nation by Hunter and was handed over to the Company of Surgeons in 1799. It was greatly expanded by 1889, primarily by the Curator from 1861, William Henry Flower. The sometimes horrendous exhibits, including numerous human abnormalities and parts of executed criminals, does not provide 'pure amusement' for many, and some members of The Baskerville Hounds who visited the Museum had to vacate the premises rather rapidly! It is not open to the general public.

151.18 ~ Poor Sir Charles's head was of a very rare type, half-Gaelic, half-Ivernian. This is a dreadful piece of nonsense, in that the terms used are not strictly applicable to comparative anthropology, or to anything else. Gaelic is a linguistic term, but it might most-easily be accepted as involving Scottish Celts. There is no such word in English as 'Ivernian', although the English word 'Hibernian', which is probably what is intended, is a corruption of the Greek word 'Iverna', meaning Ireland. Mortimer seems to be indicating that Sir Charles had a part-Scottish, part-

Irish ancestry. It has been suggested that Sir Charles was closer to ACD than to the real Baskervilles, who came from Normandy, but ACD was merely born in Scotland, with his ancestry being primarily Irish, although he did have Norman ancestors. Sir Henry, in being small with a dark complexion, might more-appropriately be thought to have more Iberian ancestry than Hibernian!

151.26 ~ there rose in the distance a grey, melancholy hill, with a strange jagged summit. W S Baring-Gould suggests that this was Brent Tor, but one would have to be travelling from Lydford towards Coryton (W S Baring-Gould's station for 'Baskerville Hall') to see this sight, and one would already have seen plenty of Dartmoor on the way from Exeter to Lydford on this route, quite apart from it being on totally the wrong side of Dartmoor.

151.37 ~ a small wayside station. This is not, as far too many commentators have suggested, one of the main line stations which Watson, Sir Henry and Mortimer might have passed through, like Newton Abbot or Totnes, since it is a wayside station. Better candidates would be Staverton (which fits the description superbly) or Buckfastleigh on the Ashburton line, or, less probably, Bovey Tracey or Lustleigh on the Moretonhampstead line. W S Baring-Gould probably got it more wrong than anyone else, choosing Coryton station, purely to fit Lew House being 'Baskerville Hall'.

151.38 ~ a waggonette with a pair of cobs. A waggonette was a lightweight four-wheeled carriage, usually drawn by two horses, often with a removable hood, generally used by large households or hotels. It had four or six seats behind the driver, running laterally and facing inwards. Cobs were short-legged, very strong horses.

152.01 ~ hart's-tongue ferns. (*Phyllitis scolopendrium*) A fern which grows in shady, moist and rocky places, which makes it ideal for parts of Dartmoor. Unusually for a fern it has undivided leaves.

152.26 ~ Selden, the Notting Hill murderer. It has been mooted that Selden was the name of a vicious warder in Dartmoor Prison in 1901, but the records are not readily available. A well-known, early detective story, published in 1865, was *The Notting Hill Mystery*, written by the otherwise unknown Charles Felix. It does not involve the ferocious crime and insanity credited to Selden.

153.12 ~ Swan and Edison. Sir Joseph Wilson Swan (1828-1914), an English inventor and manufacturer, and Thomas Alva Edison (1847-1931), an American inventor and manufacturer. W S Baring-Gould quite rightly points out that the lamps manufactured by Swan and Edison were different in principle, so Sir Henry may have said 'Swan or Edison', as no joint-operation has been identified.

153.35 ~ behind the high iron dogs. The running canine joke again? Iron dogs are the metal supports which prevent logs falling out of the grate of a fire.

154.35 ~ the modern-billiard-room. ACD had recently built a modern billiard-room as a central feature of his new house, 'Undershaw'. He was a county class player.

154.42 ~ half moon. W S Baring-Gould was correct in stating that in the year of his dating for the case, 1888, on the night he calculates Watson as having just arrived at 'Baskerville Hall', 29 September, the moon was only one day past half moon, and there was thus 39% of its disc illuminated (not quite half-Moon). Watson clearly states, however, that he and Sir Henry retired early after dinner, and he implies that he saw the Moon when he got to his room. The Moon did not rise on the Eastern side of the Moor until 11.40 pm on 29 September 1888 (as viewed from Hayford Hall), and could not have come into view from Watson's window on the South side of 'Baskerville Hall' until after 2.47 am on 30 September. On 5 October 1889, the Moon was past half-moon (85%), but it arose at 4.15 pm and was within view of Watson's window throughout the whole evening. The choice here is between Watson seeing no Moon (1888) and Watson seeing more Moon than he recorded (1889). W S Baring-Gould's suggestion that Watson stayed up later than he thought is ludicrous, unless Watson did not consider it worthwhile mentioning that he stayed up until after 3.00 am to see the Moon. It can similarly be shown that most of W S Baring-Gould's astronomical pronouncements do not fit the facts of the case, and they can therefore be ignored. After all, he did start with the wrong day, month and year!

156.41 ~ The postmaster, who was also the village grocer. W S Baring-Gould suggests that Watson must have visited the Postmaster at his home, not his shop, since the day was a Sunday. It was a Sunday, but less attention was paid to such matters in villages on the Moor with no church, and in some villages, such as Hexworthy, the publican provided postal and grocery services all week from the establishment which was also his home.

157.12 ~ the first to dog the new heir. That dog joke again!

157.33 ~ I am Stapleton of Merripit House. W S Baring-Gould states that: "a glance at our 'very-large'-scale map will show Merripit, in the heart of the moor." There is, in fact, no such place, although we do have Lower, Middle and Higher Merripit (which are the names of farmhouses) and Merripit Hill.

159.14 ~ I saw one of the moor ponies wander into it. Moor ponies rarely wander into mires, as they can sense them better than Man, but SBG mentioned ponies getting 'stugged' in *A Book of Dartmoor*. In four decades of Moor exploration this commentator has seen only two get stuck, but newcomer Stapleton sees two in two days!

160.20 ~ a bittern booming. The bittern (*Botaurus stellaris*), a long-legged bird inhabiting marshy areas, makes a deep booming noise, similar to that made by someone blowing across the mouth of a very large bottle or jug.

160.23 ~ the last of the bitterns. In 1889 bitterns were thought to be approaching extinction in Britain, with very few pairs being noted in Norfolk (close to where *The Hound* was born) and Lancashire, and with some in the New Forest in Hampshire (where ACD recorded them in his *The White Company* when he stayed in the New Forest in the 1880s). The situation was not as bad as thought at that time, but it has become worse since.

160.32 ~ his hearth. R Hansford Worth had labelled a 'hearth-stone' in his drawing of Hut 3 at Grimspound in SBG's 1900 book, *A Book of Dartmoor*.

160.35 ~ Neolithic man - no date. There are thousands of prehistoric remains on Dartmoor. The Oxford edition claims that: "… at Grimspound near Widecombe there is a metropolis of neolithic (last period of the Stone Age, 6,000 - 3,000 BC) huts." Three Neolithic (4500 - 2300 BCE) settlements have been found on Dartmoor, but Neolithic huts were primarily biodegradable, and there are only two or three debatable Neolithic stone huts. There are, however, over 5,000 known stone hut circles (the generally circular stone remains of huts), and practically all of these are Bronze Age (2300-700 BCE), with Grimspound being Middle Bronze Age, in having been occupied between 1400 and 1000 BCE. The Oxford edition further suggests that Stapleton's lectures on prehistory are probably one of the clearest imprints of BFR, but they are more-probably the influence of the early archaeological works of SBG, since he too initially used the incorrect term 'Neolithic' for antiquities which were from the Bronze Age.

160.40 ~ Cyclopides. There is no such fly or moth, although many unsatisfactory candidates have been offered, including a group of hover-flies called *Cyclorrhapha*.

161.04 ~ I had heard someone describe her as being a beauty. Watson's memory is failing, as it was Holmes who told him this at Paddington Station the day before.

161.23 ~ orchid. Experts at the internationally-renowned Orchid Centre in Newton Abbot, close to Dartmoor, have suggested that it is possible that some forms of orchid, such as the bog orchid (*Malaxis paludosa*), could have been growing in sheltered spots on Dartmoor in early-October.

161.23 ~ mare's-tails. A perennial plant (*Hippuris vulgaris*) which can grow in stagnant or gently-flowing water, which conditions occur frequently near mires on the Moor.

161.39 ~ commoner. Watson was correct in stating that he was a commoner, but then so, technically, was Sir Henry, since he was not a Peer of the Realm.

162.08 ~ as if in answer to my thought. Holmes had performed an even-more amazing reading of Watson's mind the year before, in 'The Cardboard Box'.

164.04 ~ One page is missing. The two letters which are reproduced seem to be complete, but the missing page might be the report which Watson wrote for Holmes on 16th October.

164.09 ~ Oct 13th. The Oxford edition suggests that those Holmesian commentators who date the case as beginning in September are wrong, in that there seems to be no convincing reason to assign the first chapters before October, as only a brief interval between Chapters VII and VIII makes much sense, since Holmes expects regular reports from Watson. This suggestion is correct, but only if one ignores the day when Mortimer left his walking stick at '221B', in that it can be calculated that Mortimer first met Holmes and Watson on Tuesday 1 October 1889, and that Watson reached Dartmoor on Saturday 5 October. Holmes does not, however, instruct Watson to report regularly, as he merely suggests that Watson should report carefully, giving facts in the fullest possible manner, and Watson indicates in Chapter VII that he considers that he should report only when he has something to report.

164.16 ~ graves and the huge monoliths. There are many different types of prehistoric grave on the Moor, with the smallest being the kistvaens, which are rectangular box-shaped coffins made of six slabs of stone, usually being around two feet in width, three feet in length, and two feet in depth, which indicates that they probably did not contain whole bodies, but ashes. Tombs were often used more than once. Larger remains exist with those graves which were covered with stones and earth, to form barrows, as large mounds. The biggest graves are the few Neolithic tombs, which can be large chambered tombs comprising enormous slabs of rock to form the walls, floor and roof, with the covering of small stones and earth often having been removed in recent centuries. Tombs were sometimes surrounded by a circle (or circles, with up to four concentric rings) of stones. There are often avenues of stones leading to tombs, and these sometimes end with an extra large column of stone, known as a monolith, although monoliths do exist in splendid isolation on the Moor. This account is a gross simplification of the wonderful variety of prehistoric monuments which exists on the Moor, and everyone is encouraged to read one of the archaeological accounts included in the Select Bibliography, with Sandy Gerrard providing an excellent overview and Jeremy Butler's atlases providing superb detail.

164.21 ~ I am no antiquarian. The Oxford edition suggests that the basic information for these archaeological speculations came from BFR, but that the mixture of disciplines involved is characteristic of ACD. Once again, the basic information more-probably came from SBG, although the conclusion is very typical of ACD's prehistorical speculations. It is ACD, rather than BFR, who would more-appropriately describe himself as not being an antiquarian at that time, in that the Fletcher Robinson household clearly had an interest in the antiquities of Devonshire. It is difficult to understand the meaning of the Oxford edition's suggestion that: "Watson's thesis argues the survival of the unfittest as providing the bases of archaeological conclusions." Both the fit and the unfit leave archaeological evidence, and the prehistoric men who took up residence on the Moor might be considered to have been pioneers, rather than the unfittest, in extending the environment in which they lived. They survived subsequently by abandoning their residences on the Moor when climatic conditions made continued residence unsuitable.

164.24 ~ uninteresting to your severely practical mind. The Oxford edition suggests that as Holmes was by then occupying a Neolithic dwelling, Watson's digression was very practical. This nicely highlights yet another example of the wonderful irony which repeatedly appears in this story, but Holmes would, in fact, have been staying in a Bronze Age hut when he stayed on the Moor, although he points out later that he stayed mostly in Coombe Tracey.

164.24 ~ your complete indifference. This is a reference to the first Holmes story, where Holmes said that it made no difference to his cases whether the Earth went round the Sun or round the Moon. It also reflects how ACD was influenced by what he saw and heard in what he wrote. In February 1884 ACD attended a lecture given by his friend, Major-General Alfred Drayson, at the Portsmouth Literary and Scientific Society (wherein ACD became a joint Honorary Secretary with a certain Dr Watson!), on

"The Earth and its Movements". This was some two years before ACD wrote the first Holmes story, *A Study in Scarlet*, in Portsmouth. General Drayson, who studied astronomy and taught mathematics, is considered to have been a model for Professor Moriarty.

165.12 ~ the spot where the legend of the wicked Hugo is supposed to have had its origin. This needs to be close to the route from the South-Eastern edge of the Moor to the South-Western edge of the Moor, and it should lie in a dip or goyal. Deadman's Bottom provides an appropriately evocative name and location, as does Evil Combe, although the Giant's Basin area does provide the required fang-like rocks, with all of these being close to the upper waters of the River Plym and to tracks leading from Lud Gate to Sheepstor.

165.15 ~ cotton grass. A grass-like plant (*Eriophorum augustifolium*, the Common Cottongrass) which bears what look like bolls of cotton, and which is very common in the miry areas of the Moor. Another form is the *Eriophorum vaginatum*, which is popularly known as the Hare's-tail Cottongrass, which might easily have been confused nominally with the Hare's-tails already mentioned.

165.40 ~ He has been excavating a barrow at Long Down. A barrow is a burial which has been covered by rocks and frequently also by soil to form a mound. There are numerous barrows on Dartmoor, and indeed the predecessor of the Dartmoor Exploration Committee within the Devonshire Association was the Barrow Committee. There is no '*Long Down*' on Dartmoor, but the ridge of Hamel Down does form a very long down, and along this down there are several remarkable barrows, including 'Broad Barrow', which is the second largest barrow on Dartmoor, and 'Two Barrows', a pair of barrows. The latter were known to have been excavated by Spence Bate, an archaeological rival of SBG, in 1872, but the original excavator of 'Broad Barrow' does not seem to have been recorded, and he might therefore have been Mortimer! Alternatively, there is the magnificent Neolithic burial chamber near Corringdon Ball Gate, which is recorded on the Ordnance Survey map as 'Long Barrow', where the excavator also seems to be unrecorded, and where the earlier age of this tomb may have caused the confusion in Watson's mind over Neolithic huts. Incidentally, the largest barrow on the Moor is one of those known as 'Three Barrows', close to 'Long Barrow'.

165.40 ~ a prehistoric skull. No prehistoric skulls have been found anywhere on the Moor. This may partly be due to the prehistoric burials having involved cremation, and there

are signs of this, but it would also be due to the nature of the soil on the Moor, which quickly destroys bone.

166.15 ~ Fernworthy. Possibly the former hamlet of Fernworthy, now submerged beneath the Fernworthy Reservoir. The Fernworthy which W S Baring-Gould proposes is off the North-Western border of the Moor, and too far from Frankland's location to be appropriate.

166.25 ~ he dug up the neolithic skull in the barrow on Long Down. This supports the suggestion that the barrow at '*Long Down*' might be the real Long Barrow near Corringdon Ball Gate, in that if a skull were found in that Neolithic barrow, then it might well have been Neolithic. As no skull is recorded as having been found there, and as the original excavator does not seem to have been recorded, might it be that Mortimer failed to register his skull find because he kept the skull in his personal collection, or because of Mr Frankland's threat of prosecution for opening a grave without the consent of the next-of-kin?

166.28 ~ having brought you up to date in the escaped convict. The 'in' here, repeated in the first book edition but changed to 'on' in many other editions, seems to be either a case of 'in' being printed instead of 'on', or of the omission of some words after 'in', such as 'connection with'.

168.08 ~ a budget. This might readily be read as meaning 'an allowance', but the Oxford edition more-pertinently points out that 'budget' was sometimes used to mean 'a weekly summary of news', as with the *Pall Mall Gazette* (which is mentioned in one of the short Sherlock Holmes stories, 'The Blue Carbuncle', and which published one of ACD's non-Holmes stories, *The Mystery of Cloomber*, in serial form), having its weekly *Pall Mall Budget*.

169.03 ~ Plymouth. With Exeter, one of only two large cities close to '*Baskerville Hall*', with the '*Hall*' being about 25 miles from Plymouth, the city where ACD lived for six weeks in 1882.

170.35 ~ either he or I ought to be in a strait-jacket. There are several similar references associated with madness in connection with Sir Henry, and noting the references to Atavism, some might infer that there is a possible explanation for the Phantom Hound of the legend here, as opposed to Stapleton's very real hound, in that it may have resulted from some form of insanity which allowed Baskervilles to see the Phantom Hound and die as a consequence. Given the seeming obsession of so many Houndian commentators with matters psychological, one looks forward with trepidation to reading the first PhD thesis on 'The Psychosomatic Hound'!

171.44 ~ tangled skein. A common and obvious metaphor in Holmesian adventures, with the intended title of the first Holmes story, *A Study in Scarlet*, originally having been *A Tangled Skein*.

174.15 ~ Cleft Tor. There is no 'Cleft Tor' on Dartmoor, although there are many Tors which have clefts cut into them by nature. There is a Cleft Rock above the River Dart at Holne Chase, and SBG was photographed in Chaw Gully, near Grimspound, at a point which had all the appearance of being a cleft Tor.

174.34 ~ a thin rain began to fall. W S Baring-Gould comments that '" Foggy and misty in the south and south-east of England" said the *Times* of London.', and several of his other attempts at matching the weather described in *The Hound* similarly refer to areas of England where the weather could easily have been vastly different to that of Dartmoor, especially as Dartmoor tends to create its own micro-climate. There is still much local research to be done on this topic.

174.36 ~ hunting-crop. A short, stiff riding whip, sometimes with a tape-like lash and often with a handle at right-angles to the whip and with a strap which attaches to the wrist to prevent the whip being lost when riding. Holmes once stated that his preferred weapon was a loaded hunting-crop, which is one where the handle has been drilled out and refilled with lead.

175.08 ~ country-side. The Oxford edition suggests that this word appears thus hyphenated here, but that the hyphen is unsatisfactorily dropped later. The word does, in fact, appear unhyphenated when it is first used, in Chapter III, followed by six hyphenated usages, concluding with the one referenced here, and then by two unhyphenated usages. Unfortunately, there are no examples of the word in the readily-available manuscript of Chapter XI to see ACD's preference.

176.20 ~ We were both fair runners and in good condition. American editions tend to change this phrase to read 'We were both swift runners and in fairly good training'. The only explanation for this change seems to confirm the suggestion that the English and the Americans are two nations divided by two different languages, if one may be permitted to update Oscar Wilde!

176.32 ~ peat. Compressed, long-term rotted vegetable matter which appears in many parts of the Moor, which can be dug up and air-dried then burnt to provide heat, although it is not as efficient as coal and produces no flame.

177.05 ~ you could come down to us. This phrase ends Chapter IX in the *Strand* edition, but American editions

have an additional sentence: *"In any case you will hear from me again in the course of the next few days."*

179.18 ~ and there is the repeated reports. In the first book edition this is changed to: *"... and there are the repeated reports ..."*

179.36 ~ upon the Tor. An example of the inconsistent use of 'tor' and 'Tor' in the *Strand* edition.

179.41 ~ a stranger then is still dogging us. It's that canine joke again!

180.22 ~ But he will never trouble anyone. The 'But' is changed to 'And' in the first book edition. As conjunctions, both are wrong, but this might be deliberate, in being meant to suggest that Barrymore was not well educated.

182.14 ~ the Black tor. This is changed to 'the Black Tor' in the Oxford edition, but there is no certainty that Watson was referring to a specific Black Tor. There are, in fact, several Black Tors on Dartmoor, and probably the best candidate for *"... the Black tor ..."* upon which the mystery man stood is that Black Tor which exists above the River Aune near Shipley Bridge.

182.35 ~ dog-cart. Another canine joke? A lightweight, one-horse, two-wheeled cart with four seats running transversely, back-to-back. They were never, as is sometimes claimed, drawn by dogs, but were originally designed for carrying shooters and dogs to shooting venues, with the latter often being carried in a special box underneath the cart.

183.01 ~ Coombe Tracey. A fictitious town. This appeared as 'Newton Abbott' throughout the chapter of the manuscript which still exists, with an alteration to 'Coombe Tracey' being made by ACD in that manuscript. There is a town called Newton Abbot, not 'Newton Abbott', located close to the boundary of Dartmoor. There are various 'Combes' around the Moor, and there is Bovey Tracey, although none of these are suitable candidates for *'Coombe Tracey'*, in that express trains from London did not stop at any of them.

183.28 ~ écarté. A French card game for two, involving elements of whist and draw poker. It was extremely popular in England in the mid-Nineteenth Century, but was out of fashion with serious card players by 1889 through having been over-analysed.

183.32 ~ three days ago. The Oxford edition claims that this was the day before Barrymore was confronted, and that Barrymore would have taken supplies out to the Moor by day. This is totally incorrect. This conversation takes place on 17th October, and Barrymore was confronted at some time after 2.00 am on 16th October. Barrymore says that Selden's signal was to show the point to which the supplies were to be delivered, and Barrymore would thus have had to follow the candle signal to find the spot. This is why the candle was still burning when Watson and Sir Henry reached *'Cleft Tor'*. In addition, on the night when Watson first saw Barrymore signalling, he subsequently heard a key turning in a lock, which was almost certainly Barrymore going out onto the Moor to make a delivery, or coming back, which was during the early hours of 14 October, which was the last time that Barrymore saw Selden, which was, as Barrymore says, three days before the conversation of 17th October (ACD:QED!).

183.43 ~ a week ago or more. This mysterious Man on the Moor thus arrived there sometime between 5 October (the date when Watson arrived) and 10 October.

184.15 ~ some lay of his own. Having some purpose of his own, which is an ironical point and an almost inevitable one in most of Holmes's cases, in that numerous people seem to have lays of their own.

185.23 ~ a Remington typewriter. In 1889 Laura Lyons might have had the latest in the Remington range, the Model 5, introduced in 1888, although the Model 2 of 1878 remained the most popular model until 1908. In 1889 typists were generally known as 'typewriters' in England, which had already led to music hall jokes about gentlemen working with typewriters on their knees or marrying their typewriters! ACD used the term 'type-writist' in other Holmes cases.

185.28 ~ the sulphur rose. *Rosa sulphurea*, a yellow double rose, and a typical example of Watson's romantic writing in connection with ladies having seemingly Hispanic backgrounds.

186.32 ~ a passage of your letter. 'the postscript' was changed to *"… a passage …"* in the manuscript, yet Watson shortly afterwards still refers to this passage as *"… the postscript …"* in the amended text.

186.44 ~ But why a rendezvous … a bachelor's house. These two sentences were inserted into the manuscript, and the first word of the next sentence was changed from 'And' to *"Well"* in the manuscript.

187.28 ~ the law is upon his side. ACD making a political point with Mrs Lyons, in that he later became the President of the Divorce Law Reform Union, supporting easier divorces for women.

187.30 ~ I had learned … could be met." This phrase was inserted into the manuscript, in place of the original

phrase which read: '… I had learned that if a certain sum of money could be found for his expenses my husband was willing to leave the country.'

187.39 ~ finding if she had … of the tragedy. This phrase was inserted into the manuscript, in place of the original phrase which read: '… obtaining the last English address of the husband, and discovering whether he had indeed left England at the date she named.'

187.41 ~ It was unlikely that … the stone huts upon the moor. The surviving manuscript of this chapter indicates that there was a re-writing of most of this paragraph, in that all but the first two dozen words were written on a half-sheet of paper which seems to have been inserted into the manuscript to replace a now-missing sheet and a lengthy section of deleted manuscript text on the sheet which contains the next paragraph which was included in the printed text.

187.42 ~ a trap would be necessary to take her there. A trap is not a specific type of vehicle, but a general term for any two-wheeled, lightweight carriage, usually being one-horsed.

187.45 ~ baffled and disheartened. A major change was made here in the manuscript, with only part of the change being determinable, and with the new section being written on a separate sheet of paper, which was inserted between the existing sheets. The immediately preceding section has been changed in an unknown way and the following passage, which still exists within the manuscript, was deleted *en bloc*: '… disheartened. Either she was an accomplished actor and a deep conspirator, or Barrymore had misread the letter, or the letter was a forgery - unless indeed there could by some extraordinary coincidence be a second lady writing from Newton Abbott whose initials were L. L. For the time my clue had come to nothing and I could only turn back to that other one which lay among the stone huts upon the moor.' Significantly, the 'Newton Abbott' which appears in this deleted section is not changed to *'Coombe Tracey'* in the manuscript, which suggests that the passage was deleted before the changes were made to the name of 'Newton Abbott' throughout the chapter.

188.09 ~ the summit of the Black Tor. This does appear as 'Black Tor' in the manuscript, but changes shortly thereafter and therein to 'black Tor'. The Oxford edition accepts the 'Black Tor' usage.

188.35 ~ Sir John Morland. This was changed from 'the Mayor of Plymouth' in the manuscript, and the change must have been done immediately, as the new words were written along the same line as the earlier ones, and on to the next line, without an insertion having to be made between the lines.

188.38 ~ Frankland *v.* Morland. A legal case, Frankland *versus* Morland, wherein Frankland raises an accusation against Morland. The fact that the word *"... Morland ..."* is included without alteration further supports the suggestion that the change from the manuscript's original 'the Mayor of Plymouth' above was made immediately.

188.45 ~ Frankland *v.* Regina. A legal case, Frankland *versus* the Queen, where Frankland has some grievance against the Queen's legal representatives, although the Queen (Victoria in this case, of course) would not have had to appear in court.

189.20 ~ my telescope upon the roof. Being an amateur astronomer, Frankland would almost certainly have had an astronomical telescope, which would have presented an inverted image to the viewer, but Jim Ferreira suggests that the way in which Watson seems to use the telescope easily indicates that Frankland also had a terrestrial telescope, which was used here. The Oxford edition interestingly points out that ACD's Jesuit school, Stonyhurst College, had an excellent astronomical observatory, and that the College suffered from the complaints of an obsessive litigant when ACD was a pupil there.

189.30 ~ that Black Tor. This appears as 'that black Tor' in the manuscript, in contrast to the 'Black Tor' which appears in the manuscript shortly before this usage. The Oxford edition accepts the 'Black Tor' usage here.

189.37 ~ Every day and sometimes twice a day, I have been able -. This phrase was inserted into the manuscript, in place of the phrase which originally read: 'Without my telescope it would of course have been impossible -'

190.20 ~ Belliver and Vixen Tor. Real locations on the Moor, with 'Belliver' usually now being spelled Bellever, although ACD's version is not an error, as it is merely an alternative spelling which was used on some maps.

190.27 ~ this must be the burrow where the stranger lurked. To illustrate this burrow, or stone hut, W S Baring-Gould reproduces a photograph (used also in his 'biography' of Holmes), taken by Stuart Black, which the photographer claimed was of one of the huts at Grimspound. It does not, in fact, look like any of the stone huts at Grimspound, even as reconstructed by the Victorians, but it might be connected with a hound, in that it looks very much like one of the granite slab dog kennels built into the wall at Ditsworthy Warren House. Watson's description of looking down on this stone hut in the text is exactly like

the view of the hut which had been restored in the centre of Grimspound when ACD visited that site in 1901, as seen from Hamel Down.

190.37 ~ that very stone slab ... a rude grate. R Hansford Worth labelled a 'stone platform' upon which ancient men may have slept and the crude 'cooking hole' and 'hearth stone', in his plan of Hut 3 at Grimspound in SBG's 1900 book, *A Book of Dartmoor*.

190.41 ~ pannikin. A small, metal drinking-vessel.

190.41 ~ a half-full bottle of spirits. This phrase, without the hyphen added by *The Strand Magazine*, was inserted into the manuscript to replace the phrase which originally read 'a half empty bottle of spirits'. An interesting change from a pessimistic to an optimistic philosophy!

191.15 ~ Great Grimpen Mire. An inconsistency in the *Strand* edition, as it is "... the great Grimpen Mire ..." elsewhere in that text.

191.18 ~ and yet as I looked ... was bringing nearer. This phrase was added to the previous section in the manuscript in place of the following unfinished phrase: 'and yet here was I waiting for some crisis, waiting with my nerves in a quiver, knowing that'. The change was clearly made immediately, in that the original phrase was unfinished and the replacement phrase was continued on the next line without any writing having to be inserted between lines.

192.09 ~ the rude lintel. SBG shows a lintel over the door of Hut 3 at Grimspound, in his *A Book of Dartmoor*, but this was later removed by archaeologists.

197.35 ~ He appears to have broken his neck by falling over these rocks. The Oxford edition claims that Watson is lying here. He may actually be telling the truth, in that Selden may indeed have broken his neck falling over the rocks, although he is not telling all of the truth in avoiding mentioning how Selden came to fall over the rocks, but then Stapleton would, of course, have been aware of the reason why Selden fell, so there would have been no point in Watson lying about the broken neck, as he merely has to conceal that he knows why Selden fell.

198.25 ~ the silvered slope which showed where the man was lying who had come so horribly to his end. In some book editions, notably the Doubleday edition, Chapter 12 ends here, and the rest of the *Strand* text of this chapter is included in Chapter 13.

198.30 ~ we have never had a foeman more worthy of our steel. Another fencing image. This is also the clearest indication that the Baskerville case is pre-1891, for in that year Holmes encountered Professor Moriarty, the ultimate criminal.

199.14 ~ Sufficient for to-morrow is the evil thereof. Seemingly a misquotation of *The Bible*: "Sufficient unto the day is the evil thereof." (Matthew 6-34).

201.10 ~ Kneller. Sir Godfrey Kneller (1646-1723), a Court painter to Charles II.

201.11 ~ Reynolds. Sir Joshua Reynolds (1723-92), a portrait painter who lived near Dartmoor.

201.17 ~ Rodney. Baron George Brydges Rodney (1719-92), the British Admiral primarily responsible for defeating the French Navy in the West Indies in 1782.

201.19 ~ Pitt. Probably William Pitt the Younger (1759-1806), Prime Minister of Britain 1783-1801 and 1804-06.

201.20 ~ Cavalier. A supporter of King Charles I, during the English Civil War.

201.34 ~ love-locks. Curls of hair on the forehead, with the generally aristocratic Cavaliers being known for fancy and decorative dress, in contrast to the austere appearance of their Roundhead opponents.

201.44 ~ It is the first quality of a criminal investigator that he should see through a disguise. Holmes failed to do this on more than one occasion.

204.16 ~ York. The county city of Yorkshire, in the North of England, possibly close to where Stapleton (Vandeleur) had his Yorkshire school.

205.12 ~ Grodno, in Little Russia. Grodno was actually in Belorussia, not in Little Russia, which was in the Ukraine.

205.17 ~ the reverential way in which Lestrade gazed at my companion. It has been suggested that Lestrade did not have this sort of reverence for Holmes in 1889, but it must be recalled that Watson prepared the recording of this case for publication some 12 years after the events, and he might not have wished to have resurrected earlier antagonistic feelings, in 1901.

205.23 ~ we will take the London fog out of your throat. A nicely ironic touch, in that Lestrade is shortly to have his throat filled with Dartmoor fog!

206.19 ~ Temple Coombe. Templecombe is some 70 miles from the Moor, in Somerset. This is clearly a typographical error in the *Strand* edition, and it was changed to *'Coombe Tracey'* in the first book edition.

206.22 ~ as long as I have my trousers I have a hip-pocket. The implication here is that what Lestrade has in his hip-pocket is the revolver which he later produces, but it would have been extremely uncomfortable and dangerous to have carried a revolver in the hip-pocket of one's trousers. The more-likely content of a hip-pocket might be the hip-flask which Lestrade also later produces. Perhaps, when he was asked *"Are you armed?"*, he misheard this as 'Are you

alarmed?', and was replying that he always had some Dutch (or rather French) courage in his pocket! Slight deafness is justifiable on the grounds that Lestrade seems to have misheard most of Holmes's essentially vocal advice throughout his career!

208.03 ~ Thank Heaven. The Oxford edition has "Thank God" here, even though the explanatory notes indicate that it is "Thank Heaven" in the *Strand* and first book editions, and even though the notes also explain that Newnes had house rules against using exclamations involving God. The notes do, at least, highlight the fact that Watson twice uses the word 'God' improperly when Selden is chased to his death and Mrs Stapleton twice uses it improperly after The Hound is killed, with Sir Henry using it improperly once after the death of The Hound. The Oxford notes do not mention the other six occasions when the word 'God' might be thought to have been used improperly in *The Hound*.

208.21 ~ its muzzle and hackles and dewlap were outlined in flickering flame. A large number of people, especially those from the USA, have been found to have read the first part of this statement as indicating that The Hound wore a muzzle, but the word 'muzzle' here means the snout and mouth of a dog's face, being the part of the face over which a full muzzle is normally fitted. Hackles are the feathery neck hairs around the head of a dog. The dewlap is the fold of loose skin which hangs down the lower half of the face of some dogs.

208.24 ~ broke upon us out of the fog. Although the penultimate chapter of the *Strand* version stops here, and an intermediate chapter numbered "Chapter XIV. (continued)" follows after the usual chapter break, the whole of Chapter XIV is one continuous chapter in the first book edition. The rather artificial break, although it does introduce a cliff-hanger, was primarily intended to produce a set amount of text for the magazine edition. It must have been a very frustrating month-long break for the magazine readers, and it must have encouraged those who could afford the six shillings to buy the complete book when it came out on 27 March 1902, prior to the release of the final episode in *The Strand Magazine* in April.

209.14 ~ Holmes had emptied five barrels of his revolver into the creature's flank. Most commentators suggest that Watson is wrong here, and propose that he should have said 'five chambers'. As a former professional armourer, this commentator can assure everyone that Watson was not wrong. Firstly, the chambers of most revolvers are not emptied when such a gun is fired, in that they still retain the empty cartridge cases. Secondly, when the charge of each cartridge is discharged out of the chamber it first fills the barrel behind the bullet as the bullet travels down the barrel, and the charge is then emptied out of the barrel after the bullet leaves the barrel. When five bullets have been fired, then five barrels will have been emptied, although one might more-correctly say that the barrel had been emptied five times. The term 'emptied five barrels' is a perfectly reasonable colloquialism, and Watson was not alone in using it.

209.26 ~ it appeared to be a combination of the two. The Oxford edition states that a combination of a mastiff and a bloodhound is impossible, but some dog experts say that it is perfectly possible, and the 1880s and 1890s were a time of great experimentation with first-breed crosses in dogs in England. It should also be noted that Watson only says that The Hound *appeared* to be a combination of the two breeds, and he was therefore describing the appearance, not the exact blood lines. The result of the combination is clearly something extraordinary and probably unexpected. Perhaps it was the result of the cross-breeding of the two dogs which appeared to have failed to deter intruders in another great mystery story, *The Moonstone*: a bloodhound and a mastiff!

209.31 ~ Phosphorous. It must, as Holmes said, have been a very cunning preparation of phosphorous, since pure phosphorous would have poisoned The Hound, as well as ruining its sense of smell, but the full effects were not known in 1889.

212.04 ~ wands. Thin sticks of wood, or the stems of plants used to mark a safe route to the centre of the mire.

212.24 ~ miasmatic. More-correctly miasmic, causing an infectious or obnoxious emanation.

212.25 ~ the dark, quivering mire, which shook for yards in soft undulations around our feet. This is an excellent description of what is known on the Moor as a 'feather-bed' mire, and one can sometimes see undulations travelling outwards in waves for scores of yards.

214.04 ~ our sitting-room in Baker Street. After this initial sentence in Chapter XV, a new section was added to the first book edition, as follows:

Since the tragic upshot of our visit to Devonshire he had been engaged in two affairs of the utmost importance, in the first of which he had exposed the atrocious conduct of Colonel Upwood in connection with the famous card scandal of the Nonpareil Club, while in the second he had

defended the unfortunate Mme. Montpensier from the charge of murder which hung over her in connection with the death of her step-daughter, Mlle. Carére, the young lady who, as it will be remembered, was found six months later alive and married in New York.

In excerpt ~ Nonpareil Club. A non-existent club.

In excerpt ~ New York. The state city of New York State. Holmes had a contact, Wilson Hargreave, who was an official in the New York Police Bureau in 1898.

214.22 ~ blotting out what has passed. After this second sentence in this paragraph, a new section was added to the first book edition, as follows:

The barrister who has his case at his fingers' end, and is able to argue with an expert upon his own subject, finds that a week or two of the courts will drive it all out of his head once more. So each of my cases displaces the last, and Mlle. Carére has blurred my recollection of Baskerville Hall. To-morrow some other little problem may be submitted to my notice, which will in turn dispossess the fair French lady and the infamous Upwood.

214.22 ~ the Hound. An inconsistency in the *Strand* edition, in that it is 'hound' elsewhere.

214.41 ~ only two lives intervened. Holmes is wrong here. The only two whose lives intervened were Charles and Henry Baskerville, for James Desmond was a distant cousin and therefore inferior to Stapleton in terms of inheritance. In the next paragraph Holmes suggests that Stapleton may not have known about Henry, and in that case Henry could not have been one of those that Stapleton thought of as intervening.

215.12 ~ Ross and Mangles. A fictitious establishment.

215.12 ~ Fulham Road. A major thoroughfare between West and South-West London.

216.15 ~ The Mexborough Private Hotel. A fictitious establishment, with Mexborough having been a small coal-mining town in South Yorkshire.

216.16 ~ Craven Street. A short thoroughfare running between the North Embankment and The Strand, and within 50 yards of The Northumberland Arms. There were some small hotels in Craven Street.

216.27 ~ the boots. The servant, often a boy or a man too old for further public appearance in an hotel, responsible for cleaning boots and shoes.

216.28 ~ chambermaid. The bribing of a chambermaid might have been necessary for the return of the first missing boot to the inside of Sir Henry's suite, since the boots would normally collect dirty items from outside of the suite door and leave them there after cleaning, and the chambermaid might also have been necessary if Sir Henry, having lost one boot from outside his door, had refused to leave any more boots outside the door.

216.33 ~ outré. French for 'out of the ordinary', which is often the characteristic which attracted Holmes to a case.

216.41 ~ Folkestone Court. As far as can be determined, a fictitious address in the West Country.

217.20 ~ white jessamine. More commonly known as White Jasmine, a sweet smelling shrub, used for making a distinctive perfume.

218.39 ~ It is a formidable difficulty. It is indeed, since Holmes's explanation of how Stapleton might have claimed his inheritance if he had succeeded in killing Sir Henry without being caught is not really satisfactory. The intention could only have been to make his claims from overseas, without ever subsequently visiting the Dartmoor estate again.

219.01 ~ 'Les Huguenots'. A French opera (1836) by Giacomo Meyerbeer (1791-1864).

219.02 ~ the De Reszkes. Jean de Reszkes (1850-1925), a tenor, and Edouard de Reszkes (1853-1917), a bass. Polish operatic brothers.

~ Marcini's. A fictitious restaurant.

SIDNEY PAGET'S ILLUSTRATIONS

Paget's drawings for *The Hound* are sometimes used as evidence in solving problems which exist within the text, but these drawings, evocative though they are, cannot be relied upon, since Paget clearly did not have all of the text available to him when he produced some of the drawings, and in others he makes obvious mistakes. On at least one occasion, his printer failed him. In Chapter II, for example, he produces a drawing of Barrymore as being relatively short, stout and ugly, when ACD had at that time published no description of Barrymore. In Chapter VI the butler is described as being "... *a remark-able-looking man, tall, handsome* ...", and Paget drew him like that in that chapter and thereafter. In Chapter II, the wicked Hugo's roysterers are shown in Eighteenth Century dress, rather than that of the Seventeenth Century. The most famous illustrative error in the *Strand* edition occurs at the beginning of Chapter III, where Holmes and Watson are shown walking down Regent Street, and where Watson might be thought to have fastened his coat on the female side. This is not Paget's fault, however, for his faint signature can be seen at the foot of the drawing, and it is in mirror-writing, as the *Strand* printed the drawing reversed. It can still be seen that way, with Holmes on the left of the drawing, in some later editions which copied the *Strand*. In Chapter III Holmes is seen looking at a map, and it appears to be about the right size for the one-inch-to-the-mile Ordnance Survey map of Southern Dartmoor. In Chapter VIII, Paget correctly shows Barrymore as being shoeless, but in Chapter IX, where one might expect that Barrymore would once again have taken the precaution of removing his shoes, he is shown to be wearing them, although ACD and Dr Watson do not comment upon this situation. In Chapter XI, the tripod mount shown with Frankland's telescope would be totally unsuitable for astronomical purposes, but Frankland may have mounted it temporarily like this for his terrestrial observations, or this may, indeed, be a terrestrial telescope, rather than the astronomical one which is mentioned specifically in the story. In Chapter XIII, Holmes arrives at '*Baskerville Hall*' without luggage, and Watson records that he and Sir Henry soon supplied Holmes's wants. According to Paget, they provided Holmes with a full dinner jacket outfit, yet Sir Henry was very short and Watson was considerably shorter than Holmes, as was Sir Charles, according to Paget. Barrymore would probably not have had a dinner jacket, as it was only gentlefolk who had recently taken to wearing them. It is therefore difficult to see where Holmes's outfit came from. Holmes seems to have a flat cap when he meets Laura Lyons, yet he has a soft Trilby or Homburg when he meets Lestrade shortly afterwards. There seems to have been a game of musical hats when the three men go onto the Moor, for Watson, who is wearing a bowler hat when he creeps up to *'Merripit House'* is wearing a flat cap when Sir Henry emerges from that residence, and Watson or Lestrade appears to be wearing a flat-crowned Trilby or Homburg when chasing after Holmes, but both have their bowlers on again when they reach Sir Henry and The Hound! In the penultimate picture of Holmes beside his fire at *'221B Baker Street'*, Holmes seems to have aged considerably, and to have put on a great deal of weight, but he rejuvenates and loses a lot of weight before leaving for *'Mancini's'*. A picture may sometimes be worth a thousand words, but some of Sidney Paget's pictures would require more than a thousand words in order to explain away their inconsistencies!

A retrospection
Holmes here looks like the description of his portly,
older brother, Mycroft.

Be ready in half an hour
Within a very short time, Holmes has reverted to his
previous slim self.

Selected Bibliography

It has been impossible to incorporate footnotes within the Investigation and Annotations without disrupting the appearance of the book excessively, and so in order to provide those who wish to extend the studies contained within this volume, an extensive bibliography is provided below. Square brackets within the reference indicate information added by the present commentator, such as where the title of the reference is not self-explanatory. Any references where the titles are not self-explanatory, but where there is no additional information may be assumed to be general background information, although it may well be the author who is of significance. Some recent editions of books have been referenced, although original publication dates have been indicated, and unless otherwise stated, all publishers are from the UK. Researchers should be warned that some of the sources referenced are included only for the sake of completeness, in terms of previous discussions which have taken place, and some of these are unreliable over the material or arguments which they include. There are several references to *The Hound*, the journal of The Baskerville Hounds which has been published annually since 1992. Most of the articles in this journal are relevant to the discussions in this present book, but only those of a very specific nature or of a particular importance are included in this listing. There are hundreds of articles connected with *The Hound of the Baskervilles* in other Holmesian journals (see bibliography by Ronald De Waal detailed below, which has been the main source of Holmesian bibliographical references). Every effort has been made to include all of the worthwhile ones, as well as some of the less worthy, although many more of the latter have deliberately been omitted! There are thousands of articles and books about various aspects of Dartmoor (see the bibliography by Peter Hamilton-Leggett detailed below), but only a selection of the more important ones with a direct association or reference to *The Hound of the Baskervilles* have been included here. The relevant Dartmoor books of SBG are included, plus some of the articles and books by SBG from other areas of interest which are pertinent to studies of *The Hound*, including some published after 1901, but further details of his books are available (see the bibliography by Roger Bristow below).

Adye F, *The Queen of the Moor*, J & R Maxwell, 1885.

Allen A, 'Cry Wolf - A History of the Wolf in Devon', *Devon Life, No 259*, 1988.

Allen G, 'An Ancient Lake Bottom', *Longman's Magazine*, June 1884.

Allen G, 'A Corner of Devon', *The Cornhill Magazine*, November 1882.

Allen G, 'From Moor to Sea', *The English Illustrated Magazine*, December 1889.

Allen G [with ACD], *Hilda Wade*, Grant Richards, 1900.

Allen G, *Scallywag*, Chatto & Windus, 1893.

Anderson D, 'Grim Suggestiveness: Sense of Place in The Hound of the Baskervilles', *Baker Street Miscellanea, No 24*, USA, Winter 1980.

Anon ['Merthyr Tydfil Correspondent'], 'Baskerville anger over holiday home offer' [interview with Major Hopton - main Baskerville family branch descendant], *The Times*, 9 November 1981.

Anon [possibly Adye F] (introduced & annotated by Weller P L), *The Baskerville Guide to 'The Tale of a Dartmoor Fog'*, 2nd Edition, Sherlock Publications, 1999.

Anon, 'A Devon Coachman Whose Name Has Become Immortal' [on Harry Baskerville], *The Western Times & Gazette*, 1 November 1957.

Anon, 'His Name Has Gone Down in Mystery - Harry Baskerville', *South Devon Journal*, 17 October 1951.

Anon, '"Hound of the Baskervilles" - Harry Baskerville Dead; Conan Doyle Used Name', *New York Herald Tribune*, USA, 2 April 1962.

Anon, 'Splendid old place this, Dear Watson' [Brook Manor], *Western Evening Herald*, 23 September 1989.

Athenæum, Letter from Librarian, Dodgson S J, to Weller P L, dated 27 January 1997, on ACD dining with a group at the Athenæum on 30 April 1901.

Atholl J, *Prison on the Moor: The Story of Dartmoor Prison*, John Long, 1953.

Austin B, 'Dartmoor Revisited or Discoveries in Devonshire', *Austin's Sherlockian Studies - The Collected Annuals*, Magico, USA, 1986.

Austin B, 'The Play's the Thing' [a dubious play version], *Baker Street Miscellanea, No 24*, USA, Winter 1980.

Bamberg R W, *Haunted Dartmoor - A Ghost Hunter's Guide*, Peninsula Press, 1993.
Barclay The Rev J G, *Random Reminiscences* [on Black Shuck], Privately Printed, Undated.
Baring-Gould S, 'The Black Dog in Heraldry', *Devon and Cornwall Notes and Queries, Vol X*, 1919.
Baring-Gould S, *The Book of Dartmoor*, Methuen, 1900.
Baring-Gould S, *A Book of Folk-Lore*, Praxis, 1993 [originally 1913].
Baring-Gould S, *Bladys of the Stewponey*, Methuen, 1897.
Baring-Gould S, *A Book of the West - Volume 1 - Devon*, Methuen, 1899.
Baring-Gould S, *Dartmoor Idylls*, Methuen, 1896.
Baring-Gould S, *Devonshire Characters and Strange Events - 1st Series*, J Lane, 1908.
Baring-Gould S, *Devonshire Characters and Strange Events - 2nd Series*, J Lane, 1908.
Baring-Gould S [Anonymous], *Eve*, Chatto & Windus, 1889.
Baring-Gould S, 'The Exploration of Grimspound', *The Western Morning News*, 29 June 1894.
Baring-Gould S (with Burnard R, Gray W A G, Worth R H & Worth R N), 'The Exploration of Grimspound', *Report & Transactions of the Devonshire Association*, 1894.
Baring-Gould S, *Freaks of Fanaticism*, Methuen, 1891.
Baring-Gould S, *Furze Bloom*, Methuen, 1899.
Baring-Gould S, *Guavas the Tinner*, Praxis Books, 2000 [originally 1896].
Baring-Gould S, *John Herring*, Smith, Elder & Co, 1888 [originally 1883].
Baring-Gould S, *Kitty Alone: a Story of Three Fires*, Praxis, 2001 [originally 1894].
Baring-Gould S, *The Life of Napoleon Bonaparte*, Methuen, 1897.
Baring-Gould S, *Little Guide to Devon*, Methuen, 1907.
Baring-Gould S, *Margery of Quether and Other Stories*, Methuen, 1891 [main title story originally in *The Cornhill Magazine* in April & May 1884, and 'At the Y' in *Belgravia* in April & May 1884].
Baring-Gould S, *Old Country Life*, Methuen, 1889.
Baring-Gould S, 'The Old Manor Houses in South Devon', *Western Antiquarian, Vol 3*, 1884.
Baring-Gould S, *Red Spider*, Praxis, 1993 [originally 1887].
Baring-Gould S, *Royal Georgie*, Methuen, 1901.
Baring-Gould S, *Urith: A Tale of Dartmoor*, Methuen, 1891
Baring-Gould W S, *Sherlock Holmes - A Biography of the World's First Consulting Detective*, Rupert Hart-Davis, 1962.
Baring-Gould W S, *The Annotated Sherlock Holmes, 2 Vols*, John Murray, 1979.
Bedford M & Dettman B, 'A Cunning Preparation' [on phosphorous], *Baker Street Journal, Vol 16 No 4 (NS)*, USA, December 1966.
Bellamy R, *Postbridge - The Heart of Dartmoor*, Devon Books, 1998.
Black S, 'The Adventures of Sherlock Holmes on Dartmoor', *John O'London's*, 21 November 1952.
Blackmore R D, *Christowell*, Sampson Low, Marston,

Searle, & Rivington, 1881.
Blackmore R D, *Maid of Sker*, Blackwood, 1872.
Bookman Article (Williams J E H), 'Arthur Conan Doyle', *The Bookman*, [UK Version], April 1902.
Bookman Editorial, 'Coronation Honours' [ACD's knighthood], *The Bookman*, USA, August 1902.
Bookman Editorial, 'The Footprints of the Baskerville Hound', *The Bookman*, USA, February 1902.
Bookman Editorial, 'More Sherlock Holmes Theories', *The Bookman*, USA, May 1902.
Bookman Editorial, 'The New Sherlock Holmes Story', *The Bookman*, USA, October 1901.
Bookman Editorial, 'A Sherlock Holmes Number', *The Bookman*, USA, April 1902.
Bookman Editorial, 'Some Inconsistencies of Sherlock Holmes', *The Bookman*, USA, January 1902.
Bookman Review [Maurice A B], 'Conan Doyle's "The Hound of the Baskervilles"', *The Bookman*, USA, May 1902.
Booth M, *The Doctor, The Detective and Arthur Conan Doyle - A Biography of Arthur Conan Doyle*, Hodder & Stoughton, 1997.
Bray A E, *Traditions, Legends, Superstitions and Sketches of Devonshire*, John Murray, 1838.
Briggs C, *The Mana of Lew* [on SBG's house], Praxis Books, 1993.
Bristow C R, *A bibliography of the works of S. Baring-Gould*, Privately Printed [primarily for The Sabine Baring-Gould Appreciation Society], 1999.
Brodie B, 'The Existence of an Heir in Canada', *The New Baker Street Pillar Box, No 37*, July 2001.
Brody H, 'The Location of Baskerville Hall', *Baker Street Journal, Vol 29 No 4 (NS)*, USA, December 1979.
Brown A, *The Cabells and Their Kin*, Houghton Mifflin, USA, 1939.
Brown P, 'Escapes From Dartmoor Prison', *The New Baker Street Pillar Box, No 37*, July 2001.
Brown T, *Devon Ghosts*, Jarrold, 1992.
Brown T, 'The Black Dog in Devon', *Report and Transactions of the Devonshire Association*, 1959.
Burton M L, 'On the Hound' [the breed], *The Baker Street Journal, Vol 25 No 3 (NS)*, USA, September 1975.
Butler A, 'Dartmoor and the Great Rebellion', *The Hound, Vol 2*, 1993.
Butler J, *Dartmoor Atlas of Antiquities, Vols 1-5*, Devon Books, 1991-97.
Butler S, *Dartmoor Century*, Devon Books, 2000.
Butler S, *Dartmoor Century II*, Devon Books, 2001.
Butler S (ed), *A Gentleman's Walking Tour of Dartmoor 1864*, Devon Books, 1986.

Cabell Djabri S, 'The Cabell Legend - A Source for "The Hound of the Baskervilles"', *The Hound, Vol 1*, 1992.
Cabell Djabri S, 'The Cabell Legend and the Hound of the Baskervilles', *Hound and Horse, A Dartmoor Commonplace Book*, The Sherlock Holmes Society of London, 1992.
Cabell Djabri S, *The Story of the Sepulchre - The Cabells of Buckfastleigh and the Conan Doyle Connection*, The Shamrock Press, 1989.
Cabell J B, *Ladies and Gentlemen*, Robert M McBride & Co, USA, 1934.

Cabell J B, 'The Original Wicked Hugo - as recorded by James Branch Cabell', *The Hound, Vol 5*, 1996.

Campbell M, 'The Hound of the Baskervilles: Dartmoor or Herefordshire?', *Guy's Hospital Gazette* Reprint, 1953.

Carr J D, *The Life of Sir Arthur Conan Doyle*, John Murray, 1949.

Chadderton M, 'The Opening Chapter - Setting the Scene', *The New Baker Street Pillar Box, No 37*, July 2001.

Chadderton M, 'That Eponymous (and Ambiguous) Hound', *The Hound, Vol 5*, 1996.

Chambers P, 'Baskerville (of hound fame) used to live here' [on Harry Baskerville], *The Daily Express (Holiday Express)*, 19 July 1975.

Chapman M, 'Finding clues to the site of Baskerville Hall - It is elementary, my dear Watson' [Clyro Court], *Western Mail*, 28 July 1992.

Cherry B & Pevsner N, *The Buildings of England (South Devon)*, Penguin, 1989.

Christ J F, 'A Very Large Scale Map', *Sherlock Holmes Journal, Vol 6 No 3*, Winter 1963.

Christensen P, 'The Nature of Evil in The Hound of the Baskervilles', *Baker Street Journal, Vol 29 No 4*, USA, December 1979.

Christie A, *The Sittaford Mystery*, Collins, 1996 [originally 1931].

Chudleigh J, *An Exploration of Dartmoor's Antiquities - 1892*, John Pegg, 1987 [originally 1892].

Coates H, 'The "Reel" Hound of the Baskervilles' [an analytical model for film versions], *The New Baker Street Pillar Box, No 37*, July 2001.

Collier W F, *The Hound and the Horn* [about Harry Terrell and Dartmoor hunting], Halsgrove, 2000.

Coxhead J R W, *Legends of Devon*, Westward Press, 1954.

Crossing W, *Crossing's Guide to Dartmoor*, David & Charles, 1981 [originally 1912].

Crossing W, *Folklore and Legends of Dartmoor*, Forest Publishing, 1997 [originally articles from 1914].

Crossing W, *A Hundred Years on Dartmoor*, David & Charles, 1967 [originally articles from 1900].

Curjel H, 'The Dartmoor Campaign', *Sherlock Holmes Journal, Vol 12 No 2*, Winter 1975.

Curjel H, 'Green Glows the Goyal', *Baker Street Journal, Vol 30 No 1 (NS)*, USA, September 1976.

Dakin D M, *A Sherlock Holmes Commentary*, David & Charles, 1972.

Davies B, 'The Back Yards of Baker Street' [the definitive identification of *'221B'*], *The Sherlock Holmes Journal, Vol 4 No 3*, Winter 1959.

Davies B, 'Railways and Roads in "The Hound ..."', *Sherlock Holmes Journal, Part 1 - Vol 14 No 2, Part 2 - Vol 14 Nos 3-4*, Winter 1979 & Summer 1980.

Davies D S, *Starring Sherlock Holmes* [films - unseen, due release Summer], Titan, 2001.

Dam H J W, 'Arthur Conan Doyle - An Appreciation of the Author of "Sir Nigel," the Great Romance Which Begins Next Sunday' [important BFR material], *Sunday Magazine* of the *New York Tribune*, USA, 26 November 1905.

Day K F, *Eden Phillpotts on Dartmoor*, David & Charles, 1981.

De Waal R B, *The Universal Sherlock Holmes, Vols 1-5* [*the* bibliography of Holmesian studies], Metropolitan

Toronto Reference Library, Canada, 1994.

Dickinson B H C, *Sabine Baring-Gould - Squarson, Writer & Folklorist 1834-1924*, David & Charles, 1970.

Doyle A C, *Adventures of Gerard*, Newnes, 1903.

Doyle A C, *The Complete Sherlock Holmes*, Penguin, 1987.

Doyle A C, *The Complete Sherlock Holmes Long Stories*, John Murray, 1929.

Doyle A C, 'Dry Plates on a Wet Moor, *The Hound, Vol 3*, 1994 [originally 1882].

Doyle A C, *The Exploits of Brigadier Gerard*, Newnes, 1896.

Doyle A C, 'The Man on the Tor' [manuscript of Chapter XI of *The Hound of the Baskervilles*], The Berg Collection, New York Central Library, USA, undated.

Doyle A C (edited with annotations by Klinger L S), *The Sherlock Holmes Reference Library: The Hound of the Baskervilles*, Gasogene Books, USA, 2001.

Doyle A C, *The Hound of the Baskervilles*, McClure, Phillips & Co, USA, 1902.

Doyle A C, *The Hound of the Baskervilles*, Newnes, 1902.

Doyle A C, *The Hound of the Baskervilles*, Penguin, 2001.

Doyle A C (introduced by Robson W W, with annotations), *The Hound of the Baskervilles*, OUP, 1998.

Doyle A C, 'The Hound of the Baskervilles', *The Strand Magazine*, August 1901 - April 1902.

Doyle A C, *The Hound of the Baskervilles - A Study Edition*, Sherlock Publications, 2001.

Doyle A C, 'The King of the Foxes', *The Green Flag and other Stories of War and Sport*, Smith Elder & Co, 1900 [story originally published in 1898].

Doyle A C, *Memories and Adventures* [autobiography], Oxford UP, 1989 [originally 1924].

Doyle A C (selected & introduced by Doyle A M), *A Treasury of Sherlock Holmes*, Hanover House, USA, 1955.

Doyle A C, *The Winning Shot*, Sherlock Publications, 1995 [originally 1883].

Doyle Dame J L C, Personal Letter to Weller P L, dated 3 February 1997, on absence of records of payments to BFR.

Endle R, *Dartmoor Prison*, Bossiney Books, 1979.

Evans P, 'The Mystery of Baskerville', *The Daily Express*, 16 March 1959.

Eyles A, *Sherlock Holmes - A Centenary Celebration*, John Murray, 1986.

Ferreira J, 'The Question of the Rooftop Telescope', *The Hound, Vol 5*, 1996.

Fox H, 'Brook Manor, Buckfastleigh', *Devon Life, No 134*, 1977.

Frayling C, *The Hound of the Baskervilles* [Introduction & Notes], Penguin, 2001.

Frayling C, *Nightmare - The Birth of Horror* [section on *The Hound*], BBC Books, 1996.

Fuller T (ed Freeman J), *The Worthies of England* [abridged] [on Gubbins], George Allen & Unwin, 1952 [originally 1662].

Gawne E & Sanders J, *Early Dartmoor Farmhouses*, Orchard Publications, 1998.

Gerrard S, *Book of Dartmoor - Landscapes Through Time*, Batsford, 1997.

Godfrey A, 'On the Alternative Use of the Long and Short S', *Baker Street Journal, Vol 12 No 3 (NS)*, USA, July, 1962.

Green C, 'The Story of Nun's Cross Farm', *Dartmoor Magazine, No 6*, 1987.

Green C M, 'A Study of the Legend of the Hound of the Baskervilles', *Baker Street Journal, Vol 31 No 1 (NS)*, USA, March 1981.

Green Richard L, 'Bertram Fletcher Robinson: An Old and Valued Friend', *Hound and Horse, A Dartmoor Commonplace Book*, The Sherlock Holmes Society of London, 1992.

Green Richard L & Gibson J M, *A Bibliography of A Conan Doyle*, [*the* ACD bibliography], Hudson House, USA, 2000 [originally 1983].

Green Richard L, 'Conan Doyle's Norfolk Connections', *Sail and Steam - Norfolk Expedition - September 2000*, The Sherlock Holmes Society of London, 2000.

Green Richard L, 'The Snake of Longmore Hall and the origin of "The Hound of the Baskervilles"', *Sherlock Holmes Gazette*, Issue 16, 1996.

Green Richard L, *The Uncollected Sherlock Holmes*, Penguin, 1983.

Green Roger L, 'Baskerville Hall', *Sherlock Holmes Journal, Vol 8 No 2*, Spring 1967.

Griffiths D M (ed), *The Archaeology of Dartmoor - Perspectives from the 1990s - Proceedings No 52*, Devon Archaeology Society, 1994.

Guerra S, Salvatori G & Solito E, 'The Mastiff of the Baskervilles' [on the Italian translation of 'Hound'], *The New Baker Street Pillar Box, No 37*, July 2001 [also in Italian in *The Strand Magazine*, the journal of Uno Studio in Holmes (Italy)].

Haining P, *The Television Sherlock Holmes*, Virgin, 1994.

Hamilton-Leggett P, *The Dartmoor Bibliography*, Devon Books, 1992.

Hammer D, *The Game is Afoot*, Gasogene Press, USA, 1983.

Harris H, *Industrial Archaeology of Dartmoor*, David & Charles, 1986.

Harris V, *Dartmoor Prison - Past and Present*, Brendon, Undated [c 1875].

Haydock R, *Deerstalker! - Holmes and Watson on Screen*, The Scarecrow Press, USA, 1978.

Haydock R, 'Sherlock Holmes and the True Legend of the Hound of the Baskervilles', *The History of Sherlock Holmes in Stage, Films, TV, & Radio Since 1899*, E-GO Collector's Series No 1, USA, 1975.

Hemery E, 'Phantom hounds of demon Dewer', *Western Morning News*, 8 March 1983.

Hemery E, *High Dartmoor* [badly flawed on The Hound, but invaluable on Dartmoor], Robert Hale, 1983.

Hermon A, 'Elementary Watson, we can't be in two places at once', *Western Morning News*, 11 October 1986.

Hirayama Y, 'A Defence of Mr Jack Stapleton', *The New Baker Street Pillar Box, No 37*, July 2001.

Hirayama Y, 'Some Hound Scholarship from Japan', *The Hound, Vol 1*, 1992.

Holloway E, *Elinor with the Pleading Eyes* [on Fowelscombe], Privately Printed, Undated [after 1983].

Howlett A D, *Some Observations on the Dartmoor of Sherlock Holmes*, Privately Printed, 1972.

Howlett A D, 'The Curse of the Cabells - The Legend of the Hound of the Baskervilles', *Hound and Horse, A Dartmoor Commonplace Book*, The Sherlock Holmes Society of London, 1992.

Jenkins S C & Pomroy L J, *The Moretonhampstead and South Devon Railway*, The Oakwood Press, 1989.

Jones K I, 'The Geography of The Hound of the Baskervilles', *Sherlock Holmes Journal, Vol 7 No 3*, Winter 1965.

Jones K I, *The Mythic Hound*, Oakmagic Publications, 1996.

Jones K I, *The Mythology of The Hound of the Baskervilles*, Sir Hugo Books, 1986.

Jones K I, *The Psychology of the Hound*, Oakmagic Publications, 1997.

Johnson R, *Ready When You Are, Mr Rathbone*, Northern Musgraves, 1992.

Kay P, *The Ashburton Branch - A New History*, Peter Kay, 2000.

Kelley G E, *Sherlock Holmes Screen and Sound Guide*, The Scarecrow Press, 1994.

King R J, 'Folklore of Devon', *Fraser's Magazine*, May 1873.

Kirk-Smith H, *Now the Day is Over - The Life and Times of Sabine Baring-Gould 1834-1924*, Richard Kay, 1997.

Klinefelter W, *Ex Libris A. Conan Doyle: Sherlock Holmes*, Black Cat Press, USA, 1938.

Klinefelter W, *Origins of Sherlock Holmes*, Gaslight Publications, USA, 1983.

Klinger L S, *The Sherlock Holmes Reference Library: The Hound of the Baskervilles*, Gasogene Books, USA, 2001.

Knight W H K, *Romances of the West Country written by the Rev. Sabine Baring-Gould*, Doidge & Co, 1898.

Knight-Bruce J H W, *Dartmoor Days with the Forest Hunt*, John Murray, 1916.

Lauder R, *Vanished Houses of South Devon*, Rosemary Lauder, 1997.

Lysons Rev D & S, *Magna Britannia, Vol 6* [including Devonshire], 1822.

Maggs C G, *Branch Lines of Devon - Exeter and South, Central and East Devon*, Alan Sutton, 1994.

Maggs C G, *Branch Lines of Devon - Plymouth, West and North Devon*, Alan Sutton, 1995.

Manaton - The People of, *The Book of Manaton*, Halsgrove, 1999.

Maurice A B, 'Conan Doyle's "The Hound of the Baskervilles"', *The Bookman*, USA, May 1902.

McClure M W, 'Myth Conceptions Regarding The Hound of the Baskervilles', *The Devon County Chronicle, Vol 2 No 2*, USA, April 1989.

McNabb J, *The Curious Incident of the Hound on Dartmoor*, Bootmakers of Toronto Occasional Papers No 1, Canada, 1984.

McNabb J, *My Friend, Mr. Fletcher Robinson …*, unpublished manuscript, Metropolitan Toronto Reference

Library, Canada, Undated [pre-1984].

McCowen J L, 'Letter to Editor' [reference to the Baskervilles of the Welsh border], *The Baker Street Journal, Vol 27 No 1 (NS)*, USA, March 1977.

McQueen I, *Sherlock Holmes Detected - The Problems of the Long Stories*, David & Charles, 1974.

Meade L T & Eustace R, 'Followed', *The Strand Magazine*, December 1900.

Mildren J, *125 Years with the Western Morning News*, Bossiney Books, 1988.

Moore R, *The Birds of Devon*, David & Charles, 1969.

Morley C, *Sherlock Holmes and Dr. Watson: A Textbook of Friendship*, Harcourt, Brace & Co, USA, 1944.

Nesbitt F, 'Response to Query on the Legend of The Hound of the Baskervilles', *Devon and Cornwall Notes and Queries, Vol XVII Note 145*, A Wheaton & Co, 1933.

Nicholas J, *The North Devon Line*, Oxford Publishing Co, 1992.

Nordon P, *Sir Arthur Conan Doyle - L'homme et L'œuvre*, Didier, France, 1964. Partial translation available as: Nordon P (translated Partridge F), *Conan Doyle*, John Murray, 1966.

Pemberton M, 'Ghost Hound of the Marshes' [Norfolk hound legend], *The Citizen*, 28 June 1939.

Phillpotts E, *The American Prisoner*, Methuen, 1904.

Phillpotts E, *Children of Men*, Heinemann, 1923.

Phillpotts E, *Children of the Mist*, A D Innes & Co, 1898.

Phillpotts E, *Demeter's Daughter*, Methuen, 1911.

Phillpotts E, *Down Dartmoor Way*, Osgood M'Ilvane, & Co, 1896.

Phillpotts E, *The Master of Merripit*, Ward, Lock & Co, 1914.

Phillpotts E, *Miser's Money*, Heinemann, 1920.

Phillpotts E, *The River*, Methuen, 1902.

Phillpotts E, *Sons of the Morning*, Methuen & Co, 1900.

Phillpotts E, *The Three Brothers*, Hutchinson, 1909.

Pohle R W Jnr & Hart D C, *Sherlock Holmes on the Screen*, A S Barnes & Co, USA, 1977.

Pointer M, *The Pictorial History of Sherlock Holmes*, W H Smith (Bison), 1991.

Polwhele R, *History of Devonshire, Vols 1-3*, Kohler & Coombes, 1977 [originally 1797-1806].

Pollock D K, 'The Hound of the Baskervilles: A Bibliography', *Baker Street Miscellanea, No 24*, USA, Winter 1980.

Purcell W, *Onward Christian Soldier - A Life of Sabine Baring-Gould*, Longmans, 1957.

Ransom B, *Dartmoor's Greatest Walk: A Guide to the Perambulation of the Forest of Dartmoor*, Devon Books, 1987.

Rendell P, 'An Abandoned Mine - An Exploration of the Whiteworks Area', *The Hound, Vol 4*, 1995.

Rhodes A J, *Dartmoor Prison: A Record of 126 Years of Prisoner of War and Convict Life, 1806-1932*, Bodley Head, 1933.

Riarty M, 'A Fundamental Question - And a Fundamentalist's Answer' [on the breed of The Hound], *The Hound, Vol 2*, 1993.

Robb C J, 'Query on the Legend of The Hound of the Baskervilles', *Devon and Cornwall Notes and Queries, Vol XVII Note 101*, 1933.

Robinson B F, *The Chronicles of Addington Peace & The Trail of the Dead* (with Fraser J M), The Battered Silicon Dispatch Box, Canada, 1998 [originally 1904 & 1905].

Robinson B F [obituary], *The Athenæum*, 26 January 1907.

Robinson B F [obituary], *The Times*, 22 January 1907.

Robinson B F (introduced & annotated by Weller P L), *The Terror in the Snow*, Sherlock Publications, 1995 [originally 1905].

Robinson B F (introduced & annotated by Weller P L), *The Tragedy of Thomas Hearne*, Sherlock Publications, 2001 [originally 1905].

Robinson J F [obituary], *Report and Transactions of the Devonshire Association, Vol 36*, 1904.

Robinson R, 'The Hound - Dartmoor or Oxfordshire?', *Sherlock Holmes Journal, Vol 13 No 2*, Summer 1977.

Rose L, 'Cave Canem Nocte - The Folklore Origins of The Hound of the Baskervilles', *Baker Street Journal (NS), Vol 26 No 3*, USA, September 1976.

Rowe S, *A Perambulation of Dartmoor*, Devon Books, 1985 [originally the 1896 edition, as updated by Rowe J B].

Ruber P A, 'Sir Arthur Conan Doyle and Fletcher Robinson: An Epitaph', *The Baker Street Gasogene, Vol 1 No 2*, USA, 1961.

Ruber P A, 'Baskerville of Hound Fame is Dead …' [retraction of much of above article], *The Baker Street Gasogene, Vol 1 No 4*, USA, 1962.

Sanderson R, *The Prison on the Moor - The Astonishing Story of Dartmoor Prison*, Westaway, 1974.

Sayers D L, *The Documents in the Case*, Coronet 1990 [originally 1930].

Sayers D L, *Unpopular Opinions*, Gollancz, 1946.

Sayle J C, 'The Typewriter', *The Hound, Vol 1*, 1992.

Schenck R T E, 'On the Footprints of a Gigantic Hound', *Baker Street Journal, Vol 2 No 4*, USA, October 1952.

Sidgwick F, 'The Hound of the Baskervilles at Fault - An Open Letter to Dr. Watson', *The Cambridge Review*, 23 January 1902.

Sliney N, 'Did Conan Doyle have rival for novel poisoned?', *Western Morning News*, 2 September 2000.

Smith H G, 'Some Letters of Conan Doyle - With Notes and Comments', *The Strand Magazine*, December 1930.

Smith M, *The Railways of Devon*, Ian Allan, 1993.

Sommerlad U, 'Stapleton's Murderous Intentions', *The New Baker Street Pillar Box, No 37*, July 2001.

Stanbrook E, *Dartmoor Forest Farms*, Devon Books, 1994.

Stashower D, *Teller of Tales - The Life of Arthur Conan Doyle*, Penguin, 1999.

Stavert G, *A Study in Southsea*, Milestone Publications, 1987.

Steinbrunner C & Michaels N, *The Films of Sherlock Holmes*, Citadel, USA, 1978.

St. Leger-Gordon R E, *The Witchcraft and Folklore of Dartmoor*, Robert Hale, 1965.

Sutton M, 'A History of the Western Morning News', *The Hound, Vol 3*, 1994.

Takahiko E, 'The Wild Hound' [in Japanese], *The World of Holmes*, Vol 21, Japan, 1999.

Thomson B H, *The Story of Dartmoor Prison*, Heinemann, 1907.

Truscott J, 'Footprints of the Baskerville Hound', *Dartmoor Magazine, No 14*, Spring 1989.

Tullett T, *Inside Dartmoor*, Frederick Muller, 1966.

Tupper B S, 'The Singular Case of Fletcher Robinson', *The Baker Street Gasogene, Vol 1 No 2*, USA, 1961.

Watt A P & Co Ltd, Letter to Weller P L, dated 30 January 1998, on absence of records of payments from ACD to BFR.

Webb J R, 'Observations on the Dime Novel', *The New Baker Street Pillar Box, No 37*, July 2001.

Weber J, 'The Hammer Hound - A 40th Anniversary', *The Hound, Vol 8*, 1999.

Weber J, 'Landscape in the Mist - Blackaton Manor' [Blackaton Manor is not Baskerville Hall], *The Hound, Vol 4*, 1995.

Weber J, 'Architecture and Abstrusity' [architecture of 'Baskerville Hall'], *The Hound, Vol 7*, 1998.

Westwood J, *Gothick Norfolk*, Shire Publications, 1989.

Weller J C, 'Felicia Hemans - Houndian Literary Links', *The Hound, Vol 4*, 1995.

Weller J C, 'A Place of Pure Enjoyment' [The Museum of the RCS], *The Hound, Vol 2*, 1993.

Weller J C, 'The Rathbone Hound' - A 60th Anniversary', *The Hound, Vol 8*, 1999.

Weller P L, (with Baring-Gould S), 'Aglow in Those Hours of Darkness', *The Hound, Vol 3*, 1994.

Weller P L, *Alphabetically, My Dear Watson*, Sherlock Publications, 1994.

Weller P L, 'Atavism Again - And Before', *The New Baker Street Pillar Box, No 32*, August 1998.

Weller P L, 'Barking Up the Wrong Yew Tree' [breed of The Hound], *The Shoso-in Bulletin, Vol 9*, Japan, 1999.

Weller P L, *The Baskerville Guide to the Game of Écarté*, Sherlock Publications, 1992.

Weller P L, 'The Birth of The Hound' [Cromer and Other Early Aspects], *The Hound, Vol 1*, 1992.

Weller P L, 'Cartographically, My Dear Stamford', *The New Baker Street Pillar Box, No 37*, July 2001.

Weller P L, 'A Contemporary (1902) Review of *The Hound of the Baskervilles*', *The New Baker Street Pillar Box, No 37*, July 2001.

Weller P L, *Chrono-Hound - The Internal Dating of 'The Hound of the Baskervilles'*, Sherlock Publications, 2001.

Weller P L, 'A Corresponding Medic', *The New Baker Street Pillar Box, No 37*, July 2001.

Weller P L, *The Dartmoor Locations of 'The Hound of the Baskervilles'*, Sherlock Publications, 1994.

Weller P L, 'The Dartmoor of the Hound', *Beaten's "Christmas" Annual*, USA, 1995-1996.

Weller P L, 'Deposits in the Vault: Together Again on the Moor?', *Stimson & Co Gazette, No 3*, USA, 1992.

Weller P L, *Elementary Holmes*, Sherlock Publications, 1994.

Weller P L, 'A Fistful of Dimes' [notes on dime novels], *The New Baker Street Pillar Box, No 37*, July 2001.

Weller P L, 'The Game is Underfoot - Archaeology on the Moor', *The Hound, Vol 5*, 1996.

Weller P L, 'A Gathering at the Athenæum', *The New Baker Street Pillar Box, No 37*, July 2001.

Weller P L, *Geographica Baskervillia* [analyses of locational references from *The Hound*], Sherlock Publications, 2001.

Weller P L, 'If the Cap Fits …' [Sidney Paget and *The Hound*], *The Hound, Vol 2*, 1993.

Weller P L, 'Il nome della Hound' [on the Italian translation of 'Hound'], *The New Baker Street Pillar Box, No 37*, July 2001 [also in Italian in *The Strand Magazine*, the journal of Uno Studio in Holmes (Italy).

Weller P L, 'It's a Wonderful Place, the Moor', *Canadian Holmes, Vol 18 No 4*, Canada, 1995.

Weller P L with Roden C, *The Life and Times of Sherlock Holmes*, Studio Editions - 1992, Bracken Books - 1993, Random House - 1994 - USA.

Weller P L, *The Manuscript Chapter of "The Hound of the Baskervilles"* [an analysis of the changes made in the *Strand* text], Sherlock Publications, 2001.

Weller P L, 'The Medics and the Cleric - Atavism and Other Topics', *The New Baker Street Pillar Box, No 29*, February 1997.

Weller P L, 'The Mire and the Moor', *The Hound, Vol 4*, 1995.

Weller P L, 'Moor Maps and Mileages', *The Hound, Vol 4*, 1995.

Weller P L, 'Northumberland Avenue and *The Hound*', *Disjecta Memoranda I*, Sherlock Publications, 1997 [originally 1991].

Weller P L, 'The Passing of the Third Floor Back', *The Hound, Vol 7*, 1998.

Weller P L, 'The Railways of the Hound - Platform One - General Survey', *The Hound, Vol 5*, 1996.

Weller P L, 'The Railways of the Hound, Platform Two - From Shingles to Cesspool', *The Hound, Vol 6*, 1997.

Weller P L, 'The Railways of the Hound - Platform Three - GWR Route to Exeter', *The Hound, Vol 7*, 1998.

Weller P L, 'The Railways of the Hound - Platform Four - LSWR Route to Exeter', *The Hound, Vol 8*, 1999.

Weller P L, 'The Railways of the Hound - Platform Five - North Devon Line', *The Hound, Vol 9*, 2000.

Weller P L [forthcoming], 'The Railways of the Hound - Platforms Six, Seven & Eight - The South Devon Line, The Moretonhampstead Line, The Ashburton Line', *The Hound, Vols 10, 11 & 12*, 2001-2003.

Weller P L, 'A Scandal-Mongering in Bohemia' [dismissing accusations that ACD murdered BFR], *The New Baker Street Pillar Box, Nos 35-36*, December 2000.

Weller P L, 'Some Reflections on ACD's Wet Moor', *The Hound, Vol 3*, 1994.

Weller P L, 'Take Moor Care - Some Considerations of Playing the Game on Dartmoor', *The Hound, Vol 3*, 1994.

Weller P L, 'To Dartmoor in Comfort' [by GWR to Dartmoor], *The New Baker Street Pillar Box, No 37*, July 2001.

Weller P L, 'The Tomb of the Baskervilles', *Grimpen Telegraph & Registered Post, No 3*, USA, Fall 1991.

Weller P L, '221B or not 221B?', *The New Baker Street Pillar Box, No 21*, Winter 1995.

Weller P L, 'You Can Have Your Tor Any Colour, As Long As It's Black', *The New Baker Street Pillar Box, No 37*, July 2001.

Wheeler E, '"Rescuer" of Sherlock Holmes' [BFR], *Western Morning News*, 24 October 1969.

Williams A R, *Legends of the Severn Valley*, Folk Press, Undated.

Williams J E H, 'Arthur Conan Doyle', *The Bookman* [UK Version], April 1902.

Wills-Wood C, 'A Humble MRCS', *The Hound, Vol 2*, 1993.

Woods S H, *Dartmoor Stone*, Devon Books, 1988.

Woods S H, *Widecombe-in-the-Moor*, Devon Books, 1996.

Woods S H, *Widecombe-in-the-Moor - Uncle Tom Cobley & All*, Halsgrove, 2000.

Woolcombe L A W, *Princetown and its Prison*, Privately Printed, 1935 [originally 1926].

Worth R H, *Worth's Dartmoor*, David & Charles, 1988 [originally 1953].

Wright D, 'The Hound of Hell is Alive and Well', *The Shoso-in Bulletin, Vol 8*, Japan, 1998.

Wynne N B, 'The Baker Street - Devon Connection: The Influence of the Sherlock Holmes Stories on Agatha Christie's Early Work', *The Baker Street Journal, Vol 27 No 1 (NS)*, USA, March 1977.

Weller P L, *The Dartmoor Locations of 'The Hound of the Baskervilles'*, Sherlock Publications, 1994.

Weller P L, 'The Dartmoor of the Hound', *Beaten's "Christmas" Annual*, USA, 1995-1996.

Weller P L, 'Deposits in the Vault: Together Again on the Moor?', *Stimson & Co Gazette, No 3*, USA, 1992.

Weller P L, *Elementary Holmes*, Sherlock Publications, 1994.

Weller P L, 'The Game is Underfoot - Archaeology on the Moor', *The Hound, Vol 5*, 1996.

Weller P L, *Geographica Baskervillia* [locational references from *The Hound* analysed], Sherlock Publications, 2001.

Weller P L, 'If the Cap Fits …' [Sidney Paget and *The Hound*], *The Hound, Vol 2*, 1993.

Weller P L, 'It's a Wonderful Place, the Moor', *Canadian Holmes, Vol 18 No 4*, Canada, 1995.

Weller P L with Roden C, *The Life and Times of Sherlock Holmes*, Studio Editions - 1992, Bracken Books - 1993, Random House - 1994 - USA.

Weller P L, *The Manuscript Chapter of "The Hound of the Baskervilles"* [an analysis of the changes made in the *Strand* text], Sherlock Publications, 2001.

Weller P L, 'The Medics and the Cleric - Atavism and Other Topics', *The New Baker Street Pillar Box, No 29*, February 1997.

Weller P L, 'The Mire and the Moor', *The Hound, Vol 4*, 1995.

Weller P L, 'Moor Maps and Mileages', *The Hound, Vol 4*, 1995.

Weller P L, 'Northumberland Avenue and The Hound', *Disjecta Memoranda I*, Sherlock Publications, 1997 [originally 1991].

Weller P L, 'The Passing of the Third Floor Back', *The Hound, Vol 7*, 1998.

Weller P L, 'The Railways of the Hound - Platform One - General Survey', *The Hound, Vol 5*, 1996.

Weller P L, 'The Railways of the Hound, Platform Two - From Shingles to Cesspool', *The Hound, Vol 6*, 1997.

Weller P L, 'The Railways of the Hound - Platform Three - GWR Route to Exeter', *The Hound, Vol 7*, 1998.

Weller P L, 'The Railways of the Hound - Platform Four - LSWR Route to Exeter', *The Hound, Vol 8*, 1999.

Weller P L, 'The Railways of the Hound - Platform Five - North Devon Line', *The Hound, Vol 9*, 2000.

Weller P L [forthcoming], 'The Railways of the Hound - Platforms Six, Seven & Eight - The South Devon Line, The Moretonhampstead Line, The Ashburton Line', *The Hound, Vols 10, 11 & 12*, 2001-2003.

Weller P L, 'A Scandal-Mongering in Bohemia' [dismissing accusations that ACD murdered BFR], *The New Baker Street Pillar Box, Nos 35-36*, December 2000.

Weller P L, 'Some Reflections on ACD's Wet Moor', *The Hound, Vol 3*, 1994.

Weller P L, 'Take Moor Care - Some Considerations of Playing the Game on Dartmoor', *The Hound, Vol 3*, 1994.

Weller P L, 'The Tomb of the Baskervilles', *Grimpen Telegraph & Registered Post, No 3*, USA, Fall 1991.

Weller P L, '221B or not 221B?', *The New Baker Street Pillar Box, No 21*, Winter 1995.

Wheeler E, '"Rescuer" of Sherlock Holmes' [BFR], *Western Morning News*, 24 October 1969.

Williams A R, *Legends of the Severn Valley*, Folk Press, Undated.

Williams J E H, 'Arthur Conan Doyle', *The Bookman* [UK Version], April 1902.

Wills-Wood C, 'A Humble MRCS', *The Hound, Vol 2*, 1993.

Woods S H, *Dartmoor Stone*, Devon Books, 1988.

Woods S H, *Widecombe-in-the-Moor*, Devon Books, 1996.

Woods S H, *Widecombe-in-the-Moor - Uncle Tom Cobley & All*, Halsgrove, 2000.

Woolcombe L A W, *Princetown and its Prison*, Privately Printed, 1935 [originally 1926].

Worth R H, *Worth's Dartmoor*, David & Charles, 1988 [originally 1953].

Wright D, 'The Hound of Hell is Alive and Well', *The Shoso-in Bulletin, Vol 8*, Japan, 1998.

Wynne N B, 'The Baker Street - Devon Connection: The Influence of the Sherlock Holmes Stories on Agatha Christie's Early Work', *The Baker Street Journal, Vol 27 No 1 (NS)*, USA, March 1977.

Serious students of *The Hound* should note that The Baskervilles Hounds and The Franco-Midland Hardware Company are publishing the most extensive and detailed study of *The Hound* ever produced, which is entitled *The Hound Centenary Study Project*. It consists of a loose-leaf binder system, to enable easy additions and amendments, with a core text which is cross-indexed to a series of specialist and technical supplements covering such subjects as: The Hound Manuscript, The Paget Drawings, Victorian Maps of Dartmoor (with examples), The Locational References and many other topics. Details can be obtained from The Baskerville Hounds.

First published in Great Britain in 2001

Original text for *The Hound of the Baskervilles* first appeared in
The Strand Magazine between August 1901 and April 1902.
A selection of Sydney Paget's original illustrations are also included in this work.
Copyright © 2001 all supplementary text Philip Weller.
Copyright © 2001 on all remaining images lies with the named archives and individuals.
Colour photography by Bryan Harper.
Main jacket photograph courtesy Carol Ballenger.
Burnard Collection photographs courtesy The Dartmoor Trust.
Taylor Collection photographs courtesy Dartmoor National Park Authority and Devon County Council.

British Library Cataloguing-in-Publication Data
A CIP record for this title is available from the British Library

ISBN 1 85522 790 8

DEVON BOOKS
OFFICIAL PUBLISHER TO DEVON COUNTY COUNCIL

in association with

HALSGROVE
PUBLISHING, MEDIA AND DISTRIBUTION

Halsgrove House
Lower Moor Way
Tiverton, Devon EX16 6SS
Tel: 01884 243242
Fax: 01884 243325
email sales@halsgrove.com
website www.halsgrove.com

Printed and bound in Great Britain by Bookcraft Ltd, Midsomer Norton